The Radio Amateur's License Manual

Edited by
Wyland Dale Clift, WA3NLO

American Radio Relay League
Newington, CT USA 06111

Foreword

By turning this page you will join the over three-and-a-half million readers over the last 50 years who have used the *Radio Amateur's License Manual*. This 78th edition continues a long-standing tradition of providing a technical, operating and regulatory education to not only simply acquire an amateur license, but to form a solid basis in knowledge for upholding our hobby as an expression of public service, technical progress and international goodwill.

This new edition covers all the topics outlined in the FCC's official study guides. We have even printed verbatim the FCC study outline for each class of license at the beginning of its corresponding chapter so you can use it as a checklist. In chapters 5, 6 and 7 we have furnished the information necessary for acquiring a Technician, General, Advanced and Amateur Extra Class license from the Federal Communications Commission, and have put the material in an order that should be smoother for teachers using this book as their text, following the suggestions of professional educators. And once again we have expanded the index in an effort to make it easier for you to find the subject you want.

As are most League publications, the *License Manual* is a team effort, so it is difficult to say that any one person is its author. Nevertheless, I would like to acknowledge the special contributions to this book of John Pelham, W1JA, who worked on the Technician/General and Advanced class chapters, and Jay Rusgrove, W1VD, who worked on the Extra Class chapter. George Woodward, W1RN and George Collins, AD0W, also contributed their technical expertise throughout the production of this book. Also, special thanks go to Margaret Koerner, K0IQ, whose underlying philosophy of explaining Amateur Radio concepts continues to influence this book, and to W. Dale Clift, WA3NLO, who, as editor, headed our effort to make this *License Manual* THE authority in amateur licensing.

Richard L. Baldwin, W1RU
General Manager

Update

Since the appearance of the first printing of this new edition, ARRL Headquarters has received suggestions from the membership for improvements. We are pleased to be able to print most of these suggestions on this, the update page for the third printing. We have also listed all the U.S. amateur rules changes, including the lifting of power restrictions on parts of 160 meters. Thanks go to all who helped prepare this page.—WA3NLO

Errata

page 5-4, middle column, paragraph immediately preceding Eq. 13, the second sentence should read: "A potential of 12 volts is measured across a *220* ohm resistor."

page 5-9, third column, fourth line should read: "Coils that have nearly the maximum possible (coefficient 1 or 100 percent) material inductance are said to be *tightly coupled*."

First column, third line from the bottom, add: "See pages 6-3 and 6-4 for more on impedance."

page 5-11, middle column, just before the section on filters at the bottom, insert: "Decibels corresponding to any given voltage ratio are figured in much the same way. The formula is

$$dB = 20 \log \frac{V1}{V2}.$$

page 5-27, diagram of an a-m receiver: The box with the word "mixer" should be blank. That's what you are supposed to know!

page 5-44, question 56, selection A should read: "Send the other station's call sign three times and your own call three times using RTTY followed by a cw i-d."

page 6-4, Fig. 6. $E_{AC} = 250$ V.

page 6-6, first column, second paragraph under the heading "Reactances Combined" should read: "We traditionally call capacitive reactance *'negative.'*"

page 6-28, Eq. 30 should be:

$$V_b = \frac{R1}{R1 + R2} \times V_{cc} \text{ volts}$$

Eq. 36 should be: $\frac{26\beta}{I_e(mA)}$

The next equation should be:

$$R_B = \frac{26 \times 100}{1.7} = 1529 \text{ ohms.}$$

Continue with the following:
and the ac base current will be

$$I_B = \frac{0.001}{1529} = 0.65 \ \mu A.$$

The collector current is then

$$I_C = I_B \times \beta = 0.65 \ \mu A \times 100$$
$$= 65 \ \mu A \text{ or } 0.065 \text{ mA.}$$

This is the current flowing into the collector through R_L, the load resistance. The output voltage developed across R_L is simply
$V_L = I_C \times R_L = 0.065 \text{ mA} \times 2k = 0.130$ V
The voltage gain is defined as

$$A_V = \frac{V_L}{V_B} = \frac{0.130 \text{ V}}{0.001 \text{ V}} = 130 \text{ V} \quad \text{(Eq.37)}$$

Because the current is flowing through R_L (... and continue to page 6-29)
Fig. 75, the 2k resistor coming off the emitter to ground should be identified as R3.

page 6-29, first column, eq. 38 should be:

$$R_{in} = \frac{1}{\frac{1}{R1} + \frac{1}{R2} + \frac{1}{RB}} = 1048 \text{ ohms}$$

Fig. 76 should have a resistor, R_L (the load) drawn in at the output and connected to ground, and in the last column, eq. 48 should be:

$$Z_{out} = \frac{I_B \times R_S}{I_B \times \beta} = \frac{R_s}{\beta}$$

page 6-36, Fig. 86(a): Length just before feed-point, marked "z," should be "x."

page 6-50, Fig. 4: The resistor at the top of the circuit to the right of the 10 k resistor should be 2.7 k.

page 7-2, Eq. 1 should be:

$$Z = \sqrt{R^2 + X_t^2}$$

page 7-15, Information on 4000-series CMOS digital integrated circuits can be found on pages 4-54 through 4-56 in ARRL's *Radio Amateur's Handbook*, 1981 or 1982 edition.

page 7-23, middle column, the first term of the equation should be

$$\frac{50}{100}.$$

Regulations Update

A reciprocal operating agreement has been signed between Canada and Ireland. A third-party agreement has been reached between Canada and Australia.

A third-party agreement has been signed between the United States and The Gambia. However, Gambian stations are not permitted to interconnect with the Gambian phone system for phone patching.

Delete Paragraph (e) in Section 97.13 of the Amateur Rules.

quency, type of emission and power.

(2) The National Radio Quiet Zone is the area bounded by 39° 15′ N. on the north, 78° 30′ W. on the east, 37° 30′ N. on the south and 80° 30′ W. on the west.

(3) If an objection to the proposed operation is received by the Commission from the National Radio Astronomy Observatory at Green Bank, Pocahontas County, West Virginia, for itself or on behalf of the Naval Research Laboratory at Sugar Grove, Pendleton County, West Virginia, within 20 days from the date of notification, the Commission will consider all aspects of the problem and take whatever action is deemed appropriate.

Amateurs located within a 50-mile radius of either Beale or Otis Air Force Base should contact Hq. for information about power restrictions on the 450-MHz band before operating.

☐ A new paragraph (c) has been added to Section 97.421 of the amateur rules as follows:

(c) Stations in telecommand operation may transmit from within the military areas designated in §97.61 (b)(7) in the frequency band 435-438 MHz with a maximum of 611 watts effective radiated power (1000 watts equivalent isotropically radiated power). The transmitting-antenna elevation angle between the lower half-power (−3 decibels relative to the peak or antenna bore sight) point and the horizon must always be greater than 10°.

Privileges restored on 160-meter band. Effective June 10, 1981, the FCC restored to U.S. Amateur Radio stations full *power* privileges on the frequencies 1800-1900 kHz, 1000 watts maximum dc plate input. However, some power and operating restrictions will continue to apply to some parts of the U.S. for the frequencies 1900-2000 kHz for protecting Loran-A radionavigation systems operated in eastern Canada. These restrictions are as follows:

	Maximum dc plate input power in watts			
	1900-1925 kHz	1925-1950 kHz	1950-1975 kHz	1975-2000 kHz
States of:	day/night	day/night	day/night	day/night
ME, MA, NH, RI	100/25	0	0	100/25
CT, DE, MD, NJ, NY, PA, VT	200/50	0	0	200/50
KY, NC, OH, SC, TN, VA, WV	500/100	0	0	500/100
FL, GA, IL, IN, MI, WI	500/100	100/25	100/25	500/100
AL, AR, IA, MN, MS, MO	1000/200	200/50	200/50	1000/200
remainder of states and territories	1000/200	1000/200	1000/200	1000/200

Mode limitations of A1 and A3 emission remain in effect for the entire 160 meter band.

☐ A new paragraph (f) has been added to Section 97.85 of the amateur rules as follows:

(f) The licensee of an Amateur Radio station, before modifying an existing station for repeater operation in the National Radio Quiet Zone, or before placing his/her amateur station in repeater operation in the National Radio Quiet Zone, shall, after May 13, 1981, give written notification thereof to the Director, National Radio Astronomy Observatory, P.O. Box No. 2, Green Bank, West Virginia 24944. Station modification is any change in frequency, power, antenna height or directivity or the location of the station.

(1) The notification shall include the geographical coordinates of the antenna, antenna height, antenna directivity, if any, proposed fre-

☐ A new Section, 97.422, entitled *Earth operation*, has been added as follows:

Stations in earth operation may transmit from within the military areas designated in §97.61(b)(7) in the frequency band 435-438 MHz with a maximum of 611 watts effective radiated power (1000 watts equivalent isotropically radiated power). The transmitting-antenna elevation angle between the lower half-power (−3 decibels relative to the peak or antenna bore sight) point and the horizon must always be greater than 10°.

August 3, 1981
Newington, Connecticut
78th edition, third printing

Contents

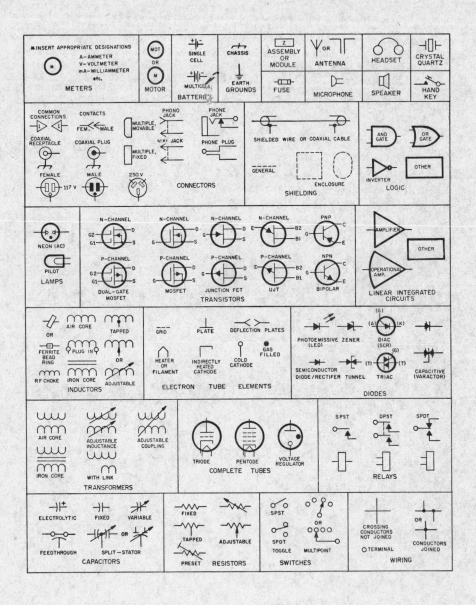

Chapter 1

Amateur Licensing

Why is there an Amateur Radio Service? Surely some must argue that the frequency spectrum used by radio amateurs should be given to commercial broadcasters, citizens band (CB) operators, the military, or some other group. Perhaps these persons have failed to remember that without the tinkerers and experimenters of Amateur Radio, the world of electronic wizardry, as we know it, would not exist.

The United States and Canadian governments have continued to recognize the importance and the purposes of this well-established and -organized hobby. Today, radio amateurs continue to serve the public as a voluntary, noncommercial communication service, especially during natural disasters or other emergencies. Hams continue to make important contributions to the advancement of the art of electronics. Amateur Radio experimentation also encourages many persons to become part of a self-disciplined group of trained operators, technicians and electronics experts — as asset to any country. This explains the term *amateur*: Hams pursue their hobby purely for *personal* enrichment in these technician and operating skills, without any consideration of remuneration.

Because radio signals know no territorial boundaries, hams have the unique ability to enhance international good will. A ham becomes an ambassador of his country every time he promotes that special camaraderie for which hams are so famous.

Amateur Radio has been around since before World War I. Yet, it is as up to date as tomorrow! Hams relay signals through their own space satellites in the *OSCAR* series (*O*rbiting *S*atellite *C*arrying *A*mateur *R*adio) or bounce them off the moon. They talk from hand-held rigs on mountain peaks or from transceivers in their cars. They send their own pictures by television, chat by voice around the world or, keeping alive a proud, distinctive skill of amateurs since yesteryear, tap out messages in Morse code. And when needed, radio amateurs send their signals from

Note to Canadian Readers of the License Manual

For purely practical reasons the *License Manual* has been written to reflect the regulations established by the Federal Communications Commission for amateurs of the U.S. Canadian amateurs are regulated by the Department of Communications. Though the privileges and responsibilities of amateurs in Canada and the U.S. are generally similar, there are differences. Many Canadian amateurs have, however, found the technical sections of this manual helpful as a study guide. Several other sources of Canadian information are listed below.

There are three classes of operator certificates in Canada: the Amateur Radio Operator's Certificate, the Amateur Radio Operator's Advanced Certificate and the Amateur Digital Radio Operator's Certificate. Examinations include written tests on radio theory and DOC regulations for all three classes of Certificates, and Morse code receiving tests for Amateur (10 words per minute) and Advanced (15 words per minute) Certificates. There is no code requirement for the Digital Certificate, but Advanced theory, Advanced regulations plus a digital theory exam must be written. There is an annual fee of $13 for the station license, which is renewable before April 1 each year. There is no minimum age requirement.

A Telecommunications Regulation Circular, TRC-24, is available without charge from local offices of DOC. Entitled "Information for the Guidance of Candidates Preparing to Attend Examination for an Amateur Radio Operator's Certificate, or an Amateur Radio Operator's Advanced Certificate, or an Amateur Digital Radio Operator's Certificate," it describes the method of periodic examinations and the study curriculum to qualify for examination for all three classes of certification. It is available in English and French. Anyone planning to take examinations is advised to obtain a copy. See pages 1-4 and 1-5 for a list of DOC offices.

The Canadian Amateur Radio Licencing Manual, written by Ralph Zbarsky, VE7BTG, and published by the Canadian Radio Relay League (the Canadian Division of ARRL), is written expressly for those wishing to become licensed in Canada. It is organized into a loose-leaf, three-ring binder format and is easily identified by its blue cover with the CRRL-ARRL diamonds on the front cover. In addition *The Canadian Advanced Amateur Radio Licencing* material is available as well as a student question book. Inquiries regarding the manual should be directed to the Canadian Radio Relay League, Box 7009, Station E, London, ON N5Y 4J9 or to Canadian Amateur Radio Licensing Manual, 3275 West 22nd Ave., Vancouver, BC V6L 1N1.

disaster-struck areas that have lost normal lines of communication.

Yes, there's much to do in ham radio. But you have to do a little work to earn your Amateur Radio license. It won't be as easy as getting on CB or licensing a transmitter for your boat, but that little work will be rewarded with a lot more fun and satisfaction. This book, and others published by the American Radio Relay League (the ham's organization in the United States and Canada), will help you get your Amateur Radio license.

In the United States, operating an Amateur Radio transmitting station is a privilege. And privileges, we know, are earned. Before receiving the privilege of operating an Amateur Radio station, applicants must demonstrate (1) the ability to send and receive international Morse code, (2) an acquaintance with the basics of radio, and (3) a familiarity with government regulations.

That sounds like a mouthful, but hundreds of thousands of Americans and Canadians have earned their Amateur Radio licenses; and you can too. The U.S. government, through the Federal Communications Commission (FCC), grants each U.S. amateur license. The Canadian government, through its Department of Communications (DOC), issues every Canadian amateur license. Licensing ensures operating skill. Without this skill, radio operators might cause interference to other services using the radio spectrum through improperly adjusted equipment or neglected regulations.

To own and operate an Amateur Radio station in the United States or possessions you must be licensed. The FCC issues licenses from its Licensing Unit at P. O. Box 1020, Gettysburg, PA 17325. An amateur license incorporates two types of authorization. For the *operator*, the license incorporates operator privileges, issued after passing a code test and written examination that tests the applicant's knowledge of Amateur Radio law and regulations and proper operation of an Amateur Radio transmitter. The Commission gives these examinations at numerous field offices throughout the country. In certain cases, the exams are given through the mail. This is explained later in this chapter and in chapter 3.

The license also authorizes an Amateur Radio *station*, i.e., operation of transmitting equipment at a specified location. It also authorizes portable and mobile operation as permitted under the regulations. The license you receive authorizing operator privileges and an Amateur Radio station at a permanent location is your *primary license*. This is a single, wallet-sized card containing the operator and station license. When operating as an amateur, it's required that you have this primary license in your personal possession.

You must obtain a license before you operate an amateur station of any kind. That's strong talk, but we have to emphasize this point. There are no exceptions to the requirement for licenses for any type of Amateur Radio activity. More than 60 years ago, the authority of the government to require the licensing of radio transmitters, whether amateur, commercial or any other kind, was established. And it's withstood every challenge since then. There are no special cases. A government license is *always* necessary. You face the loss of future operating privileges as well as the prospect of fine and imprisonment if you operate without a license. Don't think that you are an exception.

The FCC doesn't care how old you are or whether you're a U.S. citizen. If you pass the examination, the Commission will still issue you an amateur license. Adopted in November 1974, Public Law 93-505 allows any person (except an agent of a foreign government) to take the exam and, if successful, receive amateur station and operator licenses. It's important that you understand that if a foreigner receives an amateur license in this manner, then he is a U.S Amateur Radio operator. Don't confuse this with reciprocal licensing, which allows foreign visitors (from certain countries) who hold amateur licenses in their homelands to operate their own stations in the U.S. without having to take the FCC test. We'll discuss reciprocal licensing later in this chapter.

License Structure

By examining Table 1, you'll see that the present license structure provides a variety of amateur license classes, with each class having its own requirements and privileges. The FCC requires proof of the ability to operate an amateur station properly with the privileges that go with a particular license. This proficiency is demonstrated by passing a written examination (in addition to filling out an application form) to show familiarity with radio theory, operation and adjustment of basic transmitting equipment, both telegraph and phone, and with the essential parts of radio law and regulations.

The higher the class of license, the more knowledge required to earn it. The higher class tickets (licenses) offer more privileges. So as an amateur upgrades his class of license and eventually, hopefully, attains the Amateur Extra Class, offering all amateur privileges, he must pass more difficult written examinations. Each written examination is described later in this book.

In addition, an applicant must demonstrate an ability to send and receive international Morse code at the speed required for the class license he wants — five words per minute for Novice or Technician, 13 wpm for General or Advanced, and 20 wpm for Amateur Extra Class. Details on the code examination are in chapter 3. It's important to stress that although you may intend to use phone rather than telegraphy, this doesn't excuse you from the code test. Knowing the international Morse code is a basic requirement of international treaty for operating on any Amateur Radio band below 144 MHz.

Learning the code is like learning most things — a matter of practice. Instructions on learning the code, how to handle a telegraph key, and so on, can be found in an ARRL package, *Tune in the World with Ham Radio,* which includes a code cassette for beginners. Additional cassettes for code practice at speeds of 5 and 7-1/2 wpm, 10 and 13 wpm, and 15 and 20 wpm are available from the American Radio Relay League, Newington, CT 06111.

Application Procedure

Application procedures for the prospective Novice are different than those for Technician and higher-class licenses. The applicant locates a volunteer examiner who is over 18, holds a General class or higher license, and is not related to the applicant. The examiner administers the code test, certifies to it on the FCC Form 610 application, and sends it to FCC, P. O. Box 1020, Gettysburg, PA 17325. FCC will send the multiple-choice exam papers to the examiner, who should administer the test and return the papers within 30 days. More information on the Novice license is in chapter 4.

As for Technician, General and the higher-class licenses, you must appear in person to take the examination. If, however, you're physically handicapped and unable to travel, you may make special arrangements. See "Physical Disability," page 1-3.

There's a standard application blank, FCC Form 610, for individual amateur operator and station licenses. To get one, just write to the FCC engineer in charge of the district you live in (see the list on pages 3-1 and 3-3 or send a self-addressed, stamped envelope to ARRL headquarters. This form is very detailed but it comes with instructions, so there's usually no

Table 1
Amateur Operator Licenses*

Class	Code Test	Written Examination	Privileges	Term
Novice	5 wpm (Element 1A)	Elementary theory and regulations (Element 2)	Telegraphy in 3700-3750, 7100-7150, 21,100-21,200 and 28,100-28,200 kHz; 250 watts maximum input.	Five years Renewable.
Technician	5 wpm (Element 1A)	Elementary theory and regulations; general-level theory and regulations. (Elements 2 and 3)	All amateur privileges above 50.0 MHz plus Novice privileges.	Five years Renewable.
General	13 wpm (Element 1B)	Elementary theory and regulations; general theory and regulations. (Elements 2 and 3)	All amateur privileges except those reserved for Advanced and Extra Class; See Section 97.7(a) and (b)	Five years Renewable.
Advanced	13 wpm (Element 1B)	General theory and regulations, plus intermediate theory. (Elements 2, 3 and 4A)	All amateurs privileges except those reserved to Extra Class; See Section 97.7(a).	Five years Renewable.
Amateur Extra Class	20 wpm (Element 1C)	General theory and regulations, intermediate theory, plus special exam on advanced techniques. (Elements 2, 3, 4A and 4B)	All amateur privileges.	Five years Renewable.

*A licensed radio amateur will be required to pass only those elements that are not included in the examination for the amateur license currently held. See §97.21 and §97.23 in Chapter 9.

problem. Just read the form and instructions carefully. An applicant must sign the form, certifying that all statements are true. There are penalties for falsifying any information.

Application Fees Suspended

The FCC suspended all radio license fees, effective January 1, 1977. The commission no longer charges amateurs for applying for a new license, renewal, modification, or similar amateur licensing matter.

Environmental Policy

The Environmental Policy Act affects Amateur Radio. After it arrives at the FCC, an application will be classified either "major" or "minor," as far as environmental processing goes. Major applications involve antennas over 300 feet tall; dish antennas more than 30 feet in diameter; stations to be located in a wilderness area, wildlife preserve or nationally recognized scenic and recreational area; facilities which will affect sites significant in American history or those listed in the *National Register of Historic Places;* and facilities whose construction will involve extensive changes in surface features. That almost sounds as though you can't put a station anywhere, but actually it covers only a small number of amateur installations. The vast majority of amateur stations aren't affected at all by the Environmental Policy Act. Most amateurs will simply answer "no" to item 10 on the Form 610, "Would a Commission grant of your application be a major action as defined by Section 1.1305 of the Commission's Rules?"

Exemptions

When applying for a higher class license, an applicant receives credit for those examination parts which were required for his present license. For example, an Advanced class licensee going for an Amateur Extra Class ticket receives credit for the written examinations he passed for the Novice, General and Advanced licenses. He has only to pass a code test of 20 wpm and the written examination required for the Amateur Extra Class.

Under a recent rule change, the Commission will waive a code test if you present a Code Credit Certificate issued by the FCC district office for the district you are being examined in. The Code Credit Certificate is given to an applicant who passes an FCC-administered code test but fails the written portion which would have qualified him for a higher class of license. With the certificate, the applicant gets credit for the code element for one year. See §97.25(b) of the Rules in Chapter 9.

Anyone who has held, within five years, a commercial radiotelegraph license may receive code test credit (see chapter 9, Section 97.25, for details). This is discussed in chapter 3. There are no other waivers of examination elements for amateur licenses.

Applying for a License

If you're applying for a Technician class license or higher, obtain FCC Form 610 from an FCC office (or send a self-addressed, stamped envelope to ARRL, Newington, CT 06111). Fill it out carefully and bring it to the FCC office where you'll be taking the examination. There's a list of these offices on pages 3-1 and 3-3. Also, FCC exams are available in Spanish for elements 2 and 3, the exam given to applicants who do not already hold an amateur license.

If you want to take the test at one of the field *examination points* listed in chapter 3, you must file the application (FCC Form 610) at least one month ahead with the FCC district office having jurisdiction. Page 3-1 contains a list of months for examination at the different cities. Form 610 now has a space to enter your choice of an examination city. Exact information, time and place of the examination, is sent after the application is filed. This information is also your "pass" to take the examination. Don't misplace or discard it.

At one time, the Commission provided for the examination of applicants living temporarily outside the U.S.; however, it has discontinued this service because of budget constraints. The applicant wishing to be examined for a Novice class license should locate a qualified examiner to administer the exam. If a license is attained in this manner, it *does not* authorize foreign amateur operation. It may, however, be the basis for obtaining local approval to operate in a foreign country. This is outlined elsewhere in this chapter.

Physical Disability

The FCC doesn't withhold an Amateur Radio license from anyone for having a physical disability. Provided a disabled individual can qualify by passing the necessary examination, he or she can receive the privilege of operating an Amateur Radio transmitter. An invalid or shut-in genuinely incapable of traveling is entitled under Section 97.27 (see chapter 9) to take the examination for any license class.

A disabled applicant should write to the engineer in charge of the local FCC district office and ask for exemption from taking the code test and written examination at the district office or examination point. The letter should be accompanied by a certification of protracted disability from the applicant's physician. By the way, temporary sickness doesn't qualify you for exemption from appearing for the examination. You must be permanently or chronically unable to appear. If your request for exemption is approved, the Commission will appoint you an examiner, who will visit you and administer the code test and written examination.

Blindness or other disability sometimes makes it impossible to write out the examination in longhand. In these cases, the FCC permits the blind or disabled applicant to typewrite or dictate the code test and examination answers. The witness or examiner must certify that the examination comprises solely the applicant's effort or dictation, and that no outside assistance was received. The nature of the disability and, if the examination was dictated, the name and address of the person or persons who took the dictation, should be filed in the appropriate spaces on the answer sheet. The General class examination is available in Braille at FCC district offices only.

Renewals

Any amateur may renew his operator and station license upon application. Because a license incorporates operator and station authorization, both privileges are renewed at the same time on the same form. Use Form 610 for renewing your license—mail to FCC, Box 1020, Gettysburg, PA 17325, along with your old license or a photocopy of it.

You may apply for renewal of your license at any time during the life of your license. If, however, your license has expired, the Commission grants a period of grace of five years under which you may still renew your license without retesting (but, if your license has expired beyond a year's time, the Commission will issue your station with a new call sign).

If you move and apply for modification of your station license address, the Commission will also automatically renew your license. If you're going overseas for an extended period and your license will expire during this period, you may apply for renewal before departure and receive a new five-year license. For simple renewing, however, with no such special considerations, you should apply not any later than 60 days before your license expires. Such timely application means that you will be able to operate your station beyond the expiration date and before your new license arrives. But, if you apply under the grace period, your license is *not* valid and you may *not* operate your station until the new ticket arrives.

Whenever applying for renewal/modification of your license, it's always a good idea to keep a copy of your application for your records.

Modifications

You must let the Commission know of any permanent change in your address. This is more important for station licenses, however, and the procedure is discussed in further detail in chapter 2.

Duplicates

The odds are too great — out of the more than 350,000 amateurs in the U.S., someone's going to either lose, accidentally destroy or badly mutilate a license. If it happens to you, simply apply by letter for a duplicate license. Explain how the license was destroyed or lost. If the license was mutilated, send it along with the letter, explaining the cause. Mail the letter to FCC, P. O. Box 1020, Gettysburg, PA 17325.

Qualifying for Higher Grades

An amateur is free to apply for a higher class of license whenever he feels able to qualify. The holder of a Novice class license may, for instance, take the Technician, General, Advanced or Amateur Extra Class examination any time he wishes unless he failed an examination within the past 30 days. In fact, he may try to get an Amateur Extra Class license the very next day after he receives his Novice license. After qualifying for a higher class of license, the examiner will issue a temporary permit that allows you to use your new privileges immediately. When using the new privileges, a special two-letter designation is tacked onto the end of your call as an indication of the FCC office that handled your test. When your new license comes, the two-letter designator is no longer needed. (See 97.32, Interim Amateur Permits.)

Additional Station Licenses

In addition to the primary license, which every amateur has, there are special licenses for the following types of stations: military recreation, RACES, club, space radio, repeater, control-link and auxiliary. At one time, the FCC issued these special-purpose licenses to amateurs, but now allows these types of operation without prior notification or special licensing. Although the Commission will not issue, renew or modify repeater, control-link, and auxiliary-link stations, it will continue to renew and modify military recreation, RACES and club station licenses.

Some amateurs hold secondary station licenses in addition to their primary station licenses. A secondary license used to be issued to any radio amateur, giving him a separate call sign to use at his place of business, summer cottage, or the like. Once all presently existing secondary licenses expire, however, they will not be renewed. The FCC cited the tremendous growth in personal radio and the consequent shortage of personnel and funds to handle license processing as reasons for the elimination of secondary licenses.

The Commission also eliminated its past practice of issuing special licenses to commemorate special events, such as a Scout jamboree or state fair. The future of presently licensed special-event stations is unclear.

Licensing Overseas

In a few countries, where U.S. forces are stationed, special arrangements have been made for the licensing of our amateurs. Information on how to apply should be available from the base communications office, or write to International Services at ARRL. In most countries, however, any licensing of U.S. amateurs, military or civilian, is in accordance with reciprocal operating agreements, described below.

Reciprocal and Foreign Operating

The United States has entered into agreements with a number of countries around the world, allowing you, as an amateur, to receive permission to operate an Amateur Radio transmitting station in any of these countries. These agreements, because they're reciprocal, also allow foreign amateurs the opportunity to receive permission to operate while in the U.S. It should be stressed that a visiting amateur may operate only "his own station." That means in the U.S., the call sign, not the actual radio equipment which, of course, can be lent to any other amateur.

As this edition is written, agreements have been reach with the following countries: Argentina, Australia, Austria, Barbados, Belgium, Bolivia, Brazil, Canada, Chile, Colombia, Costa Rica, Denmark, Dominica, Dominican Republic, Ecuador, El Salvador, Fiji, Finland, France, Greece, Germany (Federal Republic), Guatemala, Guyana, Haiti, Honduras, Iceland, India, Indonesia, Ireland, Israel, Jamaica, Jordan, Kuwait, Liberia, Luxembourg, Monaco, Netherlands, Netherlands Antilles, New Zealand, Nicaragua, Norway, Panama, Paraguay, Peru, Philippines, Portugal, Sierra Leone, Spain, Surinam, Sweden, Switzerland, Trinidad & Tobago, United Kingdom, Uruguay, Venezuela and Yugoslavia. Negotiations are in progress with other countries.

The agreement with France includes Afars & Issas Territory (French Somaliland), Comoro Islands, Reunion, Guadeloupe, Martinique, St. Pierre and Miquelon, French Guiana, French Polynesia, New Caledonia, Wallis and Futuna Islands, French Antarctica and New Hebrides.

The agreement with the United Kingdom of Great Britain and Northern Ireland also covers the Bahamas, Bermuda, British Honduras, British Virgin Islands, Cayman, Falkland Islands, Gibraltar, Hong Kong, Montserrat, Seychelles, St. Helena, Turks & Caicos, British Solomons, New Hebrides, Gilbert & Ellice, Line Islands, Antigua, Grenada, St. Lucia and St. Vincent. For later information, check the update page of this book or write to ARRL headquarters mentioning the countries you're interested in.

Reciprocal operating between Canada and the United States is automatic; *no written permit is required.* U.S. amateurs visiting Canada and Canadian amateurs visiting the U.S. are authorized to use the privileges of mode and frequency authorized by their home license. Additionally, all visitors to Canada must stay within Canadian mode and band privileges, and all visitors to the U.S. must stay within U.S. mode and band privileges.

If you want to operate in a foreign country that doesn't have a reciprocal operating agreement with the U.S., you may still be in luck. Some countries don't allow any amateur operation by a foreigner, but many do. Each country grants permission to operate within its boundaries in a different manner. The most current information on how to obtain permission to operate in a certain country is available from ARRL headquarters.

If a visitor to the United States (except Canadian amateurs) wishes to receive reciprocal operating privileges, he should obtain FCC Form 610-A from an FCC office (or ARRL headquarters by sending a self-addressed, stamped envelope) and mail it to FCC, Gettysburg, PA 17325, at least 60 days in advance of the planned operation.

Canadian Reciprocity

Canada has reciprocal operating agreements with the following countries: Austria, Barbados, Bermuda, Belgium, Botswana, Brazil, Chile, Colombia, Costa Rica, Denmark, Dominica, Dominican Republic, Ecuador, Finland, France, Germany (Federal Republic), Greece, Guatemala, Haiti, Honduras, Iceland, India, Indonesia, Israel, Luxembourg, Netherlands, New Zealand, Nicaragua, Norway, Panama, Peru, Philippines, Poland, Portugal, Senegal, Sweden, Switzerland, United States of America, Uruguay, Venezuela and the British Commonwealth.

DOC Offices

Newfoundland: Department of Communications, P. O. Box 811, Corner Brook, NF A2H 6H6; Department of Communications, Sir Humphrey Gilbert Bldg., Room 612, Duckworth St., St. John's, NF A1C 5W1.

Prince Edward Island: Department of Communications, 180 Kent St., Charlottetown, PE C1A 1N7.

Novia Scotia: Department of Communications, 6009 Quinpool Rd., Halifax, NS B3K 5J7; Department of Communications, 500 King's Rd., Sydney, NS B1S 1B2.

New Brunswick: Department of Communications, 159 Main St., Bathurst, NB E2A 3Z1; Department of Communications, 77 Vaughan Harvey Blvd., Moncton, NB E1C 8P9; Department of Communications, P. O. Box 7285, Station A, Saint John, NB E2L 4G7.

Quebec: Department of Communications, 942 Chabanel St., Chicoutimi, PQ G7H 5W2; Department of Communications, 19th Floor, 2085 Union St., Montreal, PQ H3A 2C3; Department of Communications, 32 Frederic Hebert Ave., Noranda, PQ J9X 1V2; Department of Communications, Suite 436, 2 Place Quebec, Quebec, PQ G1R 2B5; Department of Communications, 701 Laure Blvd., Sept Iles, PQ G4R 1X8; Department of Communications, 1650 King St. West, Sherbrooke, PQ J1J 2C3; Department of Communications, 86 Edifice Publique, P. O. Box 67, Trois Rivieres, PQ G9A 5E3.

Ontario: Department of Communications, Alexandra Square, 135 James St. South, Hamilton, ON L8P 2Z6; Department of Communications, Federal Building, Room 154, Kenora, ON P9N 2X9; Department of Communications, Federal Building, Room 273, Clarence St., P. O. Box 633, Kingston, ON K7L 4X1; Department of Communications, 30 Duke St. West, Kitchener, ON N2H 3W5; Department of Communications, Government of Canada Bldg., 451 Talbot St., London, ON N6A 5C9; Department of Communications, Trebla Building, 473 Albert Street, Ottawa, ON K1R 5B4; Department of Communications, Suite 301, 222 McIntyre St. West, North Bay, ON P1B 8J5; Department of Communications, 421 Bay St., Sault Ste. Marie, ON P6A 5N3; Department of Communications, Dominion Public Bldg., 33 Court St., South, Thunder Bay, ON P7B 2W6; Department of Communications, 55 St. Clair Ave., East, Toronto, ON M4T 1M2; Department of Communications, 880 Ouellette St., Windsor, ON N9A 1C7

Manitoba: Department of Communications, 436 Thompson Dr., Thompson, MB R8N 0C6; Department of Communications, 2300-One Lombard Pl., Winnipeg, MB R3B 2Z8.

Saskatchewan: Department of Communications, 2101 Scarth St., Regina, SK S4P 2H9; Department of Communications, 206 Circle Drive East, Saskatoon, SK S7K OT5.

Alberta: Department of Communications, 205-8th Ave. S.E., Calgary, AB T2G 0K9; Department of Communications, Financial Building, Room 300, 10025-106 St., Edmonton, AB T5J 1G6; Department of Communications, 202-11117-100 St., Grand Prairie, AB T8V 2N2.

British Columbia: Department of Communications, 11-14th St. South, Cranbrook, BC V1C 2W9; Department of Communications, 471 Queensway, Kelowna, BC V1Y 6S5; Department of Communications, 3884-192-2nd St., P. O. Box 3396, Langley, BC V3A 3R7; Department of Communications, 1294-3rd Ave., Prince George, BC V2L 3E7; Department of Communications, Federal Building, Room 227, Prince Rupert, BC V8J 1G8; Department of Communications, 816 Government St., Victoria, BC V8W 1W9; Department of Communications, Room 300, 325 Granville St., Vancouver, BC V6C 1S5.

Northwest Territories: Department of Communications, Post Office Building, P. O. Box 540, Fort Smith, NWT X0E 0P0; Department of Communications, Bellanca Bldg., P. O. Box 2700, Yellowknife, NWT H0E 1H0.

Yukon Territory: Department of Communications, 201-4133, 4th Ave., Whitehorse, YT Y1A 1H8.

Chapter 2

The Station License

In 1972, the Federal Communications Commission decided that every radio operator must have a primary station license as well as an operator license. Normally, your primary station license will be issued for your home address. At times, though, this is not possible or convenient. You may have no permanent address or you might be living outside FCC jurisdiction (outside the U.S. and its possessions). What you'll need to do then is give the FCC the address of a relative or friend who will receive and forward mail to you. *You will be responsible for mail received at this address.*

When you apply for a primary station license, you combine this application with the one for operator privileges. In other words, the first time around, you apply for a license authorizing both operator privileges and station privileges. If you qualify, you receive your amateur license printed on a card known as the primary license.

There are additional station licenses, too — for clubs, military recreation, The Radio Civil Emergency Service (RACES) and space radio stations. Although the Commission decided that special licensing is no longer neccessary (and therefore will not issue new additional licenses), it will continue to renew and modify present licenses of these special stations.

The commission used to issue special licenses for repeater, control-link and auxiliary-link stations. However, under rules adopted in March 1978, the FCC decided to allow these types of operations without special licensing or prior notification by persons holding a Technician or higher-class license.

The Commission has also eliminated its past practice of issuing secondary and special-event station licenses. Once presently existing secondary licenses expire, they will not be renewed. There is only one presently existing special-event station, NN3SI. This station operates from the Nation of Nations Exhibit at the Smithsonian Institution in Washington, DC. Its license does not expire until the mid-1980s.

Visiting Other Stations

When a visiting amateur operates your station, the call sign permanently assigned to the station (your call) is always used. It doesn't matter whether you're around or not — he must use the call sign given to your station. Your visitor acts as the control operator, signing the log book and entering his own primary station call there. The control operator, whoever that may be, must never operate exceeding the privileges granted by his class of license. Let's say you hold an Amateur Extra Class license, and your visitor has a Novice class license. If he's operating your station (or any other station), he may not exceed the privileges given to Novice class licensees. What happens if the reverse occurs — you visit his station? You, as an Amateur Extra Class licensee, may use your full privileges at his station. If you operate his station the same way he would, transmitting telegraphy (A1 emission) with a maximum input power of 250 watts in a Novice subband, then you sign (identify on the air) just his call. If, however, while operating his station, you decide to operate on phone or with higher power or just on a frequency which isn't in a Novice subband, then you'll also have to sign your call sign after his. For example, his call sign is KB2XYZ and yours is W4XXX. If you operate his station using privileges that aren't given to a Novice class licensee, then you must identify on the air as KB2XYZ/W4XXX. Whenever he operates your station, he must sign W4XXX.

Unlicensed Persons

One of the fun parts of Amateur Radio is watching the grin of an unlicensed person's face as he participates in Amateur Radio by talking to a station across the country or on the other side of the world. The important term in that sentence is *participates*. An unlicensed person may never *operate* an amateur station, but he may *participate* in Amateur Radio. This means that, as a third party, he may speak over a microphone, use the keyboard of a radioteletype station, or a telegraph key or camera, depending on the mode used.

One point is very important. When a third party (which, by the way, may even be an amateur if he isn't *operating* the station) is participating in Amateur Radio at an amateur station, the station can only be in contact with countries which have third-party agreements with the U.S.

Let's give an example. You have an amateur license, but your brother-in-law, who's speaking over the microphone of your station, is your unlicensed guest. He's busy talking to a station in the States, when an amateur in Spain tries to contact your station. Your brother-in-law may not contact that Spanish station because Spain and the U.S. do not have a third-party agreement. He may, if possible, contact a station in Brazil, because the two countries involved have third-party agreements. The current list of countries which have third party agreements with the U.S. appears in chapter 8. Any recent changes are reported in *QST*, in "League Lines" or "Happenings."

Modifications

What do you do if you move permanently from the address printed on your primary station license? That's simple. You notify the FCC of this address change by sending Form 610 (fill it out as usual, but check the "change mailing address" box). FCC will automatically renew a license, even if the application is for modification only.

Whether you're applying for a license renewal or a license modification, you must send the Form 610 and your existing license (or a photocopy of it). These should be mailed to FCC, P. O. Box 1020, Gettysburg, PA 17325. Even if you are changing only your name or the mailing address, and the transmitter location is staying the same, you must file an FCC Form 610. When you change your address from one call sign district to another, FCC *will not* change your call sign to reflect this change unless you request a new call sign. See Table 2. If, for some reason, you are taking an operator examination before a district engineer in charge at the same time that you want to change the address of your station, you'd return Form 610 to the engineer in charge.

Renewals

All primary station licenses are renewable. The primary station license is renewed on FCC Form 610. Filling out completely the applicaton for renewal of operator license will also get a renewal of the station license. If you file before your license expires, you may continue operating your station past the expiration date on the license while the renewal is being processed by the Commission. You can continue this operation until you're sure what action was taken on your application.

Station Call Signs

What chaos would result if each country gave out to its amateurs any call sign it felt like! There'd be many similar call signs on the air, and more importantly, you'd have no way of knowing where a station was located by just receiving his call sign on the air. Fortunately, this isn't so!

Years ago, by international agreement, the nations of the world decided to allocate certain call sign prefixes to each country. This meant that if you heard a radio station with its call sign beginning with W or K, then you knew that the station was in the United States. Any radio station beginning with the letter F was in France, and so on.

The International Telecommunication Union (ITU) radio regulations outline the basic principles used in forming amateur call signs. According to these regulations, an amateur call sign must be made of one or two letters (one letter may, in some instances, be a numeral) as a *prefix*, followed by a numeral, and then a *suffix* of not more than three letters. In the United States, we use the prefixes W, K, N and A. For Amateur Radio, the continental U.S. is divided into 10 call districts, 1 through 0. For other areas of the U.S. and its territories, refer to Tables 1 to 3.

On March 24, 1978, the FCC replaced all prior call sign assignment policies. The Commission will not process requests of a specific nature. The digit in each amateur's call sign will be determined by the location of the licensee's bona fide

---

Table 1
Group A Call Signs

Block no.	Contiguous USA
1	K#¢¢
2	N#¢¢
3	W#¢¢
4-13	AA#¢-AK#¢
14-36	KA#¢-KZ#¢
37-59	NA#¢-NZ#¢
60-82	WA#¢-WZ#¢
83-92	AA#¢¢-AK#¢¢
93	Group B

The following prefixes will *not* be assigned to stations in the contiguous 48 states: AH KH NH NL NP WH WL WP. Pacific-area stations will be assigned AH#¢ KH#¢ NH#¢ WH#¢, then Group B. Alaska-area stations will get AL7¢ KL7¢ NL7¢ WL7¢, then group B. Atlantic-area stations will be assigned KP#¢ NP#¢ WP#¢, then Group B.

Group B Call Signs

Block no.	Contiguous USA
1[1]	KA1¢¢
2-23	KB#¢¢-KZ#¢¢
24-46	NA#¢¢-NZ#¢¢
47-69	WA#¢¢-WZ#¢¢
70	Group C

[1]KA prefixes will be assigned only to persons living in the first call district. Other KAs are assigned to U.S. personnel living in Japan.
The following prefixes will *not* be assigned to stations in the contiguous 48 states: KH KL KP NH NL NP WH WL WP. Pacific-area stations will be assigned calls in the format, AH#¢¢; Alaska-area stations, AL7¢¢; and Atlantic-area stations, KP#¢¢. Once these blocks are used up, assignments will be made from Group C call signs.

Group C Call Signs

Block no.	Contiguous USA
1	K# ¢¢¢
2	N# ¢¢¢
3	W# ¢¢¢
4	Group D

Pacific-area stations will be assigned KH#¢¢ NH#¢¢ WH#¢¢, in that order; Alaska-area stations KL7¢¢ NL7¢¢ WL7¢¢; Atlantic-area stations NP#¢¢ WP#¢¢. After these are depleted, Group D will be used.

Group D Call Signs

Block no.	Contiguous USA
1-23[1]	KA#¢¢¢-KZ#¢¢¢
24-41	WA#¢¢¢-WZ#¢¢¢

[1]Except KC4AAA-AAF and KC4USA-USZ
The following call-sign formats will *not* be assigned to stations in the contiguous 48 states:
KH #¢¢¢ KL# ¢¢¢ KP# ¢¢¢ WC#   WH# ¢¢¢
WK#¢¢¢ WL#¢¢¢ WM# ¢¢¢ WP#¢¢¢ WR#¢¢¢
WT#¢¢¢ Pacific-area stations will be assigned KH#¢¢¢ WH#¢¢¢; Alaska-area stations KL7¢¢¢ WL7¢¢¢; Atlantic-area stations KP# ¢¢¢ WP#¢¢¢.

---

mailing address. When the mailing address is modified, however, the station will automatically retain the current call sign *even if the new address no longer conforms to the digit or prefix for that location*. If a licensee wants a call sign with a number corresponding to his new

---

call sign area, he must request it. See §§97.47(c) and 97.51 of the rules.

All amateur call signs assigned after March 24, 1978, can be categorized in five major groups (see Tables 1 and 2). Each group corresponds to a specific class or classes of license: Group A — Amateur Extra; Group B — Advanced; Group C — General and Technician; and Group D — Novice. Group X contains WC, WK, WM, WR and WT-prefixed call signs, which are reserved for assignment to RACES, club, military recreation, repeater and temporary stations. Many amateurs hold call signs which do not conform to the class of license held. This is perfectly okay. However, the Commission will permit all Amateur Extra Class licensees to request a Group A call sign if they so desire.

As of this writing, the second phase of the Commission's call sign assignment system permits an Advanced Class licensee to request a Group B call sign if he does not already have one. However, the Advanced Class operator must meet an additional requirement by requesting a change *no sooner* than 60 days before the expiration date on his license.

Remember, call sign changes are optional. Any licensed amateur may retain his current call sign no matter what his class of license or U.S. call sign district. For details about Phase II, refer to January 1979 QST, page 62 or write to ARRL Membership Services Department and request a copy of Phase II of the call sign assignment system.

Logging

Amateurs in this country were once required to log every contact. In 1974, the FCC simplified the logging requirements. Information required by Section 97.103 (see chapter 9) now is limited to the call sign of your station, your signature, locations and dates of your operation (start and finish) and, when necessary, similar information for portable operation. When operating mobile, you don't need to keep any log at all, unless traffic is handled. If you're not the licensee but are operating the station, then you must enter the dates and times that you operated the station, plus your signature and your own call sign in the log of the station you're operating. If any third party traffic is sent or received, you should log this with names of the third parties and a brief description of the message. A log may be kept in any recorded form, including a tape recorder, but must be converted to written form if necessary. The Commission may require more information in certain station logs.

Round Tables and Nets

You'll find that when you get on the air many contacts involve more than two stations at a time. Because this is so commonplace, the FCC informally approved a

Table 2
Phase II of the FCC Call Sign Assignment System

Category	Amateur Extra Class	Advanced Class	General/Technician Class	Novice Class
New licensees	A-Only	B-Only	C-Only	D-Only
Licensees upgrading	If no change is requested, the present call sign will be retained.			
	B to A	C to B	D to C	
	C to A	D to B		
	D to A			
Licensees moving to a new district.	If no change is requested, the present call sign will be retained.			
	A to A	A to B	A to C	A to D
	B to B	B to B	B to C	B to D
	C to C	C to C	C to C	C to D
	D to D	D to D	D to D	D to D
Licensees requesting a call sign change	B to A		not accepted	not accepted
	C to A	C to B*		
	D to A	D to B*		
Licensees wanting their existing secondary call signs on their primary license	The exchange may be made any time during the term of the secondary license. The secondary license will be cancelled at the time of the exchange.			

*Only requests submitted no sooner than 60 days before expiration will be honored.

---

simplified method of identifying group transmissions. You may hear on-the-air transmissions such as, "W1XYZ and the group, this is W5QRA," or "Podunk Hollow Sideband Net, this is W6QTH." These are fine.

Civil Defense

An amateur may wish to participate in amateur communications which help during times of emergency in coordination with the civil defense. The FCC established a Radio Amateur Civil

Table 3
FCC-Allocated Prefixes for Areas Outside Continental U.S.

Prefix	Location
AH1, KH1, NH1, WH1	Baker, Canton, Enderbury, Howland Is.
AH2, KH2, NH2, WH2	Guam
AH3, KH3, NH3, WH3	Johnston Is.
AH4, KH4, NH4, WH4	Midway Is.
AH5K, KH5K, NH5K, WH5K	Kingman Reef
AH5, KH5, NH5, WH5	(except K suffix) Palmyra, Jarvis Is.
AH6, KH6, NH6, WH6	Hawaii
AH7, KH7, NH7, WH7	Kure Is.
AH8, KH8, NH8, WH8	American Samoa
AH9, KH9, NH9, WH9	Wake, Wilkes, Peale Is.
AH0, KH0, NH0, WH0	Northern Mariana Islands
AL7, KL7, NL7, WL7	Alaska
KP1, NP1, WP1	Navassa Is.
KP2, NP2, WP2	Virgin Is.
KP3, NP3, WP3	Rancador Key, Quita Sueno Bank, Serrana Bank, Serranilla Bank
KP4, NP4, WP4	Puerto Rico

Emergency Service (RACES) for this purpose. These rules are Subpart F of the amateur regulations (see chapter 9).

Portable and Mobile Operation

Any amateur station license (except a military recreation or special-event station license) authorizes operation as portable or mobile, as well as fixed.

For operation from a ship or aircraft, see the special provisions for these types of operation in Section 97.101 of chapter 9. Are you planning to operate outside the continental U.S. and possessions? Then your operation is subject to Section 97.95(b) as well. Licensing in other countries is discussed in chapter 1.

An amateur, whenever and wherever he or she is operating, must always have the original (or a photocopy) of his license with him. Additionally, it's always a good idea to have a copy of the license displayed prominently at your station in the event that another operator may be using your station. If you are guest-operating a friend's station, you must have, in addition to your own license (or photocopy), the original or photocopy of the station license whose call sign is used.

Station Identification

When on the air, give the station's call sign at the start of a transmission or series of transmissions, and at intervals not to exceed 10 minutes during a single transmission or series of transmissions of more than 10 minutes' duration. At the end of a communication, also give the call sign of the person you've been talking to (or the name of a network or group when this applies) followed by your own call sign. You're permitted to speak in a modern foreign language, but the call signs required must be given in English (see Section 97.84, chapter 9). If you're

guest operating with privileges you're entitled to, but greater than the licensee's, add your primary call sign to his each time you send it (see the beginning of this chapter).

Identification of Portables and Mobiles

In 1976, the FCC made it no longer necessary for amateurs to notify the Commission of portable operation. In addition, you don't need to identify your station as portable or mobile if you're not operating from the assigned location of your station license. However, aliens operating within the U.S. under reciprocal operating privileges must still identify according to Section 97.313 (see chapter 9). By the way, you're free to sign as portable or mobile even though it's no longer required.

What if you're mobile over or on the high seas (outside our 200-mile limit and also outside the territorial waters of any other nation)? Maritime and aeronautical mobile stations on or over the high seas customarily indicate which of the three regions they're in. The International Telecommunication Union, worldwide regulatory body for communications, places Europe, Africa, the Near East and the USSR in Region 1. North and South America are in Region 2 and the remainder of the world is in Region 3. The exact boundaries are described in Section 97.95(b)(2) in chapter 9. However, amateurs are no longer *required* to indicate ITU regions, nor do they have to identify their positions with latitude and longitude degrees.

Repeater Operation

Amateur Radio stations in repeater operation are usually located on a high spot to receive signals from other amateur stations in the area, then automatically retransmit them on another frequency.

Usually, the amateur stations in the area are mobile. Fancier systems may link the signals to additional repeaters in different locations or *crossband* them to the other authorized amateur bands. The aim is to improve coverage. Frequencies available for repeater operation are

29.5-29.7 MHz
52.0-54.0 MHz
144.5-145.5 MHz
146.0-148.0 MHz
220.5-225.0 MHz
420.0-431.0 MHz
433.0-435.0 MHz

and any other amateur frequency above 438.0 MHz.

Stations in repeater operation must identify by voice or international Morse code every 10 minutes while in use with modulation sufficient to be heard over the conversation in progress. The speed should not exceed 20 words per minute when an automatic device is used for code identification.

Stations in repeater operation may be controlled from a number of points, including mobile and portable stations. In all cases, though, the controlling frequency must be different than the frequency of the receiver input. It must also be above 220.5 MHz. Auxiliary operation is not permitted at 431-433 MHz and 435-438 MHz. The frequencies 435-438 MHz are not used for this purpose, since these frequencies are available internationally for amateur satellite communications. There must be a provision to close down a station in repeater operation (or any remotely controlled transmitter) within three minutes in the event of control failure.

For more complete information on repeater operation, remote control, auxiliary links, etc., see FCC rules in chapter 9, especially Sections 97.3, 97.61, 97.67, 97.84, 97.85, 97.86, 97.88, 97.103, 97.127 and Appendix 5.

Antenna Height Regulations

Amateurs have to watch how high they put their antennas. A portion of the FCC rules governing the Amateur Radio Service deals with restricting the height of antennas, to decrease air navigation hazards. Only a small percentage of amateurs are affected by these restrictions on antenna height, but every amateur should be aware of these conditions to be certain the planned antenna installation is legal.

Section 97.45 (chapter 9) outlines when an amateur must make a certain additional application. Few if any amateurs have antennas higher than 200 feet above ground, and so whether you'll be affected by these regulations will have to do with how close you are to an airport. Say, for instance, that your antenna will be near an airport. It can't exceed 1 foot in height for each 100 feet it is from the nearest end of the runway. Any antenna lower than 20 feet above ground or 20 feet above a house or other supporting structure is all right. But if your planned 60-foot antenna tower is only a mile from the local airport, you'll need to answer "yes" to question 14 on FCC Form 610 and then file Form 714 with your application.

For most amateurs, the filing of this form will be the end of the problem. The Federal Aviation Administration won't be notified if the antenna tower is shielded by existing structures and will be located in a congested area. Since many amateurs live close to high buildings, church steeples or tall trees, they'll probably have their antenna towers classified as "shielded by existing structures."

Environmental Policy

Like most other activities, Amateur Radio must now conform to the Environmental Policy Act. Please see the discussion in chapter 1 for more information on the environmental statement you may need to make.

Citations

The Federal Communications Commission has a very good monitoring system, and occasionally an amateur will be found violating some amateur regulation. In minor cases, such as harmonics falling within another amateur band, the amateur will receive only an "advisory notice" from the Commission, to point out what was done wrong. This notice does not require a reply. It serves only to warn the amateur that his operation is not allowed according to the strictest sense of the rules. It's not considered a serious violation. In more serious matters, the Commission will send the offending amateur an official citation which does require a reply within 10 days.

Both notices, the advisory notice and the official citation, are sent to the licensee of the station being operated. In other words, should some amateur friend of yours operate your station improperly, *you* will receive the Commission's notice, and you may have to reply to the FCC, depending on the citation.

Suppose you do receive an advisory notice. Act quickly to clear up the problem. In the case of an official citation, follow its instructions to the letter. The Commission will usually accept any good explanation of a rule infraction as long as the reply spells out that steps are being taken to prevent any further similar problems. Nothing is more serious, though, than ignoring a citation or failing to answer it altogether. In fact, some amateurs have had their licenses revoked, mainly for not answering a citation and the FCC's followup letter. In addition, the FCC now has the power to fine amateurs who willfully or repeatedly violate certain regulations up to $100 per offense and $500 total. The FCC can levy a fine on an amateur without having to go through the federal court system.

An amateur causing television interference (TVI) may receive form letters from the FCC, probably based on a complaint by a neighbor, asking him to cooperate in clearing up the trouble. Receiving such a letter doesn't mean the FCC points its finger at you. The letter is simply attempting to advise you of the complaint and to obtain your cooperation in working with your neighbor on this trouble (the neighbor, or whoever complained, receives a form letter also). Several such notices may arrive, especially if you're located in a fringe area for television. Simply answer each notice promptly and completely. The Commission will often judge the situation depending on how cooperative you are and how quickly you reply to the notice.

Quiet Hours

The FCC may impose quiet hours on any amateur station that continually causes interference with either television or broadcast radio over a general area. This is seldom done except when the amateur is uncooperative, or hasn't changed his transmitting equipment so that it's no longer at fault, according to the FCC.

The first order for such quiet hours will keep the amateur off the air between the hours of 8 P.M. and 10:30 P.M., local time, each evening, and also between 10:30 A.M. and 1 P.M. on Sundays. If after all this, the neighbors are still not pleased and the amateur fails to show an ability to reasonably improve his interference problems, then the FCC may stick him with even stiffer quiet hours (see Sections 97.131, 97.133 and 97.135 of chapter 9). Quiet hours are removed as soon as the interference is cleaned up and the situation is demonstrated to the FCC.

Radio-Controlled Models

Amateurs may use their equipment to control models, such as airplanes and boats. Section 97.99 makes special provisions for this type of activity, so it's no longer necessary to put a lot of time into logging and identifying these special transmissions (using radio-control transmitters with a power output of 1 watt or less).

Prohibited Operations

One-way transmissions are usually prohibited. For instance, you can't legally get on phone and "broadcast" a message to your nonham relatives or friends. However, you can make certain one-way transmissions. These include sending code practice or bulletins relating to Amateur Radio in general, emergency drills, and round-table or net operations (see Section 97.91).

You can't transmit music, although tones of short duration may be transmitted for testing your equipment. Tone modulation may be used for transmitting code practice over phone stations. Otherwise, tone modulation is restricted to amateur bands above 50.1 MHz.

You can't use a code or cipher on the air. Code groups may be used for on-the-air code practice, provided there is no intent to deceive. There should also be frequent identification as practice material. The usual Q signals and common amateur abbreviations may be used. You may use your foreign language talents when ragchewing with a foreign station, but you must identify your station in English, according to Section 97.84.

The American Morse code stretches back to the days of the Wild West. If was the code every railroad station keeper received on his clicker. You may still use the American Morse code on the air, even though it differs from the international Morse code. You must, however, identify each transmission in the International Morse code.

If you've ever listened to the amateur bands below 144 MHz on a weekend, you know they're crowded. For this reason, only signals using a pure dc carrier may be sent on these bands. An amateur must also have some way of checking the frequency of his transmitter signal. This method has to be different from what is being used to control the transmitter frequency. In other words, you may not rely on the calibration of a crystal in your crystal-controlled transmitter; you have to use some other method. A good receiver will usually work all right, assuming that operation too near the edges of an amateur band is not planned.

Duplex and Crossband Operation

When two or more stations are in communication with each other and are using different frequencies (or even different amateur bands), and the transmitter carrier remains on during periods of reception, we call this type of operation *duplex*. For a good reason, duplex operation is permitted only in the amateur bands above 51 MHz (where A0 emission is allowed). It reduces congestion in the bands where "skip" communication is common.

On the other hand, when two or more stations are communicating, and each operator turns off the carrier while listening, this is *crossband* operation. This is legal on any of the amateur bands and modes in the U.S. Let's say you're a Novice class licensee using cw (telegraphy) on 7140 kHz. You may communicate with an Amateur Extra Class station transmitting phone on 3780 kHz.

Chapter 3

Passing the Exam

It must be a basic human characteristic to save our own energy. Most of us try to do as little work as possible when on a certain job or task. So it's not unusual to hear a prospective radio amateur asking, "How can I get out of all that studying for the written examination?" And for us who are already amateurs, that's easy to answer. "You can't!" There's just no way anyone can get out of *all* that studying, but most of us use time-savers, making it easier.

One of the best time-savers is getting hold of the right reading material. Of course, in our opinion, the best source of information is the very book you're now reading. It can't be only our opinion, though, as more than three million copies of *The Radio Amateur's License Manual* have been sold through the years. Although we wrote this book to include information you'll need to know for

taking the written examination for either the Technician, General, Advanced or Amateur Extra Class licenses, other ARRL publications may come in handy. We recommend *The Radio Amateur's Handbook, Understanding Amateur Radio, A Course in Radio Fundamentals,* and *ARRL Q & A* manuals if you want more information on any amateur subject. For someone going for a Novice class license, the ARRL's beginner package, *Tune in the World with Ham Radio,* is the best route.

Another time-saver is to study with someone else, especially a good friend. There's nothing like a little rivalry to get your adrenalin flowing. In addition, if one of you can't quite grasp a point, the other might be able to explain it differently. There's no doubt that, in general, studying with a partner will help you both. And you can look forward to meeting your

fellow student on the air after you both pass the exam and get your tickets.

A third time-saver is to take an Amateur Radio theory class given by an ARRL-affiliated club. If you're interested in this approach, drop a note to the Club and Training Department, ARRL, Newington, CT 06111. You'll receive dates, times and places of classes near you. Most of the classes are held in high schools, colleges and YMCAs. There may be a small charge covering texts and rent of the meeting room.

Examination Points

You take the Novice test right there in your home town, with a local amateur (General class or higher) who is not related to you and is 18 or over, as the examiner. Further discussion on this is in chapter 4.

To take any other amateur examina-

FCC Field Office Exam Schedule

FCC Field Office	Examination Schedule	FCC Field Office	Examination Schedule
Alaska, Anchorage	By appointment only, one week in advance.	Michigan, Detroit	1st, 2nd and 3rd Wednesday and Friday of each month. Code — 9 A.M. No Code 9 A.M.-1 P.M.
California, Long Beach	Code — Wednesday 8 A.M. and 12:30 P.M. No code — 8 A.M. to 2 P.M. Tuesday, Wednesday and Thursday.	Minnesota, St. Paul	Friday 9 A.M.
California, San Diego	By appointment only, one week in advance.	Missouri, Kansas City	Tuesday 9 A.M.
California, San Francisco	Code — Wednesday 8:30 A.M., 10:30 A.M. and 12:30 P.M. No code — Wednesday 1 P.M.	New York, Buffalo	Code — Friday 9 A.M. No code — Friday 10 A.M. Groups of 10 or more, by appointment.
Colorado, Denver	2nd and 4th Wednesday of each month. Code — 9 A.M. No Code — 10 A.M.	New York, New York	Wednesdays: Extra Class 9 A.M., General and Advanced class 10 A.M., Technician class 12 noon.
Florida, Miami	Code — Thursday 9:30 A.M. No code — Thursday 8:15 A.M. to 1 P.M.	Oregon, Portland	By appointment only, one week in advance.
Florida, Tampa	By appointment only, one week in advance.	Pennsylvania, Philadelphia	Code — Tuesday and Wednesday 9:00 A.M. No code — Monday, Tuesday and Wednesday 10 A.M. to 12 noon.
Georgia, Atlanta	Tuesday 8:30 A.M. to 12 noon.		
Georgia, Savannah	By appointment only, one week in advance.	Puerto Rico, San Juan	Code — Wednesday 10 A.M. No code — Wednesday and Thursday 8:30 A.M. (or 1 P.M. by appointment)
Hawaii, Honolulu	Code — Wednesday 8:30 A.M. No code — Wednesday 1 P.M.		
Illinois, Chicago	Tuesday and Friday 8:45 A.M.	Texas, Beaumont	By appointment only, one week in advance.
Louisiana, New Orleans	Code — 1st and 3rd Tuesday of each month, 10 A.M. to 12 noon; 1st and 3rd Wednesday of each month, 8:30 A.M.-12 noon. No Code — 1st and 3rd Tuesday of each month, 8:30 A.M.	Texas, Dallas	1st and 3rd Tuesday of each month. Code — 8:30-10 A.M. No Code — 8:30 A.M.-12 noon.
		Texas, Houston	2nd and 4th Wednesday of each month. Code — 8:30 A.M. No Code — 10 A.M.
Maryland, Baltimore	Code — Monday 8:30 A.M. No code — Monday and Thurs. 8:30 A.M. to 12 noon.	Virginia, Norfolk	Code — Thursday 9 A.M. No code — Thursday 10 A.M.
Massachusetts, Boston	By appointment only. Exams given 1st, 2nd and 3rd Wednesday of every month. Appointment must be made one week in advance.	Washington, Seattle	By appointment only, one week in advance.

tion, you come face to face with an FCC examiner.

There are 28 FCC field offices (listed elsewhere in this chapter) spread around the country which administer amateur examinations either every week, every other week or by appointment. A prior appointment is not necessary, except when indicated on the examination schedule included in this chapter or if the applicant is blind. No examinations are conducted on legal holidays.

There are also 72 other cities at which examiners from the various field offices administer examinations from time to time. In addition, the FCC sends examiners to many ham conventions and hamfests, and many hams have taken their exams by this convenient method.

When planning to take an examination at any of the 72 cities listed in this section, you must make an appointment with whatever FCC field office will be administering the exam. You do this by completing FCC Form 610, indicating in Section II-B what examination point you plan to visit, and sending it along to the FCC field engineer in charge of the particular field office. You'll receive in the mail an appointment slip indicating the exam date. Keep this! It's needed to get into the examination room. For examinations at conventions and hamfests, check the "Coming Conventions" column in *QST* for information on making an appointment.

The Moment of Truth

By the time the day of the examination rolls around, you should have already prepared yourself. And this time we don't mean studying the material in this manual. We mean getting your schedule, supplies and mental attitude ready. Plan your schedule so that if everything goes right you'll get to the examination with plenty of time to spare. There's no harm in being early. In fact, you might have time to discuss hamming with another applicant, which is a great way to calm yourself (you'll be nervous at this point). Try not to discuss the material that will be on the examination, as this may make you even more nervous. Besides, it's too late to study. If you get lost, hung-up in traffic or just make a misjudgement of travel time, you'll have two strikes against you when you finally do show for the exam: You'll be *late* and nervous!

What supplies will you need? Bring with you several sharpened no. 2 pencils and two pens (blue or black ink). If the pencils do not have erasers, bring one.

If you're taking the exam at an FCC field office, you'll be required to fill out a Form 610. You've already done this if you have an appointment to take the exam at an examination point. After all this comes the code test, if required.

The code test is very different from what it was until recently. The examiner will hand you a piece of paper which has space to copy on. The test will begin with about one minute of practice copy, which should relax you somewhat (or make you more tense if you're unprepared!). Then comes the actual test. You may copy the entire text word for word or just take notes on the content. At the end of the transmission, the examiner will hand you 10 questions about the text. Simply fill in the blanks with your answers. If you get at least 7 correct, you pass! The format of the test is similar to one side of a normal amateur conversation, so you should be familiar with it.

You no longer have to pass a sending test. The Commission decided that if a person can demonstrate a receiving ability, chances are he or she can also send at that speed.

If all has gone right with the receiving test, then comes the written examination. The examiner will give all applicants a test booklet, an answer sheet and scratch paper. After that you're on your own. The first thing to do is read directions. Reading them after it's all over is a nice way to ruin your whole day. Don't forget to fill in all requested information. And sign your name every place it's called for. Do all this at the very beginning to get it out of the way.

Next, check the examination to see that all pages and questions are there. If not, report this to the examiner immediately. When checking the questions, you should pay attention to what number is the first question on the exam (not all exams begin with question 1 — in fact, most don't). Make sure that whatever number the first question is, you answer it in the same number block on the answer sheet. Otherwise, all your answers will be out of place.

Answer the easy questions first by going through the whole exam. Then go back to the beginning and try the rougher questions. Last, do the really tough ones, even though you might need to guess (which can only help you). You'll see that some of the questions will have one, and sometimes two, obviously incorrect distractors. Of the remaining responses, more than one could be correct; only one, however is the *best* answer. In other words, if you have to guess, do it intelligently, not just haphazardly. But one thing is important: To the applicant who is fully prepared, there are obviously incorrect distractors to each question. Nothing beats preparation.

And after you're finished, check the examination thoroughly. You may have read a question wrong or goofed in your arithmetic. Don't get overconfident. There's no rush so take your time, think, and check your answer sheet. When you feel you've done your best and can do no more, it's time to turn in the test booklet, the answer sheet and the scratch paper to the examiner.

A convenient new plan was put into effect by FCC in March 1977 — we call it "instant upgrading." The examiner will grade your examination while you wait. If you hold a license already, and you pass, the examiner will give you an interim amateur permit allowing you to use your new privileges the minute you leave the testing place. The permit will include a two-letter designator which you'll add to your call while waiting for the new permanent license to arrive. It is necessary to use the identifier so that you won't get cited by a monitor for improper operation.

A list of FCC radio districts appears below, followed by a table showing when those district offices conduct amateur examinations. Then there is a list of additional examining points the FCC visits during the year. Finally, there is an example of an FCC answer sheet; be sure you match the question you're answering with the right number on the answer sheet.

United States Radio Districts

District No. 1, 1600 Customhouse, India & State Sts., Boston, MA 02109. The states of *Connecticut, Maine, Massachusetts, New Hampshire, Rhode Island and Vermont.*

District No. 2, 201 Varick St., corner of Houston St., New York, NY 10014. In the state of *New York,* the counties of Albany, Bronx, Columbia, Delaware, Dutchess, Greene, Kings, Nassau-New York, Orange, Putnam, Queens, Rensselaer, Richmond, Rockland, Schenectady, Suffolk, Sullivan, Ulster and Westchester; in the state of *New Jersey,* the counties of Bergen, Essex, Hudson, Hunterdon, Mercer, Middlesex, Monmouth, Morris, Passaic, Somerset, Sussex, Union and Warren

District No. 3, 601 Market St., Philadelphia, PA 19106. In the state of *Pennsylvania,* all counties; in the state of *New Jersey,* the counties of Atlantic, Burlington, Camden, Cape May, Cumberland, Gloucester, Ocean and Salem; and the county of Newcastle in the state of *Delaware.*

District No. 4, 1017 Federal Building, 31 Hopkins Plaza, Baltimore, MD 21201. The state of *Maryland* (except that part lying in District 24); the counties of Kent and Sussex in the state of *Delaware*; in the state of *West Virginia,* all counties.

District No. 5, Military Circle, 870 North Military Highway, Norfolk, VA 23502. The state of *Virginia* except District 24; and the state of *North Carolina,* all counties.

District No. 6, 1365 Peachtree St., N.E., Room 440, Atlanta, GA 30309. The states of *Georgia, South Carolina* and *Tennessee,* and the state of *Alabama* except that part lying in District 8.

District 6S, P.O. Box 8004, Savannah, GA 31402. Specialized office with no designated administrative area.

District No. 7, 51 S.W. First Ave., Miami, FL 33130. The state of *Florida* and in the state of *Alabama*, Baldwin and Mobile Counties.

District 7T, ADP Building, Suite 601, 1211 North Westshore Blvd., Tampa, FL 33607. Specialized office with no designated administrative area.

District No. 8, 829 F. Edward Hebert Federal Bldg., 600 South St., New Orleans, LA 70130. The states of *Arkansas, Louisiana* and *Mississippi.*

District No. 9, 5636 Federal Building, 515 Rusk Ave., Houston, TX 77002. In the state of *Texas,* the counties of Angelina, Aransas, Atascosa, Austin, Bandera, Bastrop, Bee, Bexar, Blanco, Brazoria, Brazos, Brooks, Burleson, Caldwell, Calhoun, Cameron, Chambers, Colorado, Comal, DeWitt, Dimmit, Duval, Edwards, Fayette, Fort Bend, Frio, Galveston, Gillespie, Goliad, Gonzales, Grimes, Guadalupe, Hardon, Harris, Hays, Hidalgo, Jackson, Jasper, Jefferson, Jim Hogg, Jim Wells, Karnes, Kendall, Kenedy, Kerr, Kinney, Kleberg, LaSalle, Lavaca, Lee, Liberty, Live Oak, Madison, Matagorda, Maverick, McMullen, Medina, Montgomery, Nacogdoches, Newton, Nueces, Orange, Polk, Real, Refugio, Sabine, San Augustine, San Jacinto, San Patricio, Starr, Travis, Trinity, Tyler, Uvalde, Val Verde, Victoria, Walker, Waller, Washington, Webb, Wharton, Willacy, Williamson, Wilson, Zaputa and Zavala.

District 9B, Room 323, 300 Willow St., Beaumont, TX 77701. Specialized office with no designated administrative area.

District No. 10, Rm. 13E7 Fed. Bldg., 1100 Commerce St., Dallas, TX 75202. The state of *Texas* except that part lying in District 9 and the state of *Oklahoma.*

District No. 11, Suite 501, 3711 Long Beach Blvd., Long Beach, CA 90807. The state of *Arizona*; in the state of *Nevada,* the county of Clark; in the state of *California*, the counties of Imperial, Inyo, Kern, Los Angeles, Orange, Riverside, San Bernardino, San Diego, San Luis Obispo, Santa Barbara and Ventura.

State	City	Month in Which Examination Administered	FCC Office Administering Examination	State	City	Month in Which Examination Administered	FCC Office Administering Examination
Alabama	Birmingham	Mar, Sep	Atlanta, GA	Nebraska	Omaha	Jan, Apr, Jul, Oct	Kansas City, MO
	Montgomery	June, Dec	Atlanta, GA	Nevada	Las Vegas	Jan, July	Long Beach, CA
	Mobile	Jan, Apr, July, Oct	New Orleans, LA		Reno	Apr, Oct	San Francisco, CA
Alaska	Fairbanks	Jan, Apr, July, Oct	Anchorage, AK	New Mexico	Albuquerque	Jan, Apr, July, Oct	Denver, CO
	Juneau	May, Nov	Anchorage, AK	New York	Albany	Mar, June, Sep, Dec	New York, NY
	Ketchikan	May, Nov	Anchorage, AK		Syracuse	Ian, Apr, July, Oct	Buffalo, NY
Arizona	Phoenix	Jan, Apr, July, Oct	Long Beach, CA	N. Carolina	Wilmington	May, Nov	Norfolk, VA
	Tucson	Apr, Oct	Long Beach, CA		Winston-Salem	Feb, Apr, Jun, Aug Oct, Dec	Norfolk, VA
Arkansas	Little Rock	Feb, May, Aug, Nov	New Orleans, LA		Charlotte	Jan, July	Norfolk, VA
California	Bakersfield	May, Nov	Los Angeles, CA	N. Dakota	Bismarck	Mar, Sept	St. Paul, MN
	Fresno	Mar, June, Sep, Dec	San Francisco, CA		Fargo	June, Dec	St. Paul, MN
Colorado	Grand Junction	Apr, Oct	Denver, CO	Ohio	Cincinnati	Feb, May, Aug, Nov	Detroit, MI
Connecticut	Hartford	Jan, Apr, July, Oct	Boston, MA		Cleveland	Mar, June, Sep, Dec	Detroit, MI
DC, Washington	Washington area	Monthly	Baltimore, MD		Columbus	Jan, Apr, July, Oct	Detroit, MI
Florida	Jacksonville	Apr, Oct	Miami, FL	Oklahoma	Oklahoma City	Jan, Apr, July, Oct	Dallas, TX
					Tulsa	Feb, May, Aug, Nov	Dallas, TX
Georgia	Albany	Feb, Aug	Atlanta, GA	Oregon	Medford	Apr, Oct	Portland, OR
Guam	Agana	Feb, May, Aug, Nov	Honolulu, HI	Pennsylvania	Pittsburgh	Monthly	Philadelphia, PA
Hawaii	Hilo	Aug, Nov, Feb, May	Honolulu, HI		Wilkes-Barre	Mar, Sep	Philadelphia, PA
	Lihue	Sep, Dec, Mar, June	Honolulu, HI	S. Carolina	Columbia	May, Nov	Atlanta, GA
	Wailuku	Aug, Nov, Feb, May	Honolulu, HI	S. Dakota	Rapid City	May, Nov	Denver, CO
Idaho	Boise	Mar, Sept	Portland, OR		Sioux Falls	Feb, Aug	St. Paul, MN
	Pocatello	June, Dec	Portland, OR	Texas	Austin	Apr, Oct	Houston, TX
Illinois	Rock Island	Feb, May, Aug, Nov	Chicago, IL		Corpus Christi	Mar, June, Sep, Dec	Houston, TX
Indiana	Fort Wayne	Feb, May, Aug, Nov	Chicago, IL		El Paso	June, Dec	Dallas, TX
	Indianapolis	Jan, Apr, July, Oct	Chicago, IL		Lubbock	Mar, Sep	Dallas, TX
Iowa	Des Moines	Mar, June, Sep, Dec	Kansas City, MO		San Antonio	Feb, May Aug, Nov	Houston, TX
Kansas	Wichita	Mar, Sep	Kansas City, MO	Tennessee	Chattanooga	June, Dec	Atlanta, GA
Kentucky	Louisville	Mar, June, Sep, Dec	Chicago, IL		Knoxville	Jan, Apr, Jul, Oct	Atlanta, GA
Louisiana	Shreveport	Apr, Oct	New Orleans, LA		Memphis	Mar, Jun, Sept, Dec	Atlanta, GA
Maine	Bangor	Feb, Aug	Boston, MA		Nashville	Feb, May, Aug, Nov	Atlanta, GA
	Portland	May, Nov	Boston, MA	Utah	Salt Lake City	Mar, June, Sep, Dec	San Francisco, CA
Michigan	Grand Rapids	Jan, Apr, July, Oct	Detroit, MI	Vermont	Burlington	Mar, Sep	Boston, MA
	Marquette	May, Nov	St. Paul, MN	Virginia	Roanoke	Mar, Sep	Norfolk, VA
Minnesota	Duluth	Apr, Oct	St. Paul, MN	Washington	Spokane	Feb, May, Aug, Nov	Seattle, WA
Mississippi	Jackson	June, Dec	New Orleans, LA		Tri-Cities	Mar, Sep	Seattle, WA
Missouri	St. Louis	Feb, May, Aug, Nov	Kansas City, MO	W. Virginia	Charleston	Mar, June, Sep, Dec	Baltimore, MD
Montana	Billings	Jun, Dec	Seattle, WA	Wisconsin	Milwaukee	Mar, June, Sep, Dec	Chicago, IL
	Helena	Apr, Oct	Seattle, WA	Wyoming	Casper	Mar, Sep	Denver, CO

District 11SD, 7840 El Cajon Blvd., La Mesa, CA 92041. Specialized office with no designated administrative area.

District No. 12, 323A Customhouse, 555 Battery St., San Francisco, CA 94111. The state of *California* except that part lying in District 11; the state of *Nevada* except the county of Clark, and the state of Utah.

District No. 13, 1782 Federal Office Bldg., 1220 S.W. 3d Ave., Portland, OR 97204. The state of *Oregon*; the state of *Idaho* except that part lying in District 14; in the state of *Washington*, the counties of Clark, Cowlitz, Klickitat, Skamania and Wahkiakum.

District No. 14, 3245 Federal Bldg., 915 2d Ave., Seattle, WA 98174. The state of *Montana*; the state of *Washington* except that part lying in District 13; in the state of *Idaho*, the counties of Benewah, Bonner, Boundary, Clearwater, Idaho, Kootenai, Latah, Lewis, Nez Perce and Shoshone.

District No. 15, Suite 2925, The Executive Tower, 1405 Curtis St., Denver, CO 80202. The states of *Colorado, New Mexico, North Dakota, South Dakota* and *Wyoming*.

District No. 16, 316 North Roberts St., St. Paul, MN 55101. The state of *Minnesota*, the state of *Michigan*, the counties of Alger, Baraga, Chippewa, Delta, Dickinson, Gogebic, Houghton, Iron, Keweenaw, Luce, Mackinac, Marquette, Menominee, Ontonagon and Schoolcraft, and Wisconsin, except for the part lying in District 18.

District No. 17, Room 320 Brywood Office Tower, 8800 E. 63rd Street, Kansas City, MO 64133. The states of *Iowa, Kansas, Missouri,* and *Nebraska*.

District No. 18, 3935 Federal Bldg., 320 S. Dearborn, Chicago, IL 60604. The states of *Illinois* and *Indiana;* in the state of *Wisconsin,* the counties of Brown, Calumet, Columbia, Crawford, Dane, Dodge, Door, Fond du Lac, Grant, Green, Iowa, Jefferson, Kenosha, Keewanee, Lafayette, Manitowoc, Marinette, Milwaukee, Oconto, Outagamie, Ozaukee, Racine, Richland, Rock, Sauk, Sheboygan, Walworth, Washington, Waukesha and Winnebago; the state of *Kentucky* except that part lying in District 19.

District No. 19, 1054 New Federal Bldg., 231 W. Lafayette St., Detroit, MI 48226. The state of *Ohio*; the state of *Michigan* except that part lying in District 16; in the state of *Kentucky*, the counties of Bath, Bell, Boone, Bourbon, Boyd, Bracken, Breathitt, Campbell, Carter, Clare, Clay, Elliott, Estill, Fayette, Fleming, Floyd, Franklin, Gallatin, Garrard, Grant, Greenup, Harlan, Harrison, Jackson, Jessamine, Johnson, Kenton, Knott, Knox, Laurel, Lawrence, Lee, Leslie, Letcher, Lewis, Lincoln, Madison, Magoffin, Martin, Mason, McCreary, Menifee, Montgomery, Morgan, Nicholas, Owen, Owsley, Pendleton, Perry, Pike, Powell, Pulaski, Robertson, Rockcastle, Rowan, Scott, Wayne, Whitley, Wolfe and Woodford.

District No. 20. 1307 Fed. Bldg., 111 W. Huron St., Buffalo, NY 14202. The state of *New York* except that part lying in District 2.

District No. 21, 7304 Prince Jonah Kuhio Bldg., 300 Ala Moana Blvd., Honolulu, Hawaii 96850. The state of *Hawaii* and outlying Pacific possessions.

District 22, 747 Federal Bldg., Hato Rey, PR 00918, *Puerto Rico* and the *Virgin Islands*.

District 23, Federal Bldg. P.O. Box 2955 — 4th and F Streets, Anchorage, AK 99510. The state of *Alaska*.

District No. 24, Presidential Building, 6525 Belcrest Rd., Suite 830, Hyattsville, MD 20782. District of Columbia and in *Maryland,* the counties of Charles, Montgomery, and Prince Georges; and in *Virginia*, the counties of Arlington, Fairfax, Loudoun, and Prince Williams.

Chapter 4

The Novice License

So Amateur Radio has caught your eye, and you've been bitten by the bug. The ham down the street let you witness some of his wizardry, and now you know that the Novice class license is the easiest U.S. amateur license to get.

You're right: The Novice ticket is the easiest to get and, therefore, offers the fewest privileges. However, it does give a taste of DX work — communicating over long distances — while it also allows you to make contact with nearby stations, such as that ham down the street. You see, as a Novice, you'll be able to operate telegraphy (A1 operation) on four different bands of wavelengths. Each band by its own nature, permits a different sort of contact. One band may be great for working (communicating with) stations on the other side of the world. Another band may be good for making local contacts, while another is better for working stations about 1000 miles away.

A Novice gets to use all three types of bands: He can operate on 3700-3750 kHz, which is in the 80-meter amateur band, a great one for working stations around his state and local area. On the 40-meter band, a good one for making contacts about 1000 miles away and occasionally even farther, a Novice can operate on 7100-7150 kHz. For working DX, the Novice may operate on 15 meters anywhere between 21.1 and 21.2 MHz and on 10 meters between 28.1 and 28.2 MHz. Both bands are excellent for communication around the world and especially across the United States. So you see, the Novice has an opportunity to "work" hams with whom he'll probably shake hands later and maybe even talk into helping with a new antenna. But a Novice can just as easily communicate with amateurs in other countries as well — friends he'll probably never visit except on the air.

The Novice class license is unique. It may be the only license you'll ever get by passing tests sent through the mail. A ham who already holds a General or higher class license will be your *volunteer examiner*. He'll have the FCC written examination sent to him after he's told the Commission that you've passed the Morse code test. That's right — there are two examinations you'll have to pass to get your Novice ticket. The first is an international Morse code test at five words per minute. The other is a written examination covering basic amateur regulations, radio theory and operating practices. After you pass both examinations, the FCC will send you a primary license, which will be your station and operator licenses in one. It will have printed on it your call sign, which is yours alone.

A lot more information about the Novice class license is in ARRL's beginner package, *Tune in the World with Ham Radio* ($7 postpaid from ARRL). This package consists of a 112-page book, a 60-minute tape cassette, and a 45-page student work-book. The book explains the radio theory and regulations you'll need to know to pass the written examination for a Novice class license. Experience is the best teacher, they say, so top-notch operators pass along some tips on assembling your first station and operating it correctly. The tape cassette not only teaches the Morse code, but also gives examples of how on-the-air contacts really sound.

Novice Limitations

You probably wonder what privileges a Novice class licensee has. We've already told you the frequencies a Novice may use, but there are other limitations. First, the input power of a Novice's transmitter must not exceed 250 watts. That's still enough to communicate around the world, because the effectiveness of an amateur station depends on much more than just power. In addition, a Novice may operate only Morse code, or *cw*, as hams call it.

Why is a Novice allowed to use only cw? The Novice class license is the first step in U.S. Amateur Radio. It's there to introduce Amateur Radio to the beginner helping him develop his Morse code skill and radio theory knowledge, and learn more about the hobby.

A Novice needs to become more skillful in Morse code and to learn more about radio theory and regulations in order to upgrade his license class. (To upgrade for the Technician class, a Novice has to pass only the written exam; he receives credit for the five wpm code requirement.)

If you don't qualify for a higher grade license and time is running out, you can renew your Novice ticket. The Novice license used to be nonrenewable, but now you can renew it just like the other license classes. However, if you build your code speed and study chapter 5 of this book you can try for the General class license. You may even want to plunge ahead and take the examinations for the Advanced and even the Amateur Extra Class license. Of course, you don't need to aim as high as the General class, but may take the written examination for a Technician license.

There's one thing you should remember, though, and that is that no one needs an amateur license in order to take an exam for *any* amateur class license. In fact, there have been cases when a non-ham has taken a code test and all the required written examinations in one sitting before an FCC examiner and strolled away knowing that he would soon receive an *Amateur Extra Class* license with his own call sign.

Since the Novice class license has the fewest privileges, what can Novices *not* do that other class licensees can do? The most obvious restriction is that a Novice cannot transmit anything other than telegraphy. He can't speak over a microphone or use radioteletype or send television signals from a station he's *operating*. His transmitter input power cannot exceed 250 watts, while all other class licensees may operate a kilowatt (1000 watts) maximum on most bands, except in the Novice bands where they, too, must operate no more than 250 watts.

A Novice may operate any licensed Amateur Radio station, assuming that it is capable of telegraphy in a Novice subband with an input power not over 250 watts. What this means is that a Novice can operate using only Novice privileges, no matter what station he's using. For example, you're a Novice class licensee and visit a ham friend of yours, who holds a General ticket, and want to operate on 15 meters from his station. What are you allowed to do? Actually, you may do nothing more than you're permitted to do at your own station — operate Morse code (A1 operation) in the Novice 15-meter subband, 21.1 to 21.2 MHz, with a transmitter input power of 250 watts or less. You must identify your transmissions with *his* call sign.

When this friend visits your station, he may operate according to the privileges granted to his General class license, but he must add his own call to yours. For instance, your call sign in KA6XYZ and his is WA2XXX. He would have to sign "KA6XYZ/WA2XXX" if he operates your station outside of a Novice subband. If he operates using the same privileges you have, then he may sign just "KA6XYZ."

What to Expect

Traditionally, the Novice code test consists of 25 five-letter groups sent at a rate of five words per minute. You'll be expected to copy accurately at least 25 consecutive letters — one full minute. A recent change allows for a different testing procedure. Your volunteer examiner may now send a five-minute plain English message and give you a multiple-choice or fill-in-the-blank examination testing your general comprehension of the message. A passing grade is on accuracy of 70 percent or higher. Your receiving and sending tests might include simple punctuation and numerals.

After you pass the code test, your volunteer examiner will send you Form 610, with verification of his eligibility to administer and your eligibility to take the exam, to the FCC in Gettysburg. Soon after than, he'll receive your written examination in the mail, and will have you take the test in his presence. He'll then return it to the FCC for grading. For the Novice license, the written test is 20 questions on basic amateur regulations and certain radio theory and operating practices. The questions are all multiple choice, as explained in chapter 3. The study guide below will show you the subject matter the Novice exam will cover. A passing grade is 74 percent, which allows you to get five answers wrong and still qualify for your Novice ticket.

A few weeks later, if you passed the exam, you will receive your license in the mail and can then get on the air!

FCC Study Outline
Novice Class Amateur Radio Operator License Examination

(Element 2 Syllabus)
(This material is covered in ARRL's beginner package, *Tune in the World with Ham Radio*)

A. Rules and Regulations

Define:
1) Amateur Radio Service 97.3(a)
2) Amateur Radio operator 97.3(c)
3) Amateur Radio station 97.3(e)
4) Amateur Radio communications 97.3(b)
5) Operator license 97.3(d)
6) Station license 97.3(d)
7) Control operator 97.3(o)
8) Third-party traffic 97.3(v)

Novice class operator privileges:
9) Authorized frequency bands 97.7(e)
10) Authorized emission (A1) 97.7(e)

Prohibited practices:
11) Unidentified communications 97.123
12) Intentional interference 97.125
13) False signals 97.121
14) Communication for hire 97.112(a)

Basis and purpose of the Amateur Radio Service rules and regulations:
15) To recognize and enhance the value of the Amateur Radio Service to the public as a voluntary, non-commercial communication service, particularly with respect to providing emergency

communications. 97.1(a)
16) To continue and extend the Amateur Radio operators' proven ability to contribute to the advancement of the radio art. 97.1(b)
17) To encourage and improve the Amateur Radio Service by providing for advancing skills is both the communication and technical phases. 97.1(c)
18) To expand the existing reservoir within the Amateur Radio Service of trained operators, technicians and electronics experts. 97.1(d)
19) To continue and extend the radio amateurs' unique ability to enhance international good will. 97.1(e)

Operating rules:
20) U.S. Amateur Radio station call signs 2.302 and FCC Public Notice
21) Permissible points of communications 97.89(a)(1)
22) Station logbook, logging requirements 97.103(a), (b); 97.105
23) Station identification 97.84(a)
24) Novice-band transmitter power limitation 97.67(b), (d)

25) Necessary procedure in response to an official notice of violation 97.137
26) Control operator requirements 97.79(a), (b)

B. Operating Procedures

1) R-S-T signal reporting system
2) Choice of telegraphy speed
3) Zero-beating received signal
4) Transmitter tune-up procedure
5) Use of common and internationally recognized telegraphy abbreviations, including: CQ, DE, K, SK, R, AR, 73, QRS, QRZ, QTH, QSL, QRM, QRN

C. Radio Wave Propagation

1) Sky wave; "skip"
2) Ground wave

D. Amateur Radio Practice

1) Measures to prevent use of Amateur Radio station equipment by unauthorized persons

Safety precautions:
2) Lightning protection for antenna system

3) Ground system
4) Antenna-installation safety procedures

Electromagnetic compatability — identify and suggest cure:
5) Overload of consumer electronic products by strong radio frequency fields
6) Interference to consumer electronic products caused by radiated harmonics

Interpretation of SWR readings as related to faults in antenna system:
7) Acceptable readings
8) Possible causes of unacceptable readings

E. Electrical Principles

Concepts:
1) Voltage
2) Alternating current, direct current
3) Conductor, insulator
4) Open circuit, short circuit
5) Energy, power
6) Frequency, wavelength
7) Radio frequency
8) Audio frequency

Electrical units:
 9) Volt
10) Ampere
11) Watt
12) Hertz
13) Metric prefixes: mega, kilo, centi, milli, micro, pico

F. Circuit Components

Physical appearance, applications and schematic symbols of:
1) Quartz crystals
2) Meters (D'Arsonval movement)
3) Vacuum tubes
4) Fuses

G. Practical Circuits

Block diagrams:
1) The stages in a simple telegraphy (A1) transmitter
2) The stages in a simple receiver capable of telegraphy (A1) reception
3) The functional layout of Novice station equipment, including transmitter, receiver, antenna switching, antenna feedline, antenna and telegraph key

H. Signals and emissions

1) Emission type A1

Cause and cure:
2) Backwave
3) Key clicks
4) Chirp
5) Superimposed hum
6) Undesirable harmonic emissions
7) Spurious emissions

I. Antennas and Feedlines

Necessary physical dimensions of these popular high-frequency antennas for resonance on Amateur Radio frequencies:
1) A half-wave dipole
2) A quarter-wave vertical

Common types of feedlines used at Amateur Radio stations
3) Coaxial cable
4) Parallel-conductor line

Chapter 5

The Technician and General Class Licenses

The material in this chapter covers what you need to know to pass the written part for the Technician or General class Amateur Radio license. (The written test element required for either examination is FCC Test Element 3.) Printed below is the FCC's study outline, which lists the subjects the test will cover. This chapter does not follow the same subject order as the FCC's outline; we've rearranged the subjects to make studying a little easier. However, we recommend that you constantly refer to the FCC outline printed here and check off each topic as you cover it. If you have trouble with a certain subject, make a note of it on the outline so that you can come back to it.

Federal Communications Commission Study Guide
Technician/General Class Amateur Radio Operator License Examination

(Element 3 Syllabus)

A. Rules and Regulations
1) Control point §97.3(p)
2) Emergency communications §97.3(w); §97.107
3) Amateur Radio transmitter power limitations §97.67
4) Station-identification requirements §97.84(b), (f), (g); §97.79(c)
5) Third-party participation in Amateur Radio communications §97.79(d)
6) Domestic and international third-party traffic §97.114; Appendix 2, Art. 41, Sec. 2
7) Permissible one-way transmissions §97.91
8) Frequency bands available to the Technician class §97.7(d)
9) Frequency bands available to the General class §97.7(b)
10) Limitations on use of Amateur Radio frequencies §97.61
11) Selection and use of frequencies §97.63
12) Radio-controlled model crafts and vehicles §97.65(a); §97.99
13) Radioteleprinter emissions §97.69
Prohibited practices:
14) Broadcasting §97.113
15) Music §97.115
16) Codes and ciphers §97.117
17) Obscenity, indecency, profanity §97.119

B. Operating Procedures
1) Radiotelephony
2) Radio teleprinting
3) Use of repeaters
4) VOX transmitter control
5) Full break-in telegraphy
6) Operating courtesy
7) Antenna orientation
8) International communication
9) Emergency-preparedness drills

C. Radio Wave Propagation
1) Ionospheric layers; D, E, F1, F2
2) Absorption
3) Maximum usable frequency
4) Regular daily variations
5) Sudden ionospheric disturbance
6) Scatter
7) Sunspot cycle
8) Line-of-sight
9) Ducting, tropospheric bending

D. Amateur Radio Practice
Safety precautions:
1) Household ac supply and electrical wiring safety
2) Dangerous voltages in equipment made inaccessible to accidental contact
Transmitter performance:
3) Two-tone test
4) Neutralizing final amplifier
5) Power measurement
Use of test equipment:
6) Oscilloscope
7) Multimeter
8) Signal generators
9) Signal tracer
Electromagnetic compatibility; identify and suggest cure:
10) Disturbance in consumer electronic products caused by audio rectification
Proper use of the following station components and accessories:
11) Reflectometer (VSWR meter)
12) Speech processor — rf and af
13) Electronic T-R switch
14) Antenna-tuning unit; matching network
15) Monitoring oscilloscope
16) Non-radiating load; "dummy antenna"
17) Field strength meter; S-meter
18) Wattmeter

E. Electrical Principles
Concepts:
1) Impedance
2) Resistance
3) Reactance
4) Inductance
5) Capacitance
6) Impedance matching
Electrical Units:
7) Ohm
8) Microfarad, Picofarad
9) Henry, millihenry, microhenry
10) Decibel
Mathematical relationships:
11) Ohm's law

Electrical Principles

The alarm goes off, but it just seems impossible to get out of bed this morning. It happens to the best of us. Sometimes, we just can't seem to get the push needed to get up and start the day. We need that shove to get moving, and it's no different with electricity.

Electricity needs a push to help it get going. We have a name for that push, correctly called *electromotive force (emf)*. More commonly, it's known as *voltage*. You probably have heard the term *voltage* before, but never knew what it was. It simply means the electric force which pushes electrons, the parts of atoms which have negative charges, through an electric circuit. Without voltage, there's no push. Without push, there's no electric current.

"Now wait a minute! What do we mean by current?"

The word *current* comes to us from a Latin word meaning "to run," and it always implies movement. When someone speaks of the current in a river, we visualize a flow of water; a current of air can be a light breeze or a hurricane; and a current of electricity is a flow of electrons. Even when we speak of a current theory in electronics or the current issue of *QST*, we mean one that's "going around" at the present time.

Current in electricity means the movement of electrons, and it's the result of the voltage pushing those electrons through an electrical circuit. It's just the same as your movement throughout the day is the result of that original push to get yourself out of bed in the morning. Without the push in the morning, you never get yourself moving. Without the voltage, there's no current.

Current is indicated in equations, diagrams and often on the equipment itself by the letter I. Its strength is measured in *amperes*, and the equipment which does the measuring is called an *ammeter*. An ampere, however, is often too large a measurement to use. So in electronic circuits we usually measure current in *milliamperes*, each one of which is one-thousandth of an ampere, or in *microamperes*, each of which is one-millionth of an ampere. It takes 1000 milliamperes, or one-million microamperes, to make one ampere. Amperes are abbreviated amp or A; milliamperes, mA; microamperes, µA.

E = Voltage

We have already explained that the force which gets, and keeps, electrons moving and creates a current is referred to by a few different names. Sometimes we call it *voltage*. Other times, we call it *electromotive force*. And occasionally, we use the terms *difference of potential* or *electrical potential*. Voltage is its most common name, and is the term people normally use when speaking of car batteries, power lines, etc. *Electromotive force* means, literally, electron-moving force. The names *difference of potential* and *electrical potential* are based on the fact that electrons have the ability or readiness to do work. When there is a *difference* of potential between two points, that difference is measured in *voltage*. For our purposes all the names can be used interchangeably, so you can use the word voltage any time difference of potential, electromotive force, or electrical potential are mentioned in the license examinations. Voltage is indicated by the letter E or the letter V, and it's measured in volts by an instrument called a *voltmeter*.

R = Resistance

Each day of our lives, we run into resistance. *Resistance* is something which fights motion. Most of us have never been in a jungle, but from watching Tarzan movies we know that running along a highway is a lot easier than running through a jungle. The jungle offers more resistance to a runner than the highway does.

Electricity meets a similar resistance. All materials have electrical resistance. There's always some opposition to the flow of current. At times, current may flow very easily, but there's always at least a little resistance present.

Resistance is indicated by the letter R and is measured in units called *ohms* by an instrument called an *ohmmeter*. The symbol for an ohm is Ω, the Greek capital letter omega.

Resistors

Resistors are among the most basic components in electronics and radio. As

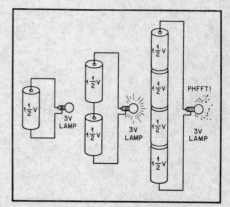

Fig. 1 — A 1-1/2-volt battery doesn't have the potential to force enough current through a 3-volt lamp, but a 6-volt battery has more than enough! One connection of a cell is called + or positive (the small electrodes when not marked) and the other is called − or negative. Voltages add when connected in series (+ to −).

their name implies, resistors are components built to oppose, defeat or at least frustrate electric current. The amount of resistance they can exert is determined by their manufacturer and is indicated on them in some way, so that the person building or repairing equipment can determine which one or ones to use for the purpose of limiting the amount of current flow and controlling the voltage to various parts of the circuit.

Electric currents commonly flow through a wire, and any piece of wire exerts a certain amount of resistance to the flow of electrons. The amount of this natural resistance depends on four things: the length of the wire (the longer the wire, the greater the resistance); its area in cross section (the larger the area, the less the resistance); its material (copper and aluminum, for example, have a low resistance); and its temperature (the higher the temperature — with some exceptions — the greater the resistance).

We do not, however, necessarily or even usually call a piece of wire or any type of conductor "a resistor," even though it exhibits a small amount of resistance. As the term is used in electronics, a resistor is a component *manufactured* to resist electric current, with the manufacturer determining how much resistance it will exhibit. He will indicate that amount on the resistor by color bands or by a printed notation. If resistors are put into situations of resisting current less than their own power rating, they will almost certainly be winners. If, on the other hand, they are matched against a strength of voltage they aren't equipped to handle, they'll burn out. For the sake of your equipment, your wallet and your personal safety, you should know three things about any resistor you plan to use:

1) its resistance in ohms;
2) its *tolerance* — a percentage, labeled on the resistor, which tells you how close to that resistance it can be counted upon to be;
3) its *power rating* in watts. Power ratings can be obtained from catalog listings, from labels on the component, or in many cases by practical experience from the physical size of the resistor.

Resistors are made of various substances. A common type is made of powdered carbon mixed with a binding material and baked into a small, rod-shaped form, with wires attached to its ends. Other resistors can be made by winding ceramic tubes with special kinds of wire, particularly alloy wires such as Nichromes, which have very high electrical resistance. Typical wirewound resistors can operate at higher temperatures and tolerate much stronger currents than the carbon ones normally used. They are usually larger and more expensive than carbon resistors.

Instead of being fixed for a definite amount of resistance, some resistors are

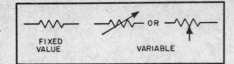

Fig. 2 — Schematic symbols for resistors.

adjustable or variable in resistance. They may have a slide contact or "tap" which makes them function as *voltage dividers*, allowing different voltages to go to different parts of the circuit. The volume control on your television set or radio is a type of variable resistor. The circuit symbols for a fixed-value resistor and a variable resistor are shown in Fig. 2.

Combining Resistors

People designing or working on radio equipment (or people taking an FCC examination) may need to know the total amount of resistance present in a circuit. The total depends on how the different resistors are wired together; that is, whether they are connected *in series*, end to end like a string of linked sausages or *in parallel*, side by side like a picket fence.

When resistors are connected in series, all you have to do to figure their total resistance in ohms, is to add them together, so

$$R_{total} = R1 + R2 + R3 + \text{etc.} \quad \text{(Eq. 1)}$$

As you do the figuring, note that the sum of any number of resistors in series is always more than the number of ohms in even the highest-valued individual resistor in the circuit. A second important factor concerning resistors in series is that the same amount of current flows through each of them, but the voltage drops down from resistor to resistor. The sum of all these voltage drops equals the source voltage (you'll understand what we're talking about here after we discuss Ohm's Law and Kirchhoff's Laws).

Combining resistors in parallel is a different story. If there are only two resistors to be combined in parallel, use this simple equation

$$R_{total} = \frac{R1 \times R2}{R1 + R2} \quad \text{(Eq. 2)}$$

If R1 = 3 ohms and R2 = 6 ohms, the total resistance is

$$\frac{3 \times 6}{3 + 6} \text{ or 2 ohms} \quad \text{(Eq. 3)}$$

When three or more resistors are combined in parallel, a more complicated equation is used. It's

$$R_{total} = \frac{1}{\frac{1}{R1} + \frac{1}{R2} + \frac{1}{R3} + \text{etc.}}$$
$$\text{(Eq. 4)}$$

If you've forgotten how to add fractions or how to divide a number into "1," you can either swallow your pride and ask someone to show you, or you can spare your pride (for later swallowing) by first combining R1 and R2, using the equation for two resistors, and then using the *result* of that combination with R3 — again using the two-resistor equation.

Example: If there are three resistors in parallel, R1 and R2 being the same 3-ohm and 6-ohm resistors we used in the last example, and R3 being a 2-ohm resistor to be combined with them, we would first combine R1 and R2, get its result of 2 ohms and then use that 2-ohm result to combine with R3. R_{total} for R1, R2 and R3 in parallel combination would then be determined as

$$\frac{2 \times R3}{2 + R3} = \frac{2 \times 2}{2 + 2} = \frac{4}{4} = 1 \text{ ohm}$$
$$\text{(Eq. 5)}$$

This is the answer you would get if you added all three resistors as fractions and then divided their fractional sum into "1," using the more complicated equation. The alternative and much simpler method can be used for any number of resistors.

Note that the total resistance of the circuit is always less than the number of ohms in even the lowest-valued resistor in the circuit. And remember this fact: When resistors are connected in parallel, the voltage stays the same across each resistor, but the current through each one may be different. In addition, the sum of all the branch currents is equal to the strength of current present at the beginning of the circuit.

Ohm's Law

Resistance, voltage and current are tied together in a very important way by what is known as *Ohm's Law*. It's expressed by a mathematical equation which you should understand and memorize.

Ohm's Law is stated by the equation E = IR. It can also be stated

$$I = \frac{E}{R} \text{ or } R = \frac{E}{I} \quad \text{(Eq. 6)}$$

Since you already know what E, I and R stand for and how they are measured, you can say the equation in words: voltage (in volts) equals current (in amperes) multiplied by resistance (in ohms); current equals voltage divided by resistance; resistance equals voltage divided by current.

Remember that in Ohm's Law, the E either stands alone (E = IR) or is on top on its side of the Ohm's Law equation.

$$\frac{E}{I} = R \text{ or } \frac{E}{R} = I \quad \text{(Eq. 7)}$$

A traditional method which students use

Fig. 3 — Ohm's Law.

to remember Ohm's Law, particularly if they're uncertain about changing from one form of the equation to another, is to draw a circle and arrange E, I and R as shown.

To find the equation for any one of these, put your thumb on top of the one you want and see what you have left. Your thumb on E says that the voltage equals IR (I multiplied by R); thumb on R says that resistance equals E over I (E divided by I); thumb on I says current equals E over R. Remember that E is placed on top of the circle, just as it is in the equations it illustrates.

When you know any two of the three things involved in Ohm's Law, you can always get the third. For example, suppose you have a circuit (electrical path) which has a current of 3 amperes and a resistance of 40 ohms, but you don't know the voltage. Since E is what you need to know, use

$$E = IR = 3 \times 40 = 120 \text{ volts} \qquad \text{(Eq. 8)}$$

If you knew the current and voltage in that same problem and didn't know the resistance, you would use

$$R = \frac{E}{I} = \frac{120}{3} = 40 \text{ ohms} \qquad \text{(Eq. 9)}$$

If you knew the resistance and voltage, and didn't know the current, you would use

$$I = \frac{E}{R} = \frac{120}{40} = 3 \text{ amps} \qquad \text{(Eq. 10)}$$

You have just worked Ohm's Law all three ways.

Always decide what it is that you want to find out and write that down first. Add an equal sign after it, and then write down the things you already know. You'll avoid a lot of mistakes if you always check your answer that way. Make up some problems of your own, and practice.

P = Power

Power, which is the rate of doing work, is measured in units called *watts* by an instrument called a *wattmeter*. It's most often indicated by the letter P in equations, but sometimes a W is used. It can be calculated (when the current we're using is direct current, which we'll mention next) by using the equation P = IE. This is an easy one to remember since it spells PIE. Written either P = IE or P = EI, it says that power (in watts) is equal to current

(in amperes) multiplied by voltage (in volts).

The Federal Communications Commission has set up definite rules as to the amount of power you're allowed to use as input power to the final stage of your amateur transmitter. For example, all licensees may use no more than 250 watts of input power on the Novice subbands. Higher classes of licensees are allowed a maximum of 1000 watts or one *kilowatt* (kW) on most amateur bands. The prefix *kilo* means 1000, as opposed to milli, which, as we've already mentioned, means

$$\frac{1}{1000}$$

The power equation can also be written

$$P = I^2R \text{ or } P = \frac{E^2}{R} \qquad \text{(Eq. 11)}$$

with R referring to resistance. You'll need to know these other equations for the test.

Let's say that the voltage to the final tube in a transmitter is measured to be 880 V, and the current is 300 mA (0.3 A). The power input to this stage is

$$P = IE = (0.3)(880) = 264 \text{ watts} \qquad \text{(Eq. 12)}$$

This power level would be illegal in the Novice subbands.

What if you knew only the voltage and resistance, and needed to know the power? A potential of 12 volts is measured across a 22 ohm resistor. How much power is the resistor dissipating? Here you must use one of the forms of Eq. 11.

$$P = \frac{E^2}{R} = \frac{(12)^2}{220} = 0.655 \text{ watts} \qquad \text{(Eq. 13)}$$

In this application you should use a resistor rated at 1 watt or higher.

Kirchhoff's Laws

There are two laws, known as Kirchhoff's Laws, which apply to any closed dc circuit. The first law states that, in any series circuit, the sum of the voltage drops must equal the sum of the voltages supplied by all sources in the circuit.

Fig. 4 illustrates this first law. The voltage drop across each resistor can be found by multiplying its resistance by the current going through that resistor (E = IR). The resistance of each resistor is given, but we need to find how much current is traveling through each resistor. Since the amount of current going through any point in a dc series circuit is the same as the amount of current going through any other point in the circuit, by taking the total voltage of the circuit, 10 V, and dividing it by the total resistance in

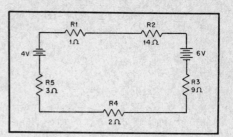

Fig. 4 — Using Kirchhoff's first law.

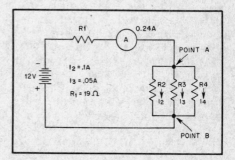

Fig. 5 — Using Kirchhoff's second law.

the circuit, 29 ohms, we find that each resistor has 0.345 A passing through it. The voltage drop across R1 is 0.345 A times 1 ohm, which equals 0.345 V. (E = IR). The voltage drops across R2, R3, R4, and R5 are similarly calculated by multiplying 0.345 A by the resistances to get the answers 4.83 V, 3.105 V, 0.69 V and 1.035 V, respectively. The sum of these voltage drops equals 10 V, which is the total voltage supplied by all sources in the circuit!

Kirchhoff's second law states that whenever a circuit branches into two or more directions, the current going into the branch point, or node, is equal to the current coming out.

Fig. 5 illustrates how this second law enables us to calculate the resistance of R4. Let's take this problem step by step. At point A, we know that there is 0.24 A. We also know that at point B there is 0.24 A because Kirchhoff's second law states that the current going into the branch point is equal to the current coming out. Taking the values of the currents flowing through R2 and R3, we can calculate the value of the current going through R4 as follows: 0.24 − (0.1 + 0.05) = 0.09. There is 0.09 A going through R4.

The voltage drop across R1 plus the voltage drop from point A to point B must equal 12 V. Therefore, subtracting the voltage drop across R1 from 12 V will give us the voltage drop from point A to point B. 19 × 0.24 = 4.56 V. Therefore, the voltage drop from point A to point B equals 12 − 4.56, which equals 7.44 V. The voltage drop across each resistor between points A and B is 7.44 V because they are in parallel. Therefore, the value of R4 can be calculated by using

$$R = \frac{E}{I}, \text{ to get } \frac{7.44}{0.09} = 82.67 \text{ ohms.}$$
(Eq. 14)

Voltage and Current Dividers

In a series circuit with a voltage source and several resistors, the voltage across each resistor is *directly* proportional to its resistance divided by the total resistance (R_T) in the circuit. The voltage-divider circuit of Fig. 6 shows how this occurs and how to calculate each voltage. This method can be expanded to include any number of resistors in series. For example, if there were five resistors in a series circuit, the voltage across a particular resistor would be the total voltage of the circuit multiplied by the ratio of the particular resistance to the sum of all five resistances. You could get the voltages by using Kirchhoff's first law, as in the example of Fig. 4, but the voltage-divider method is a short-cut in which you don't need to calculate the current in the circuit. Note how the three voltage drops equal the voltage source — Kirchhoff's first law obeyed!

In a parallel circuit with a voltage source and several resistors, the current through each resistor is *inversely* proportional to its resistance divided by the total resistance in the circuit. A current-divider example is given in Fig. 7. Calculation of each branch current is similar to the method used for the voltage divider, except that the resistance ratio is inverted, and that the total resistance consists now of resistors *in parallel*. Like the voltage-divider principle, this method can be expanded to include any number of resistors in a parallel circuit.

Direct and Alternating Current

In picturing current flow it's natural to think of a single, constant force causing the electrons to move. When this is so, the electrons always move in the same direction through a path or circuit made up of conductors connected together in a continuous chain. Such a current is called a *direct current*, abbreviated *dc*. It is the type of current furnished by batteries, by certain types of electromechanical generators, and ac-operated dc power supplies.

It's also possible to have a voltage that periodically reverses. With this kind of voltage, the current flows first in one direction through the circuit and then in the other. Such a voltage, or electromotive force, is called an alternating emf, and the current is called an *alternating current* (abbreviated *ac*). The reversals (alternations) may occur at any rate from a few per second up to several billion per second. In one cycle, the force acts first in one direction, then in the other, and then returns to the first direction to begin the next cycle. The number of cycles in one second is called the *frequency* of the alternating current. The frequency of our common house current, for instance, is 60 *cycles per second* (cps), or, as expressed in international units of measurement (and probably on the FCC written exam), 60 *hertz* (Hz). The word hertz means *cycles per second* and is not a synonym for the word cycle.

The difference between direct current and alternating current is shown in Fig. 8. In these graphs, the horizontal axis (the line going left and right) measures time, increasing toward the right, away from the vertical axis (the line going up and down). The vertical axis represents the *amplitude* or strength of the current, increasing in either the up or down direction away from the horizontal axis. If the graph is *above* the horizontal axis, the current is flowing in one direction through the circuit (indicated by the + sign) and if it's *below* the horizontal axis, the current is flowing in the reverse direction through the circuit (indicated by the − sign).

Fig. 8A shows that if we close the circuit — that is, make the path for the current complete — at the time indicated by X, the current almost instantly takes the strength indicated by the height A. After that, the current continues at the same strength as time goes on. This is an ordinary *direct* current.

In Fig. 8B, the current starts flowing with the strength A at time X, continues at that strength until time Y and then almost

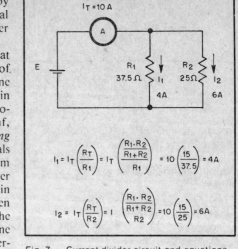

$$I_1 = I_T \left(\frac{R_T}{R_1} \right) = I_T \left(\frac{\frac{R_1 \cdot R_2}{R_1 + R_2}}{R_1} \right) = 10 \left(\frac{15}{37.5} \right) = 4A$$

$$I_2 = I_T \left(\frac{R_T}{R_2} \right) = I \left(\frac{\frac{R_1 \cdot R_2}{R_1 + R_2}}{R_2} \right) = 10 \left(\frac{15}{25} \right) = 6A$$

Fig. 7 — Current-divider circuit and equations.

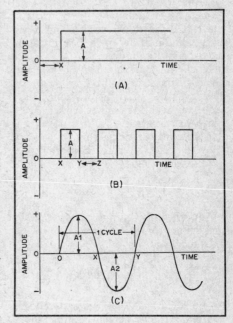

Fig. 8 — Three types of current flow. A — Direct current; B — intermittent direct current; C — alternating current.

instantly stops. After an interval YZ, the current again begins to flow and the same sort of start-and-stop performance is repeated. This is an *intermittent* direct current. We could get it by continually closing and opening a switch in the circuit. It's a *direct* current because the *direction* of current flow does not change; the graph is always on the same side of the horizontal axis (always above it in this example). Sometimes this type of current flow is called *pulsating* dc.

In Fig. 8C, the current starts at zero, increases in strength as time goes on until it reaches the strength A1 while flowing in the + direction, then decreases until it drops to zero strength once more. At that time (X) the *direction* of the current flow reverses; this is indicated by the fact that the next part of the graph is below the axis. As time goes on, the strength increases, with the current now flowing in

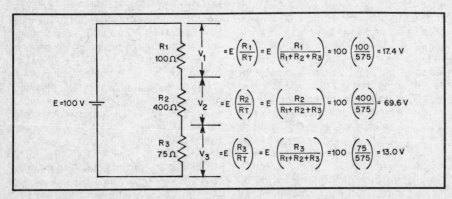

Fig. 6 — Voltage-divider circuit and equations.

the – direction, until it reaches strength A2. Then the strength decreases until finally it drops to zero (Y), and the direction reverses once more. This is an *alternating* current.

There are problems in working with alternating current, stemming from the fact that the current (or voltage) is changing throughout the cycle. In a "steady" alternating current, each cycle is like the one before it and also like the one following it. But within the cycle there is no such peaceful repose as we can easily find in the behavior of direct current. This continual restlessness leads to all sorts of effects that are absent with dc. (That is, absent except during those times when the direct current is being started or stopped, or is otherwise changed. These periods can be, and are, ignored in many instances, although not in all.)

First, there is the question of how to assign a value to an alternating current. If we follow the current throughout a cycle, we may find that at successive instants it is increasing until it reaches say, 1 ampere. At that instant, it starts to decrease, eventually dying away to nothing. Then it reverses itself to do the same thing while flowing in the opposite direction. Next, it starts the whole business over again. At no point does it stand still long enough for us to say, "*That's* the value of the current."

RMS Value of Sinusoidal AC

The clue in settling on a number to use for the current is found in a statement about power. Power makes no distinction between ac and dc. A resistor gets just as hot when current flows from top to bottom as when it flows from bottom to top. Thus the power will be the same regardless of the direction of current flow; and since this is so, it doesn't matter how rapidly the current may reverse direction. It follows that we can say we have one ampere of alternating current flowing when that current heats a given resistor exactly as one ampere of direct current would heat it. If the alternating current has the form of a sine wave when plotted on a graph, as in Fig. 10, it will have an *effective value* of 0.707 ampere when its maximum value during the cycle is about 1 ampere. The same relationship holds for the effective value of voltage. Another term for effective is *rms* (root-mean-square), this name coming from the method used to analyze such a wave mathematically.

The effects associated with alternating current are intimately related to the frequency of the current, or the number of cycles per second or hertz. One principal effect is *reactance*. Since you'll be running into reactance often, especially on the FCC examination, it needs a little detailed consideration. To appreciate reactance, however, you need first to know about energy storage in electric circuits.

Phase in Resistive Circuits

When an alternating voltage is applied to a resistance, the current flows exactly in step with the voltage. In other words, the voltage and current are *in phase*, as two musicians in an orchestra both tap their feet at the same instant. This is true at any frequency of alternating current if the resistance is "pure" — that is, is free from reactance.

There's one more thing you should remember before we continue: In a purely resistive circuit, or for purely resistive parts of circuits, Ohm's Law is just as useful for alternating current of any frequency as it is for direct current.

Reactance

A coil or capacitor will react to alternating current by storing and releasing electrical or magnetic energy as the alternating current goes through it. This is measured in ohms but is denoted by an X instead of an R.

Like the wattless watt, though, this is an ohm without resistance. It does act like a real ohm to this extent: Given a fixed frequency, the current through it will be directly proportional to the voltage applied. In other words, we can write for reactance the equivalent of Ohm's Law for resistance

$$I = \frac{E}{X} \qquad \text{(Eq. 15)}$$

Also, unlike resistance, reactance depends upon frequency as determined by the way alternating current and voltage react with coils and capacitors.

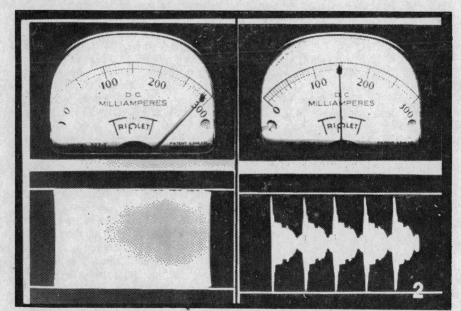

Fig. 9 — A problem with alternating current is in finding a representative value of current to use in calculations. Here, two types of alternating current from a transmitter with the same amplitude produce different meter readings of average current.

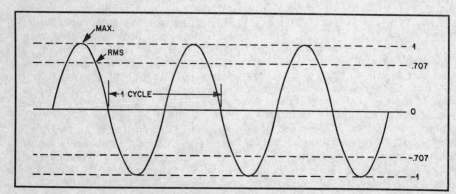

Fig. 10 — If an alternating current or voltage has the sine-wave form shown here, an effective or *RMS* value of current of 0.707 ampere exists when the peak value is 1 A, as shown by the scale at the right. This waveform also has a *peak-to-peak* (pk-pk) value of 2 volts. These ratios are the same for all sine waves. Other waveform types will have different ratios.

Effects of Reactance upon Voltage and Current

Resistors do not store energy like capacitors and coils do. As a result, they

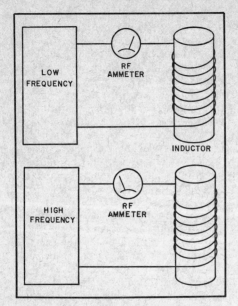

Fig. 11 — The current flowing through a given coil, or inductor, decreases as the frequency is increased. A direct current passes to a degree limited only by the resistance of the winding. The core is the form on which the inductor is wound.

do not make any distinction between current (used in the storage of magnetic energy) and voltage (used in the storage of electrical energy). Because capacitors and inductors (remember, coil is another name for inductor) *do* store electrical and magnetic energy, they affect voltage and current differently.

A discharged or "empty" capacitor looks like a short circuit. This means a lot of current flows into the capacitor before the voltage across it can build up. Only when the electrical energy becomes stored in the capacitor does the voltage follow the current. As a result, capacitors shift the *phase* of the alternating current so that the current is 90 degrees ahead of the voltage.

An inductor acts like a large resistance to a change in current. This means that a voltage appears across the inductor while the energy is being stored in the magnetic field of the coil (E = IR). When this energy is stored, the current through the coil is high but the voltage across it is low. The result is that the voltage is 90 degrees ahead of the current in inductors.

Capacitors

Capacitors are components which perform a wide variety of functions in electronic circuits. Their name comes from a Latin word meaning "to hold," and ca-

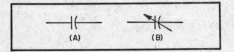

Fig. 12 — At A is the symbol for a fixed capacitor; at B, the symbol for a variable capacitor. (The curved line represents the rotor and the facing straight line, the stator.)

pacitors are holders or storers of electrons. They consist of two or more metal or other conductive-material plates which face each other and have an insulating material called a *dielectric* between them. Electrons from any electrical source can be stored temporarily on these plates and be released in microseconds, or as much as days later.

The electrical property of a capacitor is called *capacitance*, just as the electrical property of a resistor is called resistance. Capacitance is indicated in equations by the letter C. The amount of a capacitance for each capacitor depends on three things:
1) the distance between the plates;
2) the area of the plates;
3) the material of the dielectric, which can be air, mica, oil, waxpaper, a chemical, a ceramic material or even a vacuum.

The basic unit for measuring capacitance is the *farad*. To measure small amounts of capacitance, the farad becomes unwieldly, so you will see smaller units such as the *microfarad*. A microfarad is one millionth of a farad or 10^{-6} farads. A *picofarad* is one millionth of a millionth of a farad or 10^{-12} farads. A picofarad used to be known as a micro-microfarad, which may help you remember its value.

The procedure for finding the total amount of capacitance in a circuit is exactly opposite from the way total resistance is calculated. In series, capacitance is totaled like resistance in parallel, with the total for two capacitors following the

$$C_{total} = \frac{C1 \times C2}{C1 + C2} \qquad \text{(Eq. 16)}$$

equation, and three or more following the

$$C_{total} = \frac{1}{\frac{1}{C1} + \frac{1}{C2} + \frac{1}{C3} + \text{etc.}} \qquad \text{(Eq. 17)}$$

equation. In parallel, capacitance is totaled by simply adding the values of the capacitors, so

$$C_{total} = C1 + C2 + C3 + \text{etc.} \qquad \text{(Eq. 18)}$$

Capacitors are said to be *charged* when they have stored as many electrons on their plates as their physical characteristics make them capable of storing at the voltage being used. They can hold a charge even after the source current has been cut off. When a capacitor is releasing stored energy, it is *discharging*.

The size and shape of capacitors vary greatly. In many radio circuits, the capacitors weigh only a small fraction of an ounce. Some, however, can weigh 150 pounds each. Capacitors are classified commercially according to the material of

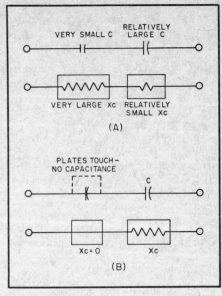

Fig. 13 — At A, all circuit voltage appears across an open circuit which leaves only a small voltage across the large C. At B is a closed circuit. There is no voltage drop, so all of the voltage appears across the smaller C.

the dielectric — mica, paper, ceramic and so on. Each type has different advantages. They are further classified by whether their capacitance is *fixed* or *variable*.

A common type of variable capacitor, which has air as a dielectric, consists of a series of metal plates, half of them immovable, the other half mounted on a rotatable shaft. The stationary plates are called the *stator*. The movable plates make up the *rotor* (short for rotator). As the shaft is turned, the rotor plates move in and out between the stator plates without touching them. This movement varies the extent of plate surfaces facing each other. The more the plates are meshed together, the greater the capacitance will be. Another type of variable or adjustable capacitor is adjusted by using a screw to change the distance between the plates. It's used for fine adjustments in tuning circuits at the time the equipment is being aligned.

Electrolytic Capacitors

Capacitors are classified according to their dielectrics. The *electrolytic capacitor* has a chemical, called an *electrolyte*, as its dielectric. It is a very thin film of insulating material (aluminum oxide) that forms on one side of the capacitor's aluminum foil plates through electrochemical action. Because of the extreme thinness of this dielectric layer, the capacitance obtained with a given plate area is large compared with that of similar size capacitors having a different material for their dielectric. It is this electrolyte which gives the capacitor its name.

Found mostly in power-supply filters, electrolytic capacitors are *polarized*. This means that they must be connected in a dc circuit in only one way. The terminals are always marked to show which one goes to the positive side of the circuit and which to the negative. A quick and easy way to ruin an electrolytic, as these capacitors are nicknamed, is to connect it backwards.

All electrolytic capacitors have a small *leakage current* — a few milliamperes flowing through the capacitor itself. This isn't serious in a power-supply filter, but prohibits using the capacitor in many other circuits. Electrolytics cannot be used on pure alternating current; that is, ac with no superimposed dc potential.

Paper Capacitors

Paper-dielectric capacitors do not have the same limitation as electrolytics. The leakage current is practically unmeasurable if the unit is not defective. And because these capacitors are not polarized, they'll work on either dc or ac.

Capacitive Reactance

The more rapidly the applied voltage changes in value, the faster the capacitor stores energy. This means that a high-frequency alternating voltage will put more current into a given capacitor than a low-frequency voltage could. As we *increase* the frequency of an ac voltage, the reactance of the capacitor goes *down*. The formula for finding the reactance of a capacitor is

$$X_c = \frac{1}{2\pi fC} \qquad \text{(Eq. 19)}$$

where

X_c = capacitive reactance in ohms
f = frequency in Hz
C = capacitance in farads
π = 3.14

You should use the proper units. For example, if capacitance were in microfarads, you would have to change them to farads before making the calculations in the above equation.

Inductors

An *inductor* can be described as a piece of wire, a strip of metal or a piece of metal tubing wound into a coil. The metal used for the winding is usually copper or aluminum, and each coil has a *core* or center. Depending on the way the coil is to be used in the circuit, this core can be air or it can be iron in some form — finely powdered, laminated in sheets, or in compound with another metal. Coils are able to store magnetic energy, in contrast to capacitors, which store electric charge.

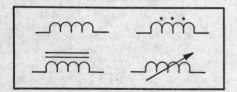

Fig. 14 — Common symbols for inductors.

They can be wound around their own solid core or wound around a supporting tube of a nonmagnetic substance such as cardboard or Bakelite. After they are wound, some coils are firm enough to hold their shape without the supporting tube and it can be removed.

The most important electrical effect of an inductor or coil is *inductance*, indicated by the letter *L* in equations. Its unit of measurement is the *henry*, but in radio work the smaller units of *millihenry* and *microhenry* are commonly used. The total amount of inductance in a circuit is calculated in henrys, using the same methods used in totaling resistors. In a series circuit, the individual inductance values are added together and L_{total} = L1 + L2 + L3 + etc. In parallel circuits, the equations are

$$L_{total} = \frac{L1 \times L2}{L1 + L2} \qquad \text{(Eq. 20)}$$

$$L_{total} = \frac{1}{\dfrac{1}{L1} + \dfrac{1}{L2} + \dfrac{1}{L3} + \text{etc.}}$$
$$\text{(Eq. 21)}$$

The word *inductance* comes from the same base as *induce* which means to lead, influence or persuade. Television commercials induce viewers to buy a particular product; drugs may be used to induce sleep or something else. In radio circuits, coils can be used to induce or create voltages, and hence currents, in other conductors without coming into direct contact with them. They accomplish this by *magnetism* and are, therefore, called *magnetic* components.

The motion of electrons, in addition to being able to produce light, heat and chemical changes, is also able to produce magnetism, and every electric current creates a magnetic field around itself as it flows. Extending out in concentric circles from around the conductor, the invisible lines of force in this magnetic field encircle it like an invisible tube. The field spreads outward as the current starts flowing and collapses back into the conductor as the current stops. It also increases in strength if the current increases and it decreases in strength when the current decreases.

When the conductor is a straight piece of wire, the force produced by this magnetic field is usually negligible compared to its effect if that same wire is wound into a coil. In coils, the magnetic field *around each turn of wire* affects the other turns. Together their fields produce one large magnetic field which can affect other nearby conductors. Much of the energy of the magnetic field is concentrated in the core, and the number of magnetic lines of force or *flux* for a given amount of current is the core's *permeability*.

The amount of inductance which a coil exhibits depends on four things:
1) the permeability of the core;
2) the number of turns;
3) the length of the coil;
4) the diameter of the coil.

If any of these is changed, the amount of inductance changes. If an iron or ferrite core is added to the coil, the permeability (and inductance) increases. If a movable iron or ferrite core is placed in a coil, the amount of inductance not only becomes greater, but can be varied as the core is moved in and out of the coil. Brass can also be used as a core material in radio-frequency variable inductors. It has the opposite effect of iron or ferrite, thereby decreasing the inductance as it enters the coil. The common symbols for various inductors are shown in Fig. 14.

A *toroid* is an important kind of coil, usually with a powdered-iron or ferrite-compound core. This coil is wound with one layer or many layers of wire and is curved into a doughnut shape. Because of its shape, it's a highly efficient inductor. There is no break in its circular core, so it keeps all of the lines of force inside it, rather than being partially outside as they would if the core were straight. In theory, a toroid requires no shield to prevent its magnetic field from spreading out and interfering with outside circuits. This self-shielding property helps keep outside forces from interfering with it and vice versa. Toroids can be mounted so close to each other that they almost touch, but because of the way they are made, there will be almost no inductive coupling between them. With ferrite or iron cores, they need only a small amount of wire and can have a very high inductance value.

Inductive Reactance

We said earlier that the more rapidly the current changes, the larger the opposing voltage generated in an inductance. A high-frequency alternating current changes more rapidly than a low-frequency one, since there are more cycles per second. This means that the higher the frequency or the larger the inductance, the harder it is for current to flow through the inductor. The current meets more opposition. The measure of this opposition is called *inductive reactance*, measured in ohms just like pure resistance.

The formula for inductive reactance is

$$X_L = 2\pi fL \qquad \text{(Eq. 22)}$$

where

X_L = inductive reactance in ohms
f = the frequency in Hz
L = inductance in henrys
π = 3.14

Impedance

If you've swallowed (and digested) what has gone before, you're ready to tackle *impedance*, a word that gets a lot of use in amateur conversations, especially on the air. Its basic definition is simple, but the details are far from that. In fact, we can't hope to do more than give you a speaking acquaintance with some of them in this discussion (just so you'll be able to join those conversations on the air). Fortunately, the FCC doesn't require us to be engineers, so we really don't need to know the inner workings of actual circuits. We should know *what* happens, but not so much *how* it happens.

In broad terms, impedance is a number you get by dividing the voltage applied to a circuit by the current flowing into it. In Fig. 18, suppose we measure the current I flowing into the box and find it to be 2 amperes when the applied ac voltage E is 250 volts. Dividing 250 by 2 gives 125 as the answer. Although this is not a dc circuit, we say that we have 125 "ohms" since the ohm got established as a unit representing the ratio of voltage to current (that is, E/I) in dc work. But we don't know what's in the box, do we? So we can't say that these "ohms" are either resistance or reactance. It would take more than a simple measurement of current or voltage to determine that, because — as we've seen — there is an element of phase to be reckoned with. The ammeter and voltmeter don't give any information about phase.

The fact is that we could get the same answer whether we had 125 ohms of "pure" resistance or "pure" reactance. But we could also get the same answer if the box contained 125 ohms of something that was a combination of both. Such a combination not only can exist but actually is likely to be more common than either alone.

Impedance is measured in ohms. In equations it's indicated by the letter Z. If you had a resistor and a reactance connected in series, their combined Z value would be equal to

$$\sqrt{R^2 + X^2} = Z \qquad \text{(Eq. 23)}$$

For example, if we had a resistance of 12 ohms connected in series with a capacitive reactance of −9 ohms, what would the total impedance of the circuit be?

$$Z = \sqrt{R^2 + X^2} = \sqrt{12^2 + (-9)^2} =$$

$$\sqrt{144 + 81} = \sqrt{225} = 15 \text{ ohms}$$
$$\text{(Eq. 24)}$$

If they were connected in parallel, their total Z would be equal to

$$Z = \frac{|RX|}{\sqrt{R^2 + X^2}} = \frac{|12 \times (-9)|}{\sqrt{12^2 + (-9)^2}} =$$

$$\frac{|-108|}{15} = 7.2 \text{ ohms} \qquad \text{(Eq. 25)}$$

Flux Density and Permeability

Flux density is the intensity of a magnetic field. It's called flux density because the lines of force in a magnetic field are known as *flux lines*. Flux density is expressed by the number of flux lines per unit of cross-sectional area perpendicular to the flux lines.

Calculating flux density is simple. Let's say we have a coil wound on an iron core having a cross-sectional area of two square inches. Sending a certain current through the coil creates 80,000 flux lines in the core. Since the area is two square inches, the flux density is 40,000 lines per square inch. Now suppose that the iron core is removed and the same current is maintained in the coil, and that the flux density without the iron core is 50 lines per square inch (it drops because iron has a higher tendency to hold magnetism than air does). A material's *permeability* is the ratio of the flux density with that material used as a core to the flux density (with the same coil and the same current) with an air core. In the case we just mentioned, the permeability of the iron is

$$\frac{40,000}{50} = 800$$

The inductance of the coil is increased 800 times by inserting the iron core as, other things being equal, the inductance will be proportional to the permeability.

The permeability of a ferromagnetic (meaning iron-like) material varies with the current. At low currents, increasing the current through the coil will cause a proportionate increase in flux, but at very high currents, increasing the current further may cause no significant change in the flux. When this is so, the iron is said to be *saturated*, just as a sponge can be saturated with water. Saturation causes a rapid decrease in permeability. Obviously, the inductance of an iron-core inductor is dependent upon the current flowing in the coil. In an air-core coil, the inductance is independent of current because air does not saturate.

Mutual Inductance

If two coils are arranged with their axes on the same line as shown in Fig. 15, a current sent through coil 1 will cause a magnetic field which "cuts" coil 2. Consequently, a voltage will be induced in coil 2 whenever the field strength is changing. The ratio of the induced voltage in the second coil to the rate of change of current in the first is called *mutual inductance* between the two coils.

If all the flux set up by one coil cuts all the turns of the other coil, the mutual inductance has its maximum possible value. If only a small part of the flux set up by one coil cuts the turns of the other, the mutual inductance is relatively small. Two coils having mutual inductance are said to be *coupled*.

The ratio of actual mutual inductance to the maximum possible value that could

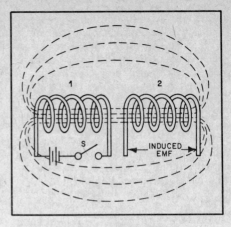

Fig. 15 — Mutual inductance. When S is closed, current flows through coil no. 1, setting up a magnetic field that induces an emf in the turns of coil no. 2.

theoretically be obtained with two given coils is called the *coefficient of coupling* between the two coils. It's frequently expressed as a percentage. Coils that have nearly the maximum possible (coefficient 1 or 100 percent) mutual inductance are said to be *loosely* coupled. The degree of coupling depends upon the physical spacing between the coils and how they are placed with respect to each other. Maximum coupling exists when they have a common axis and are as close together as possible (one wound over the other). The coupling is least when the coils are far apart or are placed so that their axes are at right angles.

The maximum possible coefficient of coupling is closely approached only when the two coils are wound on a closed iron core. The coefficient with air-core coils may run as high as 0.6 or 0.7 if one coil is wound over the other, but will be much less if the two coils are separated.

Transformers

Two coils having mutual inductance can constitute a *transformer*. The coil connected to the source of energy is called

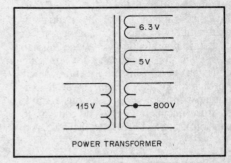

Fig. 16 — The symbol for a transformer with several windings, such as a power transformer. The numbers on the right-hand side (secondaries) represent the voltages that will be obtained when 115 volts is applied to the primary (left-hand) winding. Notice that a lead is shown from the center of the 800-volt winding; this is usually a center tap that divides the winding into two equal parts.

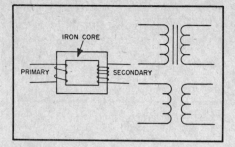

Fig. 17 — The transformer. Power is transferred from the primary coil to the secondary by means of the magnetic field. The upper symbol at right indicates an iron-core transformer, the lower one an air-core transformer.

the *primary* coil, and the other is called the *secondary* coil.

The usefulness of the transformer lies in the fact that electrical energy can be transferred from one circuit to another without direct connection, and in the process can be readily changed from one voltage level to another. Common house current is 120-volts ac. If you need a voltage of 240 volts ac, you would use a transformer that has twice as many turns on the secondary coil as it does on its primary coil. The induced voltage in the secondary would then be double the primary voltage, or 240 volts. A transformer can be used only with alternating current, because no voltages will be induced in the secondary if the magnetic field is not changing. If direct current is connected to the primary of a transformer, a voltage will be induced in the secondary only at the instant of closing and opening the primary circuit (switching the direct current on and off), since these are the only times the magnetic field changes.

The primary and secondary coils of a transformer may be wound on a core of magnetic material, such as iron. This increases the coupling of the coils so that a relatively small number of turns may be used to induce a given value of voltage with a small "magnetizing" current. A closed core (one having a continuous magnetic path), such as that shown in Fig. 17, also tends to make sure that practically all of the field set up by the current in the primary coil will cut the turns of the secondary coil.

Voltage and Turns Ratio

As we slightly mentioned already, for a given varying magnetic field, the voltage induced in a coil in the field is proportional to the number of turns in the coil. That's a complicated way of saying that a coil will have induced in it, or "get" more voltage from another coil if it has more turns. The fewer the turns, the less voltage it will get from another coil. If the two coils of a transformer are in the same field (which is the case when both are wound on the same closed core), it follows that the induced voltages will be proportional

to the number of turns in each coil. In the primary, the induced voltage is practically equal to, and opposes, the applied voltage.

The *turns ratio* is the number of turns on the primary compared to the number on the secondary in a transformer. If the secondary has twice as many turns as the primary, the primary-to-secondary turns ratio would be 1:2. The secondary would have twice the voltage of the primary, and the transformer would be a *step-up transformer*, because the voltage is stepping-up or increasing. If the secondary has only a third as many turns as the primary, the ratio would be 3:1 (primary-to-secondary), the voltage a third as much as on the secondary, and the transformer a *step-down transformer*, because the voltage would be stepping down, or decreasing.

If you know the number of turns in each coil of a transformer and know the voltage on the primary, you can figure out the voltage on the secondary by using the following equation

$$E_s = \frac{n_s}{n_p} \times E_p \qquad \text{(Eq. 26)}$$

where
E = voltage
n = number of turns
s = secondary
p = primary

Here's a problem to solve using the equation: A transformer has a primary winding (n_p) of 500 turns, a secondary winding (n_s) of 1000 turns, and a primary voltage (E_p) of 120 volts. How much voltage is there on the secondary (E_s)? The answer is

$$E_s = \frac{1000}{500} \times 120 = 240 \text{ volts} \qquad \text{(Eq. 27)}$$

The same problem could be stated in other ways. For example it might state that the transformer has a primary voltage of 120 volts and a 1:2 (primary-to-secondary) turns ratio, in which case the secondary voltage would be twice as much as the primary; or it might state that the primary has 120 volts and 500 turns, and the secondary a voltage of 240 volts. In that case, you would be asked for the number of turns on the secondary, which would be 1000 since the voltage indicates a 1:2 turns ratio.

Transformers usually have only one primary but may, and usually do, have more than one secondary. The voltage on each of these secondaries can be computed individually by using the former equation.

Whatever the induced voltages do (increase or decrease) in a transformer, the induced currents do just the opposite for a given primary current. In other words, when the induced voltage increases, the induced current decreases, and vice versa.

In a transformer, the primary current multiplied by the primary turns must equal the secondary current multiplied by the secondary turns. To find the current in either coil of a transformer, use the following equation

$$I_p = \frac{n_s}{n_p} \times I_s \qquad \text{(Eq. 28)}$$

where
I_p = primary current
I_s = secondary current
n_p = number of turns on primary
n_s = number of turns on the secondary

Transformer Efficiency

A transformer cannot create power; it can only transfer it and change the voltage. And as we previously mentioned, the power taken from the secondary cannot exceed that taken by the primary from the original voltage source. There is, in fact, always some power loss in the resistance of the coils and in the iron core, so in all practical cases the power taken from the source will exceed that taken from the secondary. An *efficiency factor* is important in transformers. We use the following equation to evaluate the power relationship in any given transformer.

$$N = \frac{P_o}{P_i} \qquad \text{(Eq. 29)}$$

where
P_o = power output from secondary
P_i = power input to primary
N = efficiency factor

The efficiency, N, is always less than 1. It is usually expressed as a percentage; if N is 0.65, for instance, the efficiency is 65 percent.

Let's solve a sample problem using this equation. A transformer has an efficiency of 85 percent at its full-load output of 150 watts. The power input to the primary at full secondary load will be

$$P_i = \frac{P_o}{N} = \frac{150}{0.85} = 176.5 \text{ watts} \qquad \text{(Eq. 30)}$$

A transformer is usually designed to have its highest efficiency at the power output it's rated for, and the efficiency decreases with either lower or higher outputs. On the other hand, the *losses* in the transformer are relatively small at low output but increase as more power is taken. The amount of power that a transformer can handle is determined by its own losses, because these heat the wire and core. Of course, there's a limit to the temperature rise than can be tolerated, because too high a temperature will either melt the wire or cause the insulation to break down. A transformer can be operated at reduced output, even though the efficiency is low, because the actual loss will be low under such conditions.

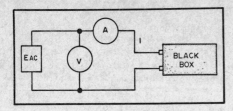

Fig. 18 — Simple measurements of voltage and current don't give a clue to what the unknown impedance may actually be.

Impedance Matching

All sources of power will deliver maximum output when the impedance of the load is equal to the internal impedance of the source. But many devices in radio work require a specific load impedance, other than the source impedance, for their *best* operation. A transformer may be used to match the actual impedance into the desired impedance. This is called *impedance matching*.

In most cases of transformer impedance matching, we use

$$\frac{n_p}{n_s} = \sqrt{\frac{Z_p}{Z_s}} \qquad \text{(Eq. 31)}$$

where

n_p/n_s = required turns ratio, primary to secondary
Z_p = primary impedance required
Z_s = impedance of load connected to secondary

Let's try an example. An audio-frequency amplifier requires a load of 50,000 ohms for best (optimum) performance and is to be connected to a loudspeaker having an impedance of 100 ohms. The turns ratio, primary to secondary, required in the coupling transformer (a transformer connected between the

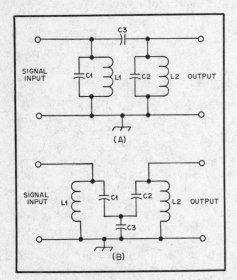

Fig. 19 — Capacitive coupling between tuned circuits. In both circuits, C3 is the shared component.

amplifier and the loudspeaker) is

$$\frac{n_p}{n_s} = \sqrt{\frac{Z_p}{Z_s}} = \sqrt{\frac{50,000}{100}} =$$

$$\sqrt{500} = 22.4 \qquad \text{(Eq. 32)}$$

The primary, therefore, must have 22.4 times as many turns as the secondary.

The Decibel

Radio amateurs very often amplify, or increase, the output power of their transmitters. Power amplification produces a *ratio* of two power levels, the output power compared to the input power. If we work with ratios, however, we have to go through a lot of multiplication to arrive at an estimate of how much we increase signal strength by increasing power. So instead there is a mathematical system for changing these ratios into simple numbers that can be added. It's handy to make the unit of such a system stand for a just-noticeable increase in signal strength. The unit we use is called the *decibel*, abbreviated dB. A one decibel power increase is about the same as multiplying the power by 1.26, which is a just-noticeable increase in signal strength.

An easy relationship to remember is that a power increase of 3 decibels is almost exactly the same as multiplying the original power by 2. A power increase of 10 decibels is the same as multiplying the original power by 10, and 20 decibels is the same as multiplying the original power by 100.

The decibel works both ways — that is, it gives the ratio of a *decrease* in power level just as readily as it gives the ratio of an increase. All you do is subtract instead of add. If you cut your transmitter power down to one-half — that is, divide it by 2 — you have decreased it by 3 dB. A decibel number with a minus sign in front of it means a decrease or a *loss* of power. If the sign is positive, or no sign is shown, there's an increase or *gain* in power.

The mathematical formula for the number of decibels corresponding to any given power ratio is

$$dB = 10 \log \frac{P2}{P1} \qquad \text{(Eq. 33)}$$

where P2 is the new power level and P1 is the old power level.

For example, if an amateur increased his power from 200 watts to 900 watts, how would this increase be expressed in dB?

$$dB = 10 \log \frac{900}{200} = 10 \log 4.5 = 6.5$$

So an increase from 200 watts to 900 watts is a power gain of 6.5 dB.

Filters

We will soon discuss one type of filter used in Amateur Radio, the power-supply

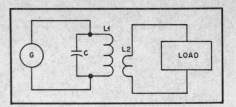

Fig. 20 — Inductive coupling between the tuned circuit and load.

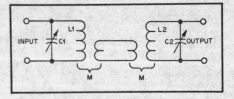

Fig. 21 — Link coupling. The mutual inductances at both ends of the link are equivalent to mutual inductance between the tuned circuits and serve the same purpose.

filter, but you should be familiar with three others: the low-pass filter, high-pass filter and band-pass filter.

A *low-pass filter* is one that passes all frequencies below a frequency called the *cutoff frequency*, but which won't let energy at frequencies above the cutoff frequency go through. What is the cutoff frequency? That changes, depending on the design of the low-pass filter. One other trait that must be incorporated into the design of the filter is its characteristic *impedance*. When used to reduce harmonic output of a transmitter, a filter must have the same characteristic impedance as that of the transmission line leading to the antenna. That's because the low-pass filter is always inserted between the transmitter and the antenna. It must be used only in lines with a low standing-wave ratio. The cutoff frequency, by the way, has to be higher than the highest frequency you're going to use for transmitting, so low-pass filters come in handy when you need to reduce vhf harmonic radiation (the kind which can bother television sets).

A *high-pass filter* is just like a low-pass filter, except that it is connected to the television set, stereo receiver, or other home-entertainment device experiencing interference. It passes all frequencies *above* its cutoff frequency, and reduces the strength of those below. These are useful in reducing the amount of lower frequency radiation that might overload a television set, causing disruption of reception.

A *band-pass filter* is one that passes without excessive attenuation (reduction of signal strength) a desired band of frequencies and rejects signals outside this band. Band-pass filters are commonly used in reception and provide the different degrees of selectivity.

Sample Study Questions

The following questions are rendered in a format similar to those on the FCC examination. When you go to take the exam, you will indicate your choices by filling in the proper spaces on the computer graded answer form with a soft-lead pencil. Remember always to choose the *best* answer since occasionally more than one choice will seem correct if you take its meaning too literally. Answers appear on page 1 of *Answers*.

1) What is the total resistance of the following circuit?

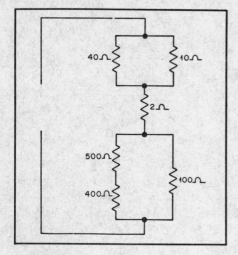

A) 100 ohms
B) 250 ohms
C) 500 ohms
D) 1000 ohms

2) If the impedance ratio of a transformer is 100 to 1, what is the corresponding turns ratio?
A) 1:1
B) 10:1
C) 100:1
D) 1000:1

3) Which equation concerning dc circuits is wrong?

A) $G = \dfrac{I}{R}$

B) $P = I^2R$
C) $E = IR$

D) $P = \dfrac{R^2}{E}$

4) How many degrees are in one cycle of a wave?
A) 90 degrees
B) 180 degrees
C) 360 degrees
D) 720 degrees

5) What is the total inductance of the following circuit?

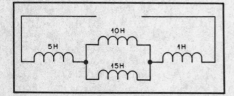

A) 0.81 henrys
B) 6 henrys
C) 12 henrys
D) None of the above

6) If a series circuit has a resistance of 5 ohms and a reactance of 12 ohms, what is the impedance of the circuit?
A) 4.6 ohms
B) 7 ohms
C) 13 ohms
D) 60 ohms

7) Which one of the following statements is *not* true?
A) Phase is measured in degrees
B) Impedance is measured in ohms
C) Apparent power is measured in watts
D) Electromotive force is measured in volts

8) What is the rms voltage of an ac wave having a peak voltage of 100 volts?
A) 66.7 volts
B) 70.7 volts
C) 141.4 volts
D) 150 volts

9) Which is a correct method to increase the inductance of a coil?
A) Decrease the voltage applied to the coil
B) Increase the Q of the coil
C) Increase the frequency of the ac voltage applied to the coil
D) Add turns to the coil

10) If the frequency of an alternating current applied to a capacitor is lowered, what happens to the reactance of the capacitor?
A) It becomes zero
B) It decreases
C) Nothing happens
D) It increases

11) What is the total reactance of the following circuit if C1 has a reactance of 10 ohms, L1 has a reactance of 15 ohms, L2 has a reactance of 5 ohms and R1 is a 20-ohm resistor?

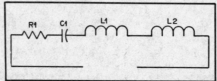

A) 10 ohms
B) 30 ohms
C) Zero
D) 50 ohms

12) What is the total capacitance of the following circuit?

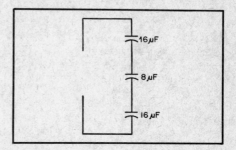

A) 4 µF
B) 8 µF
C) 18 µF
D) 40 µF

13) How much power will be used by a load connected to a transformer which has an efficiency factor of 0.65 and is connected to a power source supplying 1000 watts?
A) 65 watts
B) 650 watts
C) 1000 watts
D) 1065 watts

14) What is the voltage at the upper secondary winding of the transformer shown if the voltage applied to the primary winding is 10 volts?

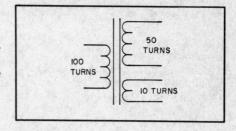

A) 2.5 volts
B) 5 volts
C) 7.1 volts
D) 20 volts

15) Which type of capacitor is polarized?
A) Mica
B) Ceramic
C) Paper
D) Electrolytic

16) If a 100-watt power level is reduced by 9 dB, what is the new power level?
A) 10 watts
B) 12.5 watts
C) 14.2 watts
D) 91 watts

Equations Used in This Section

Ohm's Law for resistance:

$$E = IR \quad I = \frac{E}{R} \quad R = \frac{E}{I}$$

Ohm's Law for conductance:

$$I = EG \quad E = \frac{I}{G} \quad X = \frac{I}{E}$$

Ohm's Law for reactance:

$$E = IX \quad I = \frac{E}{X} \quad X = \frac{E}{I}$$

Ohm's Law for impedance:

$$E = IZ \quad I = \frac{E}{Z} \quad Z = \frac{E}{I}$$

Power: $P = IE \quad P = I^2R$

Resistors in series:

$$R_{total} = R1 + R2 + R3 + \text{etc.}$$

Two resistors in parallel:

$$R_{total} = \frac{R1 \times R2}{R1 + R2}$$

More than two resistors in parallel:

$$R_{total} = \frac{1}{\frac{1}{R1} + \frac{1}{R2} + \frac{1}{R3} + \text{etc.}}$$

Two capacitors in series:

$$C_{total} = \frac{C1 \times C2}{C1 + C2}$$

More than two capacitors in series:

$$C_{total} = \frac{1}{\frac{1}{C1} + \frac{1}{C2} + \frac{1}{C3} + \text{etc.}}$$

Capacitors in parallel:

$$C_{total} = C1 + C2 + C3 + \text{etc.}$$

Inductors in series:

$$L_{total} = L1 + L2 + L3 + \text{etc.}$$

Two inductors in parallel:

$$L_{total} = \frac{L1 \times L2}{L1 + L2}$$

More than two inductors in parallel:

$$L_{total} = \frac{1}{\frac{1}{L1} + \frac{1}{L2} + \frac{1}{L3} + \text{etc.}}$$

Transformer voltage ratio:

$$E_s = \frac{n_s}{n_p} \times E_p$$

Transformer current ratio:

$$I_p = \frac{n_s}{n_p} \times I_s$$

Transformer efficiency:

$$P_o = nP_i \ (n = \text{efficiency factor as a decimal})$$

Inductive reactance:

$$X_L = 2\pi fL$$

Capacitive reactance:

$$X_C = \frac{1}{2\pi fC}$$

Like reactances in series (either all capacitors or all inductors):

$$X_{total} = X1 + X2 + X3 + \ldots \text{(with capacitive reactance, total is negative)}$$

Different reactances in series:

$$X_{total} = X_L + X_C \ (X_C \text{ is a negative value})$$

Like reactances in parallel:

$$X_{total} = \frac{X1 \times X2}{X1 + X2} \text{ or}$$

$$X_{total} = \frac{1}{\frac{1}{X1} + \frac{1}{X2} + \frac{1}{X3} + \ldots}$$

(With capacitance reactance, this total is negative.)

Impedance (resistance and reactance in series):

$$Z = \sqrt{R^2 + X^2}$$

Impedance (resistance and reactance in parallel):

$$Z = \frac{RX}{\sqrt{R^2 + X^2}}$$

Impedance matching (using a transformer):

$$\frac{n_p}{n_s} = \sqrt{\frac{Z_p}{Z_s}}$$

Rms voltage:

Rms voltage = peak voltage multiplied by 0.707

Diodes and Power Supplies

There's no doubt about it. Amateur equipment commonly referred to as "solid-state equipment" has taken over. Thousands of amateurs have switched their allegiance from strictly vacuum-tube equipment to the new type of rig: the solid-state one. What does the term "solid-state" mean? It goes back to the fact that substances exist in either gaseous, liquid or solid form. Because transistors and crystal diodes are made of solid materials, they are called solid-state devices or solid-state components. They are distinguished from electron tubes which can be thought of as "hollow state" devices because of their envelope construction around a vacuum, gas, etc.

The crystal diode and the transistor both produce electric phenomena by using a type of material called a *semiconductor*. The prefix *semi* means half, and semiconductor materials received their name because their ability to conduct electricity lies in between that of good conductors like copper and good insulators like glass.

The semiconductor materials most frequently used today in the manufacture of transistors and solid-state diodes are *germanium*, a rare chemical element; *silicon*, a more common element; and *selenium*, a fairly rare element. The atoms of these materials are arranged in orderly geometric *lattices* or patterns to form crystals. (Note: The crystals used in transmitters to control frequency are quartz crystals, which are not semiconductors and have very different physical properties. We'll talk about them later.) Early day diodes such as those used in crystal radio sets were made of semiconductor crystals which contained *natural* chemical impurities. Today's semiconductor devices depend on crystals which have had their lattice structures changed intentionally by adding certain chemicals in a laboratory.

Chemicals can change both the *resistance* and the *mechanism* of current flow within semiconductor crystals. The chemicals used in modern solid-state devices are introduced into the crystal lattice by a

laboratory process called *doping*. Depending on the choice of doping chemical, free electrons can be added to a crystal lattice or "holes" can be developed in it. These are not the usual holes we speak about. They are positions in the lattice where electrons should be — and would be — if it weren't for the doping process. Chemicals which donate electrons are called *donors* (just like blood donors donate blood). They develop current as a result of electron flow. Chemicals which make holes are *acceptors*. They create current by what is called hole flow.

We have names, of course, for the two types of materials. The material with free electrons is called n-type, and that with holes is called p-type. Neither by itself is much different from an ordinary conductor. But when the two types are formed side by side (during manufacture) to make a *pn junction*, things really begin to happen.

We can represent the junction as shown at A of Fig. 22. If a battery voltage is

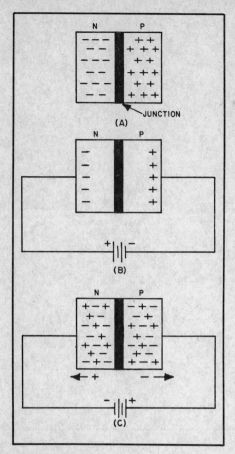

Fig. 22 — The junction diode, a semiconductor rectifier. The pn junction is shown at A, with electrons represented by − and holes +; B shows the nonconducting condition (reverse bias); C shows the conducting condition (forward bias).

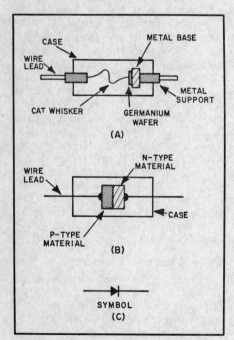

Fig. 23 — At A, a germanium point-contact diode. At B, construction of a silicon junction-type diode. The symbol at C is used for both diode types and indicates the direction of minimum resistance measured by conventional methods. At C, the arrow corresponds to the plate (anode) of a vacuum-tube diode. The bar represents the cathode elements of the tube.

applied at B, the electrons in the n-type material are attracted to the positive battery terminal and the holes in the p-type material move toward the negative terminal. Since there is no appreciable movement *through* the junction, very little current can flow in the circuit. However, if the battery polarity is reversed as in C, holes move across the junction toward the negative battery terminal, and electrons move across it toward the positive terminal. With this battery polarity, therefore, a current flows through the junction and the circuit.

The semiconductor rectifier or diode is not a perfect insulator when the voltage is applied in the reverse polarity, as in B. A small *reverse current* can flow, when the diode is *reverse biased*, meaning that the negative terminal is applied to the p-type material. In the forward direction (*forward biased*), as in C, it takes less than a volt to cause very large currents to flow — much less than it does in a vacuum-tube diode. Germanium diodes have a typical *forward voltage drop* of about 0.2 volt, while silicon diodes have a drop of about 0.6 volt.

Diode Ratings

Aside from the reverse current, which is usually a thousand times less than the forward current under normal conditions, the principal limitation of the semiconductor diode, or crystal diode, is the fact that it cannot stand very high reverse voltages. It will usually break down if the reverse voltage is just a little over the rating. Also, the semiconductor diode can't stand *any* overvoltage. In fact, unlike tubes, it can't stand overvoltage for even the tiniest moment. What, then, are the advantages of the semiconductor

diode? It's small and can conduct currents with low voltage drop. As a result, very little power is lost in the rectifier. Another advantage is that no power need be lost in heating a filament, as the semiconductor diode doesn't have one.

Junction Capacitance

With the two sections of a semiconductor diode separated by practically zero spacing, the junction forms a capacitor of pretty high capacitance. This places an upper frequency limit on the use of a semiconductor device of this type. This capacitance, called *junction capacitance*, can be reduced by making the contact area very small. This is done by means of a *point contact*. That's a tiny p-type region formed under the contact point during manufacture when n-type material is used for the main body of the semiconductor.

So far, we've discussed electrical principles and circuit components. If we combine what we know about electricity and electronics with our knowledge of circuit components, we'll end up with the practical circuits common in Amateur Radio. Your performance as an amateur depends largely on the efficiency of your station, which includes your transmitter-receiver combination (or transceiver) as well as your antenna system. And an efficient station is a result of the wise use of practical circuits.

Power Supplies

Before discussing receiver and transmitter circuits, let's look at one circuit which is found in most pieces of amateur gear: the power supply. You might be wondering why a lengthy discussion is necessary about something sitting right on your living-room wall. After all, a wall socket is

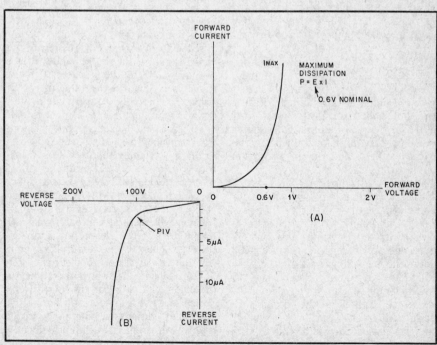

Fig. 24 — Characteristic curve for a silicon diode.

a power supply, isn't it?

No, not in ham jargon. Despite your being able to plug a floor lamp into a wall socket and have light for reading this book, the 120-volt ac current is not *exactly* what you'll need to power your ham station. First, the main lines in your house supply an *alternating* current, and most components use *direct* current. In addition, the voltage is about 120 volts, which may be too high or too low for what you want. So a power supply, then, has a double function: to increase or decrease the *value* of the voltage and to change the alternating current into direct current.

Before we continue, it should be mentioned that batteries are a source of dc. Most amateur gear, however, demands so much power that batteries are often impractical and too expensive. Most amateurs would go broke just buying new batteries to replace the dead ones. Low-power (QRP) hf rigs and vhf gear, though, are easily and commonly run off batteries.

An ac power supply consists of three basic sections: the transformer, the diode rectifier and the filter. Let's start with the transformer. Transformers are designed to operate from ac sources of specific frequencies or frequency ranges. *Power transformers* (the kind used in power supplies) usually operate at 60 hertz, because that's the frequency of common ac house current. Every transformer functions best when the alternating current passing through its windings has a frequency for which the transformer was designed.

Earlier in this chapter, we pointed out how useful a transformer can be, because it permits us to start with an ac power source of 120 volts and raise or lower the voltage level very conveniently. The *power* level remains the same, however; the transformer that delivers 360 volts at 0.1 ampere (P = IE; 360 × 0.1 = 36.0 watts) draws 0.3 ampere at 120 volts

$$(I = \frac{P}{E} = \frac{36}{120} = 0.3 \text{ amp}) \qquad \text{(Eq. 34)}$$

from the line (plus a little more because there are slight losses in the transformer itself). In other words, the power drawn by the primary must equal the power delivered by the secondary, plus the loss in the transformer.

Many power transformers have several secondary windings to provide several different voltages. For example, the power transformer in an amateur receiver might have three secondaries: one delivering 6.3 volts, one 5 volts and one delivering 200 volts. The 6.3 volts are used to heat the cathode of any tubes in the receiver, the 5-volt winding supplies voltage to heat the filament or cathode of the vacuum-tube diode rectifiers, and the 200-volt winding furnishes power that will be converted to dc by the rectifier and filter. Rather than vacuum tubes, semiconductors are more

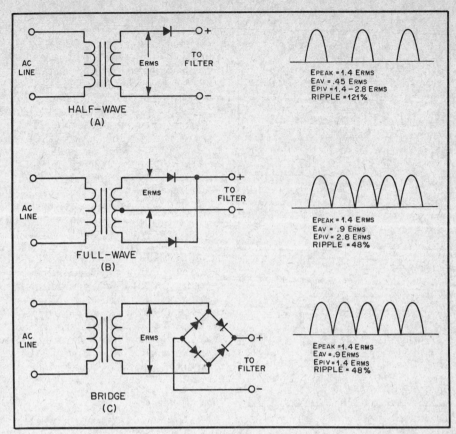

Fig. 25 — Fundamental rectifier circuits. (A) Half-wave (E_{PIV} = 1.41 E_{rms} with resistive load: E_{PIV} = 2.8 E_{rms} with capacitor-input filter). (B) Full-wave. (C) Full-wave bridge. Output-voltage values do not include rectifier voltage drops.

commonly found in today's receivers, so we use this example mostly for learning purposes.

Most tube heaters operate on "raw" ac. In some tubes, the heater and cathode are the same wire, but heaters take no direct part in circuit operation. The tube electrodes that do have such a part require *dc* power, as do semiconductors. Furthermore, it must be *pure* dc without superimposed ac, called "ripple." The rest of the power supply — the rectifier and the filter — now come to the rescue. After the transformer changes the value of the ac voltage, the rectifier converts the ac into dc, and the filter smooths out the ripple.

To understand diode-rectifier action, we'll consider a diode connected to a secondary winding of a power transformer as in Fig. 25A. During the half of the ac cycle that the applied voltage makes the anode positive with respect to the cathode, the diode rectifier will conduct. Current will then pass through whatever load is connected to the output of the rectifier (in many cases, this will be your transmitter or receiver). The current passing through the load varies with time, as the diode will allow current to pass only during one half of the cycle. During the other half of the cycle, the anode is not positive with respect to the cathode and, therefore, no current passes through the diode. The action of the diode in per-

mitting the current to flow in only one direction is called *rectification*.

If another diode is properly connected to another secondary winding (of the same transformer) supplying 400 volts, the second diode will conduct during the portions of the ac cycle that the first diode cannot. An easier and more common method of using two diodes in a rectifier is to have both anodes connected to separate ends of the same secondary winding, as in Fig. 25B. A winding, called a *center tap*, is then connected through the load to the cathodes of the diodes. The rectifier circuit with diodes working on both halves of the cycle is called a *full-wave rectifier*, as opposed to the single diode, *half-wave rectifier* that only rectifies half the cycle. This particular full-wave rectifier is known as a *full-wave, center-tap rectifier*.

Bridge Rectifier

A third type of rectifier circuit is the *full-wave bridge* shown in Fig. 25C. The output current or voltage waveshape is the same as for the full-wave center-tap rectifier. The *amplitude* of the output voltage, as compared with the voltage of the transformer secondary, is different. In the center-tap circuit, *each* side of the center-tapped secondary must develop enough voltage to supply the dc output voltage desired. In the bridge circuit no center-tap is necessary. But we can't get something for nothing; dispensing with the center tap has a price. Two additional rectifiers must be used in a bridge rectifier.

In the bridge circuit, two rectifiers are connected to the transformer secondary in the same way as the two rectifiers in the center-tap circuit shown in Fig. 25B. The second pair of rectifiers is also connected in series between the ends of the transformer winding, but in reverse. When the upper end of the transformer winding is positive, the current path is through one rectifier — the load — and through another rectifier on its way back to the other end of the secondary. During the other half of the ac cycle, the current passes through the other two rectifiers.

Rectifier Ratings

You're already familiar with the way a diode rectifier works. A power-supply rectifier is just a diode or series of diodes suitably rated to handle the current and voltage needed in a power supply. Many ratings are available.

Some important factors should not be overlooked in selecting and using power-supply rectifiers. One is the *peak-inverse voltage* rating, often abbreviated PIV (also called peak-reverse voltage, abbreviated PRV). This is the maximum voltage which may be applied to the rectifier in the *nonconducting* direction. For example, in the full-wave bridge circuit, when one rectifier is conducting, the two connected to it are not. The full transformer secondary voltage is applied to the reverse direction to the nonconducting rectifier which follows the conducting rectifier. Since the peak value of the voltage is 1.41 times the rms value, you can see that in Fig. 25C the PIV is 1.41 times the total secondary voltage. In other words $E_{PIV} = 1.41\ E_{rms}$ in a full-wave bridge circuit. The E_{PIV}, in relation to the E_{rms}, changes for different types of rectifier circuits.

The current rating of the rectifier must also be considered. Diodes are usually rated for two current values, the *average dc output current* and the *maximum peak current*. The average dc output current is the direct current flowing to the load, so if your load needs a current of 100 mA, you'd choose a rectifier having at least that output-current rating. In full-wave rectifier circuits, each diode carries half the current, so absolute minimum rating is *half* the desired output current.

The peak current rating is the largest current that can be allowed to flow through the rectifier at any time during the rectified cycle. This rating is important when a capacitor-input filter is used because most of the charging current into the first capacitor flows in a short burst, reaching a peak of as much as 10 to 20 times the average dc output current. In a choke-input filter the peak current is not much larger than the average dc output

current, so with this type of filter the peak current rating can be neglected.

Also, when a power supply is first turned on, the discharged filter capacitor looks almost like a dead short, and for an instant the rectifier passes a very high current. The peak one-cycle surge current can be 10 to 100 times the average dc output current. In practice, all these ratings would be doubled for complete protection.

Protecting Diodes

Excess heat, current surges and power-line transient voltages can destroy semiconductor diodes. Therefore, if the diodes in a power supply are not correctly protected, they may be ruined.

Thermal Protection

Because the junction of a silicon diode is very small, it must operate at a high current density. That means that it must handle a large current flow in a very small area. The heat-dissipating capability is, therefore, reduced. We need to use some form of "heat sink" to remove heat generated in diodes, especially those in high-current rectifiers. However, low-current diodes usually need only the heat sinking provided by the component leads. Forced-air cooling is sometimes used in addition to heat sinks. In all cases, the operating temperature should be kept below its maximum rating.

Surge Protection

Some form of protection is required to safeguard the diodes during the initial current surge when the power is first turned on and the power-supply filter capacitors are charging. We don't have this problem with choke-input filters. Although the dc resistance of the transformer secondary can be relied upon in some instances to provide surge-current limiting, sometimes a current-limiting device is installed in the *primary* circuit of the power transformer. This limiter permits only a small voltage to reach the transformer primary winding until the capacitor is nearly charged. After that, the full ac voltage reaches the primary winding.

Transient Voltage Protection

A common cause of rectifier failure is *transient voltages* on the ac power lines. These are short spikes that can increase the voltage applied to the rectifier to values much higher than the normal transformer voltage. Transients are caused by lightning strokes or by electric appliances going on and off, and they can cause unexpected, and often unexplained, destruction of solid-state rectifiers. There are two methods of protecting rectifiers from transient voltages. One is connecting a low-value capacitor in parallel with each transformer winding. The other form of protection is placing a selenium suppressor diode across the primary winding.

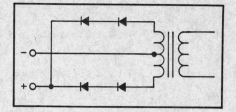

Fig. 26 — Using two semiconductor diodes in series doubles the peak-inverse voltage rating. A resistor and capacitor are placed in parallel with each diode to equalize voltage drops and guard against transient voltage spikes.

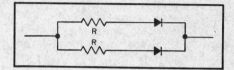

Fig. 27 — Diodes in parallel should have equalizing resistors.

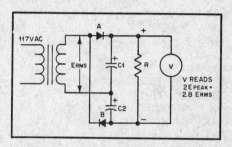

Fig. 28 — The voltage-doubler circuit. Two half-wave rectifiers, working alternately, charge capacitors connected in series.

A suppressor diode does not conduct unless the peak voltage becomes abnormally high. Then it "clips" the transient peaks.

Transient voltages can go as high as twice the normal line voltages before the suppressor diode clips them. Because capacitors cannot provide complete suppression of transients, it is good practice to use power-supply rectifiers with a PIV rating twice the expected value.

Diodes in Series and Parallel

Let's say we're building a power supply, and we'll need rectifiers rated at 1000 PIV, and we have only 500-PIV diodes on hand. Can we still use them? Yes. By connecting two 500-PIV diodes in series, the pair will withstand 1000 PIV (2 × 500 = 1000). To equalize the voltage drops and to guard against transient voltage spikes, a resistor and a capacitor should be placed in parallel with each diode (Fig. 26). Even though the diodes are of the same type and have the same PIV rating, they may have different "back" resistances when they are nonconducting. We know from Ohm's Law (E = IR) that the diode with the higher back resistance will have the higher voltage across it, and that diode may break down. If we place a "swamping" resistor across each diode, the resistance across each diode will be almost the same and the back voltage will divide equally. A good rule of thumb for determining resistor value is to multiply the PIV rating of the diode by 500. For example, a 500-PIV diode should be shunted by about 500 × 500, or 250,000 ohms.

The shift from forward conduction to high back resistance does not take place instantly in a silicon diode. Some diodes take longer than others to develop high back resistance. To protect the "fast" diodes in a series string until all the diodes are properly cut off, a 0.01 µF capacitor should be placed across each diode.

You can place diodes in parallel to increase total current-handling capability. A resistor should be placed in series with each diode to insure that each takes the same current (Fig. 27).

Power Supply Filters

The output from the rectifier is not like dc from a battery. It's neither pure nor constant. It's actually what's known as *pulsating* dc — flowing in only one direction but not at a steady value. Using this type of current as a replacement for a battery in a transmitter or receiver would introduce a strong hum on all signals. To smooth out the pulsations and eliminate the hum and its effects, a filter is used between the rectifier and the load.

The simplest type of filter is a large capacitor across the load. See Fig. 29A. If the capacitance is high enough and the current drawn by the load is not excessive, the capacitor will charge during voltage peaks. Consequently, the current through the load will never reduce to zero, as it would at the instant the ac current reverses with the capacitor disconnected. The capacitor discharges during the reversal and smooths out the ripple in the dc. You probably remember how the capacitor can do this — by storing energy. It then releases this energy and supplies load current when the rectifier isn't supplying any. This is somewhat like a basketball team with effective first and second string squads. Eventually, the coach realizes that his first string is fatigued and not playing well so he substitutes the first string with the second string, which is rested. If the coach remains alert and both squads play well, the fans shouldn't notice any lengthy slumps in the team's performance. Similarly, when the rectifier isn't putting out any current, the capacitor releases its stored energy and supplies load current.

We can design a more effective filter if we place an inductor, or *filter choke*, between the rectifier and the capacitor as in Fig. 29B. We can connect one-capacitor-in-parallel-and-choke-in-series section after another (cascade them as in Fig. 29C) to improve the filtering action still further. The two basic filters are called *choke-input* and *capacitor-input* filters, depending on which component serves as the input of the filter.

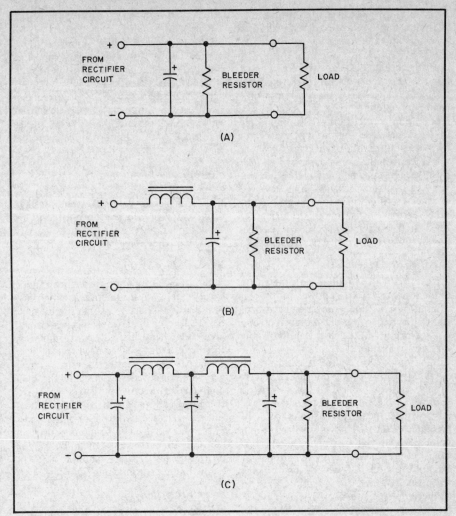

Fig. 29 — Power-supply filter circuits. (A) A simple capacitor filter. (B) A choke-input filter. (C) A capacitor-input, multi-section filter.

It's a good idea to connect a high-resistance resistor across the output of a power supply, to discharge the filter capacitors when the power-supply primary voltage is turned off. Such a resistor, called a *bleeder resistor*, bleeds the charge from the capacitors and decreases the chances for accidental electrical shock.

So far we've discussed the various parts of a power supply: the transformer, the rectifier and the filter. And we've mentioned two types of rectifiers: the half-wave and the full-wave (center-tap). But there's more to power supplies.

Ripple

Notice that in Fig. 25 there are twice as many "bumps" in the dc output voltage per cycle of line frequency when a full-wave rectifier is used as compared to half-wave rectification. This is just another way of saying that the ripple frequency is doubled with full-wave rectification. Values of the filter choke and capacitor can be half as large with full-wave rectification as with half-wave rectification, providing almost the same "smoothness" in the dc output.

The inductance and capacitance will smooth out the dc because they store energy while the voltage from the rectifier is rising, and they discharge it when the rectified voltage is falling. Less energy has to be stored, for the same overall effect, when the charge/discharge periods are closer together. That's why a filter following a full-wave rectifier requires smaller components than a filter smoothing the dc output of a half-wave rectifier.

Voltage Doubling

Several types of voltage-doubling circuits are in common use. The *voltage-doubler* circuit shown in Fig. 28 is frequently used in transmitter power supplies. How's it work? It charges the capacitors through separate half-wave rectifiers on alternate halves of the supply cycle and then discharges them in series through the load, R. When the voltage at the upper end of the transformer secondary is positive, C1 is charged to the peak value of the ac voltage through rectifier A. When the lower end of the winding is positive, C2 is charged through B in the same way. The stored voltages on the two capacitors add together, giving a total output voltage twice the voltage you'd get from a half-wave rectifier. Because both halves of the supply cycle are used, this is a full-wave rectifier circuit.

Voltage Regulation

After all this talk about power supplies in transmitters and receivers, you're probably wondering how much direct current is demanded of a power supply. As you might expect, current demand varies with the piece of equipment. But even more importantly, current demand varies *within* a piece of equipment. Say, for example, you have a cw transmitter. It will sit quite comfortably after it's turned on, not drawing much current. Once you begin tapping the telegraph key, however, the transmitter may load the supply up to the maximum current it's designed to give. This change in current affects the supply's output voltage.

Voltage regulation of a power supply is a measure of change in the output voltage with respect to current. It is usually expressed as a percentage of the output voltage at the rated load current. For example, the supply may be designed to deliver a current of 200 mA at 600 volts. If the voltage rises to 800 volts when the current is zero, the change is 200 volts. The regulation is then

$$\frac{V_{NL} - V_L}{V_L} = \frac{200}{600} \qquad \text{(Eq. 35)}$$

This is 1/3 or 33-1/3 percent.

One factor contributing to the voltage drop in the supply is the resistance and reactance of the transformer windings. Another is the voltage drop between the plate and cathode of the rectifier. The rectifier drop amounts to only a volt or so with silicon rectifiers, but can be significant if you use a tube rectifier — sometimes as high as 40 to 50 volts at full-rated current. A third cause is the resistance of the filter choke and any re-

sistors that may be used for filtering. In all of these, the voltage drops increase with current. Finally, in a capacitor-input filter the output voltage depends on the amount of energy stored in the input capacitor and how quickly the energy is released to the load. As the load current increases, so does the release rate, with a resulting voltage decrease. When there's no output current, the voltage in a capacitor-input filter builds up to the peak value of the rectifier voltages, or 1.41 times the rms voltage applied to the rectifier.

A choke-input filter using a large inductance choke will prevent this voltage buildup at small output currents and will tend to hold the output voltage at the average amplitude of the rectified waveform (only if a bleeder resistor is used to keep the load current above a minimum value). Of course, the voltage drops we mentioned in the preceding paragraph still cause the output voltage to drop off with increased current.

Sample Study Questions

17) A doping chemical which is responsible for making "holes" in a crystal lattice is
A) A dielectric
B) A donor
C) An acceptor
D) A piezoelectric

18) What component is necessary for rectification?
A) Transformer
B) Diode
C) Bleeder resistor
D) Filter choke

19) Which of the following is *not* an advantage of semiconductor diodes over vacuum-tube diodes?
A) Ability to stand overvoltage
B) Smaller size
C) Lower voltage drop
D) Less power consumption

20) A full-wave, center-tap rectifier is

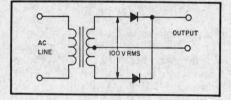

connected to a transformer as shown. What is the peak value of the pulsating dc output of this circuit?
A) 70 V
B) 100 V
C) 121.5 V
D) 140 V

21) In the circuit of the figure at the left, what is the peak-inverse voltage that the diode must withstand?
A) 70 V
B) 100 V
C) 121.5 V
D) 140 V

Emission Characteristics

What makes ham radio exciting? Many things do, but one of the best points in favor of Amateur Radio is that it offers so many different types of emission. An emission is the vehicle by which information is transmitted by radio. Just as buses and planes transport people, emissions carry information. Some emission types which hams use are as different as planes are from buses. Most radio services in the U.S. are permitted to use only one specific form of emission. For instance, an a-m broadcast station must use only amplitude modulation, and an fm broadcast station must use only frequency modulation. Citizens band operators may use only amplitude modulation (or single sideband, which is a form of it). Don't worry

for now what these terms mean. Just remember that amateurs are permitted to use 12 different emission types. (See chapter 9, §97.61)

Emission Types

The FCC classifies emissions by the two-symbol combination of a letter and a numeral. When taking the written examination for a Technician or General class license, you will be expected to know the following definitions:

A0 — A pure, unmodulated carrier. (Amplitude with no modulation.)

A1 — Telegraphy without the use of modulating audio frequency.

A3 — Amplitude-modulated (a-m) telephony, including single and double

sideband, with full, reduced or suppressed carrier.

F1 — Frequency (or phase) modulated (fm) telegraphy. It can also be described as frequency shift keying without the use of a modulating audio signal. It is usually used for radioteleprinter communications on the hf bands.

F2 — Audio, tone-modulated telegraphy of an fm transmitter. It is commonly used for automatic identification on fm repeaters.

F3 — Frequency (or phase) modulated (fm) telephony.

Appendix 3 to the Amateur Rules lists all the emission-types allowed in the Amateur Radio Service. The Amateur Rules, Part 97 of the FCC Rules, are printed in their entirety near the back of this *License Manual*.

Modulation

Almost every amateur will think of phone transmission whenever the word "modulation" crops up. The subject of modulation is a lot broader than that. However, the principles are the same whether the radio transmission is modulated by the human voice, or pulses (as in radar), by any of the varied forms of coded signals that are used in many communication systems, or by some Novice operator "shaking" a telegraph key. The process of *modulation* adds a message to what would otherwise be a plain, single-frequency radio wave that, in itself, tells you nothing except that it exists.

Your Voice

Possibly, it's easier to grasp the essence of modulation when it's put in terms of phone. Sound is a vibration in the air, a vibration usually made of many frequencies lying within the range we call *audio frequencies*. The lower and upper limits of this range are not the same for all listeners; what you can hear depends on the condition of your hearing apparatus. Experts usually say that the extremes are about 15 or 20 hertz at the bottom end and 15,000 or 16,000 hertz at the top end.

But long experience, backed by many tests, shows that a frequency range of about 200 to 3000 hertz will contain all the frequencies needed for making your voice understandable to a receiving operator. The actual range a person may have may be much greater. But if those frequencies below about 200 and above 3000 hertz are eliminated — filtered out — there's little, if any, loss in the speaker's ability to make himself understood. That is, voice *intelligibility* is high when the frequencies are kept within that range.

Microphones

In phone transmission, the first step is to translate the air vibrations into electrical vibrations having the same form. The device that does this is the familiar *microphone*. Mostly, three general types are used by amateurs. One is the carbon microphone shown in Fig. 30A. When a sound strikes the diaphragm, which is usually a thin metal sheet of circular shape, the diaphragm vibrates right along with the air, following the air vibrations pretty faithfully. The diaphragm is held rigidly around its rim, so the movement is greatest at the center, as shown by the small double arrow. The alternate back-and-forth movement varies the pressure on loosely packed carbon grains in the *button*. This changes the resistance in the circuit formed by the button, battery BT (a few volts) and the primary of transformer T. In turn, the varying resistance causes the current in the circuit to vary. Theoretically, the current will change in

proportion to the vibration of the diaphragm, and in practical microphones (of this type) it makes a reasonably good stab at doing so.

Since the resistance of a collection of carbon grains is rather low, the impedance of the transformer primary has to be low too, in order to take maximum advantage of the change in current. Values are usually around 100 to 200 ohms. So the primary will have only a few turns relatively speaking. The secondary normally has a very large number of turns. This steps up the output voltage from the microphone by a large factor.

The carbon microphone once was widely used in mobile and portable work because of its high output and the fact that generally batteries are available to run it. Its *quality*, or ability to reproduce a voice faithfully and with little distortion, is not especially good. The second type of microphone, Fig. 30B, is better in this respect. It makes use of a property of crystals that we found useful for selectivity in receivers and for frequency control in transmitters — *piezoelectricity*. We talked about piezoelectricity before, but that was concerning transmitting crystals. Here, however, the process is reversed; that is, the crystal is set into vibrations by sound waves and the vibration causes a voltage. Crystals for transmitters and receivers are cut from quartz, but those we use in microphones are made from Rochelle salts or certain ceramic materials. A microphone containing Rochelle salts is called a *crystal microphone*; one containing ceramic materials is known as a *ceramic microphone*.

The crystal or ceramic microphone generates only a few hundredths of a volt. Because this voltage is actually in series with a capacitance of about 0.03 μF, the frequency response depends on the load resistance, R (see Fig. 30B) into which the microphone works. A resistance of 1 to 5 megohms is generally used when a tube or field-effect transistor follows the microphone.

The *dynamic microphone* is very commonly used nowadays. It consists of a lightweight coil, suspended in a magnetic circuit and attached to a diaphragm. When sound hits the diaphragm, it moves the coil through the magnetic field generating an alternating current.

Changing Audio to Radio Frequency

After a microphone translates sound frequencies into corresponding electricity, what's next? We can't put these low electrical frequencies on the air directly. Even the highest audio frequency — about 15,000 hertz — would have a radio wavelength of about 20,000 meters. This is certainly nowhere near any radio frequency the FCC lets amateurs use.

The answer is that the band of voice frequencies has to be moved up in the radio-frequency spectrum to some amateur

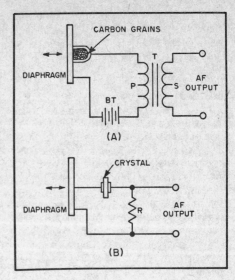

Fig. 30 — Carbon and crystal microphones and their connections.

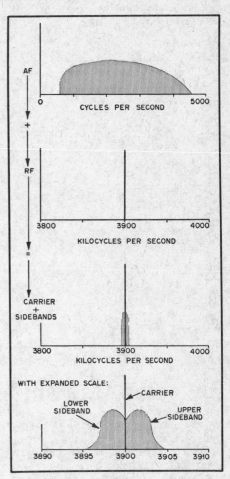

Fig. 31 — Modulation with a band of audio frequencies sets up two sidebands, centered on the carrier frequency.

band where we can make use of it. This is where *modulation* comes in. Suppose we want to operate in the 75-meter phone band, the one that lies between 3890 and 4000 kHz for General class operators. And suppose that we could get into that band just by adding some frequency in it to the voice range of frequencies, 200 to

3000 hertz. It's easier to do the arithmetic if we change the hertz to kilohertz; in kilohertz, the voice range is 0.2 to 3 kHz. If we select 3900 as the frequency to add, we should have a signal occupying the band from 3900 plus 0.2 to 3900 plus 3, or 3900.2 to 3903 kHz.

Boy, is that simple! Wait, though, there's a catch; there isn't any way to do it directly. Nature insists on doing things symmetrically, which only means that most things, like a butterfly's wings, are the same on one side as they are on the other. We can add the voice band to 3900 kHz, all right, but *at the same time* we find that we can't avoid subtracting the frequencies too. So we wind up not only with the band 3900.2 to 3903 kHz but also with another band from 3900 minus 0.2 to 3900 minus 3, or 3899.8 or 3897 kHz as in Fig. 31. Instead of a band a little less than 3 kHz wide we find ourselves with one having a total width of 6 kHz — 3897 to 3903 kHz, in fact.

Modulation Sidebands

Every modulation system gives us these "sum and difference" frequencies. So the actual frequency band occupied by a modulated signal is always twice what is actually needed for transmitting the message. This means that each signal modulated like this takes up twice as much room on the air as it really needs.

The message content of the signal is referred to as the *modulation*, while the frequency we added in order to get the signal into a ham band is called the *carrier*. In the example, the carrier is the 3900-kHz frequency and the bandwidth of the signal is 3897 to 3903 kHz. Since the carrier is between two equal bands, the signal is said to consist of a carrier and two *sidebands*. The sideband from 3900 to 3903 kHz is called the *upper sideband*, being the higher of the two in frequency, while the sideband from 3900 to 3897 kHz is called the *lower sideband*.

Now comes the theory which changed the history of Amateur Radio. The word *"carrier"* implies that something is being carried, but actually our center frequency, the carrier, doesn't carry anything. It just sort of goes along for the ride. We could throw away the carrier, not put it out on the air, and the message would still leave your transmitting antenna. This would be called a *double sideband* (dsb) signal. In fact, because both sidebands each contain the message, we can throw one of them away, too. The other sideband, whether it be the lower or upper, then, has all the responsibility of transporting the message over the air. It takes special receiving methods to "decode" the message, but it can be done. In fact, it *is* done, and we call this type of a-m signal a single-sideband emission (abbreviated ssb).

Why did this change the history of Amateur Radio? In the late forties, amateurs began using single sideband rather

than the conventional a-m. Hams learned that not only were ssb signals narrower than a-m signals, making them less vulnerable to interference, but ssb signals traveled much better than a-m signals with a given power. That's because you're not wasting power sending the worthless carrier and extra sideband. Eventually the practicality of the new version of phone won out, and the hf amateur phone subbands went almost exclusively single sideband.

Amplitude Modulation

The modulation system that gave rise to the carrier idea is called *amplitude modulation* (a-m). It's a system for doing just what we have described above. But when we come to the actual mechanics by which the signal is modulated, it's easy to *think* of it from a different viewpoint. That viewpoint is this: That the amplitude of the carrier (that is, the value of the carrier's current or voltage) is made to follow faithfully the instantaneous changes in the audio-frequency voice voltage. The general idea is shown in Fig. 32. In the amateur bands, the carrier frequency is thousands of times greater than the audio modulating frequency, so the carrier will go through a great many cycles during one cycle of even the highest audio frequency we want to transmit. This is shown by the shading in the figure; we couldn't begin to draw the actual radio frequency (rf) cycles because there would be far too many to be printed.

You're probably thinking that something is actually being done to the carrier. But this is only because it isn't possible to draw a picture of more than one aspect of modulation at a time. The picture you see in Fig. 32 is really a composite one showing the *result* of the action of three separate frequencies in a circuit that will pass all of them. The three are the carrier frequency, the upper side frequency and the lower side frequency. They all add together in such a way as to give the *appearance* of a single frequency (the carrier) whose amplitude is changing in just the same way that the signal doing the modulating is changing. But appearances can sometimes fool us. It would be more accurate to say that the actual modulation process is one of mixing, which we mentioned in our discussion of receiver circuits. Nevertheless, it's easier to grasp some things about amplitude modulation with the help of a picture such as Fig. 32, and we'll take advantage of it. Never forget, though, that the carrier does *not* actually vary in amplitude, and that the modulation is all in the two sidebands.

Modulation Percentage

One thing easier to visualize by the carrier idea is *percentage of modulation*. In Fig. 32 the modulation has just the right value to make the carrier amplitude go to zero on the audio downswing and to twice

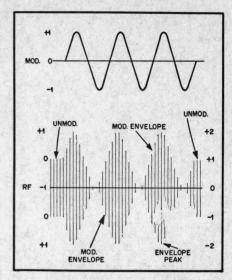

Fig. 32 — The audio-frequency waveform in the upper drawing is superimposed on an af signal, as shown by the outline, or modulation envelope. Note that the modulation envelope is duplicated on the lower side of the rf axis. Not really a separate envelope, this just looks that way! Rf amplitude changes occur symmetrically both above and below the zero axis. The positive and negative half cycles of rf must be equal.

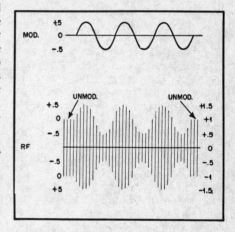

Fig. 33 — Here, the carrier is not fully modulated, as shown by the fact that the envelope peak is not twice the unmodulated-carrier amplitude while the "valley" in the envelope does not reach zero.

its unmodulated value at the peak of the upswing. This is "100-percent" modulation, which, by the way, is the maximum the FCC permits.

Now look at Fig. 33. Here we have the same carrier but the modulation signal is only half as big as in Fig. 32. The rf amplitude goes down to one-half the unmodulated value on the downswing, and up to 1.5 times the unmodulated value on the upswing. This is 50-percent modulation. The percent modulation is the ratio of the maximum swing of the modulation (either up or down) to the amplitude of the unmodulated carrier. With voice the modulation percentage is continually changing, because some sounds are loud and others are not, all within a word.

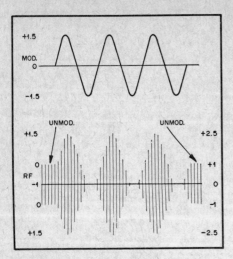

Fig. 34 — Modulating more than 100 percent produces a distorted modulation envelope. It also leads to greater signal bandwidth and "splattering" into adjacent channels.

Also, everyone raises and lowers his voice volume within a sentence.

Overmodulation

Can there be more than 100-percent modulation? Obviously, the rf output can't be reduced below zero. All we can do is fix it at zero for a slight time period. Fig. 34 illustrates this. There is a gap during which there is no output. This is undesirable. The outline of the rf signal — the *modulation envelope* — now differs considerably from the waveshape of the modulation. (In Figs. 32 and 33 the modulation envelopes are identical to the modulating signal.) As a result, the signal heard by the receiving operator isn't the same as the intended transmission. In other words, the modulation is *distorted*.

Even worse, the bandwidth of the transmission has been extended by this *overmodulation* in the downward direction. This doesn't show in the drawing, of course, because the figure doesn't show the *frequency* aspects. A simply way of looking at it, however, is that because there is distortion there must be new modulation frequencies present — harmonics of the modulation frequency or frequencies. Since harmonics are *multiples* of the frequency from which they were generated, they are the same as higher audio frequencies added to the modulation. Higher frequencies mean greater bandwidth. Downward overmodulation increases the bandwidth beyond what is necessary — sometimes far beyond — and can therefore lead to needless interference, called *splatter*, with other stations.

You can modulate upward as far as your transmitter can go. Theoretically, there's no limit; practically though, most transmitters can't go very far upward. When they can't, the peaks of modulation become *flattened*. The overall result, in its effect on the bandwidth, is just about the

same as the same degree of overmodulation downward.

Power in Amplitude Modulation

The reason why most transmitters can't be modulated very far upward will become clear on examining what happens to the power in a modulated signal. Suppose that the transmitter output without modulation is 100 watts. What is it when the signal is modulated 100 percent, as in Fig. 32? By inspection, you can see that the power will be zero at the bottom of the downswing. And since the amplitude at the peak of the upswing is twice the unmodulated amplitude, the power at this *instant* is four times the unmodulated amplitude, or 400 watts. (Remember that the amplitude refers to current or voltage; when the voltage doubles, the current also doubles, in any ordinary circuit.) When the power is *averaged* over one or more cycles of the modulation frequency, a mathematical study will show that the average power in a 100-percent modulated signal is 1.5 times the unmodulated power. So the 100 watts without modulation increases to 150 watts with 100-percent modulation.

Voice Power

The figure of 1.5 times is actually true only of single-tone modulation — that is, modulation by a sine wave. Voice waveforms are not sine waves. For the same *peak* amplitude as a sine wave, an average voice waveform will contain less than half as much power as the sine wave. It would be closer to the truth to say that with voice modulation the average power in a 100-percent modulated signal is somewhat less than 1.25 times the unmodulated power. Any two waveforms that have the same peak amplitude also have the same peak power, even though the powers averaged over one complete cycle may differ widely. It is these peaks that we must be prepared to furnish during modulation.

The extra power in the modulated signal as compared to the unmodulated signal doesn't come out of nowhere. It has to be supplied somehow in the modulation process. The extra power required is proportional to the square of the modulation percentage. This means that the 50-percent modulated signal of Fig. 33 would have only one-fourth as much extra power as the 100-percent modulated one of Fig. 32.

All the message content of a signal is in the modulation. The higher the modulation percentage, the more *talk power* we transmit to the receiving end. The goal is 100 percent — but without overshooting.

Frequency and Phase Modulation

You know by now that *fm — frequency modulation* — is the kind of emission used by broadcast stations on the vhf broadcast band. It's also the type of emis-

sion used by many amateurs nowadays on *their* vhf bands.

The modulation systems we've discussed so far operate by making the amplitude of the rf signal vary in a manner depending on the amplitude of the audio-frequency voice currents. In frequency modulation or phase modulation (pm), the varying *amplitude* of the audio-frequency signal causes the frequency of the rf signal to vary. The total amplitude of the rf signal stays just the same whether or not there is modulation.

Since the amplitude of an fm or pm signal never changes, fm or pm receivers can be made insensitive to amplitude variations in the received signal. Since most noise, particularly man-made noise, consists of pulses of changing amplitude, the signal-to-noise ratio can be improved quite a bit. There is, however, a *noise threshold*. This means that below a certain received signal level the improvement no longer exists. This signal level depends on how much the frequency is "swung" by the modulation; the greater the swing, the stronger the signal must be to overcome the noise. But once this signal level is exceeded, the noise suppression becomes better with the greater frequency swing or *deviation*. Thus a compromise between good noise suppression and weak-signal reception is necessary. A deviation of about five times the highest audio frequency in the modulation was used by hams for many years, but no longer. That is, for speech having a maximum frequency of 3000 hertz, the deviation would be 5 times 3000, or 15,000 hertz. Such deviation (15 kHz) is known as *wide-band fm* by hams (narrow-band fm is now amateur convention).

In fm, as we said earlier, the deviation is proportional to the amplitude of the audio signal. In pm the deviation is proportional to both the amplitude *and the frequency* of the audio signal. Therefore if the amplitude of the modulating audio signal stays the same, deviation will increase as the audio signal increases in frequency.

It is often easier to produce pm than fm in a transmitter, but since in pm deviation increases as the audio frequency increases, the high audio frequencies are emphasized unnaturally. This can be corrected by "shaping" the response of the audio amplifier in the transmitter so that the high audio frequencies are reduced in amplitude.

Bandwidth

Frequency deviation is defined as the instantaneous change in frequency with a given input signal. The frequency actually swings just as far in the *other* direction when modulation is going on, so the total swing is more than twice the deviation. In the example just mentioned, the wideband fm signal would occupy a total channel of over 30 kHz — 10 times the maximum

Table 1

Deviation and Bandwidth for a 3 kHz Audio Signal

FCC Definition	Ham Definition	Deviation	Bandwidth (Approx.)
Narrow band	"Sliver" band	2.5 kHz	6 kHz*
Wide-band	Narrow band	5 kHz	13 kHz
	Wide-band	15 kHz	33 kHz

*The rule of thumb does not hold for narrow deviation.

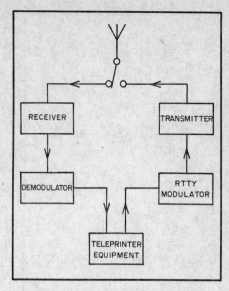

Fig. 36 — Block diagram showing the basic equipment required for amateur RTTY operation.

audio frequency. In other words, the bandwidth is 10 times the band occupied by an a-m signal or 20 times the band taken by an ssb signal. Strangely enough, bandwidth is actually greater than the frequency swing because fm sidebands occur at multiples of the modulating frequency on either side of the carrier. The rule of thumb is "that the bandwidth equals twice the maximum frequency deviation plus the maximum audio frequency. For 3 kHz maximum audio see Table 1.

Radioteleprinting Circuits

Not only can hams use cw or phone, they also can use many other types of emissions. One of them is *radioteletype*, abbreviated RTTY. Radioteletype is a form of telegraphic communication using typewriter-like machines for generating a coded set of electrical impulses. When a typewriter key corresponding to the desired letter or symbol is pressed, impulses are transmitted. A received set of such impulses is then converted into the

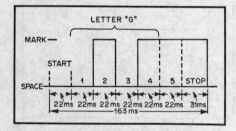

FIG. 35 — Pulse sequence in the teleprinter code. Each character begins with a start pulse, always a "space," and ends with a "stop" pulse, always a "mark." The distribution of marks and spaces in the five elements start and stop determines the particular character transmitted.

corresponding printed character. The message to be sent is typed out on a keyboard similar to a typewriter, but the printing is done at the distant receiving point. The teletypewriter at the sending point may also print the same material.

Teleprinter Code

In the special code used now in radioteletype by amateurs, *Baudot*, every character has five "elements" sent in sequence. Each element has two possible states, either "mark" or "space." Mark is indicated by a negative voltage; space by a positive voltage. An initial "start" element (space) sets the sending and receiving mechanisms in operation, and a terminal "stop" element ends the operation and readies the machine for the next character. At 60 wpm, each element takes 22 milliseconds to be sent. The stop element is 31 ms long. This process is shown in Fig. 35.

RTTY Transmission Methods

It is quite possible to transmit teleprinter signals by ordinary "on/off" or "make/break" keying such as is used in regular hand-keyed cw transmission. In practice, however, *frequency-shift keying* is preferred because it gives definite pulses on both mark and space, an advantage in printer operation.

On the vhf bands where A2 transmission is permitted, *audio frequency-shift keying (afsk)* is generally used. In this case, the rf carrier is transmitted continuously, and the pulses are transmitted by frequency-shifted tone modulation. The audio frequencies used have been more-or-less standardized at 2125 and 2975 Hz, the shift being 850 Hz. With

afsk, the lower audio frequency is customarily used for mark and the higher for space.

Below 50 MHz, F1 or fsk emission must be used. The carrier is on continuously but its frequency is shifted to represent marks and spaces. General practice with fsk is to use a frequency shift of 170 or 850 Hz, although FCC regulations permit using frequency shift up to 900 Hz. The smaller values of shift have a signal-to-noise advantage, and 170-Hz shift is currently used by amateurs.

Frequency-Shift Keyers

The keyboard contacts of the teletypewriter control a direct-current circuit that operates the printer magnets. In the "resting" condition, the contacts are closed (mark). In operation, the contacts open for space. Perhaps the simplest satisfactory circuit for frequency-shift keying a VFO uses a diode to switch a capacitor in and out of the circuit. The circuit is intended for a transmitter which heterodynes the VFO signal to the operating frequency.

The Receiver

Right now, as you read this book, hundreds of radio signals are traveling through the air. Many are from amateur radio stations, but others are signals from a-m and fm commercial broadcast stations, CB transmitters, police car two-way radios or other radio services. Why can't you hear them? How can a ham on the other side of the world communicate with the ham down the street when you can't hear a thing? The answer is pretty obvious: Our hearing can only pick up signals at *audio* frequencies. All sounds

are at audio frequencies. Radio signals, however, are much higher in frequency — so high, in fact, that our ears are useless in picking them up out of the air. Also, radio signals are electrical in nature while sound waves are caused by motion in air.

You probably know that in order to listen to radio signals we need a *receiver*; without a receiver, listening to ham or other radio signals is impossible. It is one of the three basic parts of an amateur station; the other two are the transmitter and the antenna system. So it makes sense to

devote some time to discuss receiver principles.

The major purpose of any receiver is to change radio-frequency signals (which we can't hear) to audio-frequency signals (which we can). A *good* receiver has the ability to find weak radio signals, separate them from other signals and interference, and continue to receive the one frequency on which the signal lies.

The ability of a receiver to find or detect signals is called its *sensitivity*. *Selectivity* is the ability of a receiver to separate

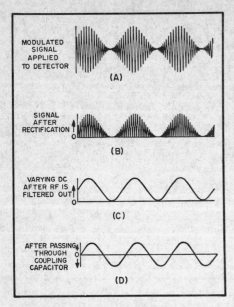

MODULATED
SIGNAL
APPLIED
TO DETECTOR

(A)

SIGNAL
AFTER
RECTIFICATION

(B)

VARYING DC
AFTER RF IS
FILTERED OUT

(C)

AFTER PASSING
THROUGH
COUPLING
CAPACITOR

(D)

Fig. 37 — The detection process.

a desired signal from undesired signals. And *stability* is a measure of the ability of a receiver to continue receiving one particular frequency. In general, then, a good receiver is very sensitive, selective and stable.

Detection

"Detect" means to discover, and the first job of any radio receiver is to detect or discover radio signals. But without the original detection of the radio signal, you're not going to get anywhere.

One of the most common detector forms is a diode rectifier, connected as a half-wave rectifier. This is an old buddy of ours, talked about in the section on power supplies. You'll recall that a diode rectifier will take an ac signal and transform it into dc. The ac fed to the diode was rectified and, through the action of a simple filter capacitor, ended up as a dc through the load, which is usually a receiver or transmitter.

Because the diode generally works at any frequency, we could have used an rf signal instead of the 60-hertz signal. The diode would operate just as well. The intelligence in the radio signal is carried by the variations in its signal strength or *amplitude*. The direct current that comes out of the rectifying detector follows these variations. In a phone signal (or a broadcast of voice or music) these variations occur at an audio-frequency rate. Once the variations are converted into sound by headphones, the signal becomes intelligible.

In a way, everything else in an actual receiver is sort of "extra equipment." It all leads to this basic process of detection. This doesn't mean, however, that this extra equipment is unimportant. Far from it! Without it, actual communication by

radio would be practically impossible. This is all needed nowadays to let you hear a very weak signal even though the air is filled with thousands of others at the same time, many of them far stronger. In other words, the rest of the receiver is there to give you a receiver with high sensitivity to weak signals, and high selectivity to let you hear the weak ones while eliminating all the ones you don't want.

Even the simplest of receivers, the crude crystal set, takes a tiny step in this direction. It often has at least a basic system of tuning or building up the response to the radio frequency of a desired signal. And *stability* is a measure of the ability of a receiver to continue to other frequencies. But a crystal set improves reception only slightly. More elaborate measures are necessary.

Selectivity

The bandwidth of a tuned circuit gets wider as the resonant frequency is raised, other things being equal. For instance, you might have a circuit with a bandwidth of 10 kHz at a center frequency of 500 kilohertz. A similar circuit at 10 times the frequency — 5000 kHz or 5 MHz — would have the same *percentage* bandwidth, but 10 times the actual number of kilohertz. In this example, the bandwidth would be 10 × 10 = 100 kHz.

One thing is in your favor: The bandwidths of the signals you want to receive do *not* increase with the operating frequency. This means that a phone signal requires no more actual bandwidth at 144 MHz than it does at 4 MHz. Its bandwidth is determined by the audio frequencies in the human voice, not by the radio frequency at which the signal goes out. Therefore, we can use the same selectivity, in kilohertz, at 144 MHz as at 4 MHz.

The quest for better selectivity in receivers led to the type of receiver in universal use today — the *superheterodyne* or "superhet." The superhet offers the same kind of selectivity in any part of the spectrum. You'll find that you can eliminate an interfering signal the same number of kilohertz away from the desired signal, no matter whether the signal is on 1000 kHz in the broadcast band or on 30,000 kHz on the other end of the hf spectrum.

Frequency Conversion

There is another advantage to the frequency-conversion process besides the constant selectivity. An amplifier having a given number of stages operating at a relatively low radio frequency — below 500 kHz, say — can be designed for considerably more gain, with stability, than a similar amplifier at high frequencies. Thus the superhet solves a major receiving problem in high-frequency reception.

However, frequency conversion also brings in some new problems that weren't there before. They aren't insurmountable,

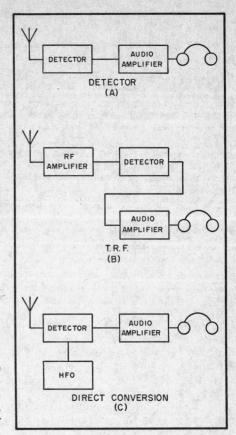

DETECTOR
AUDIO AMPLIFIER
DETECTOR
(A)

RF AMPLIFIER
DETECTOR
AUDIO AMPLIFIER
T. R. F.
(B)

DETECTOR
AUDIO AMPLIFIER
HFO
DIRECT CONVERSION
(C)

Fig. 38 — Block diagrams of three simple receivers. (HFO is the heterodyning frequency oscillator.)

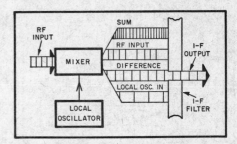

RF INPUT
MIXER
SUM
RF INPUT
DIFFERENCE
LOCAL OSC. IN
I-F OUTPUT
I-F FILTER
LOCAL OSCILLATOR

Fig. 39 — Heterodyning produces four output signals. The desired i-f signal is passed through the i-f filter, which blocks the other three signals.

but they do make a radio designer's life a little more hectic.

There is only one known method of frequency conversion that is at all useful for the purpose. This is the process known as *heterodyning* or *beating*. To get a desired new frequency — known as the *intermediate* frequency (i-f) in a superhet receiver — it's necessary to "mix" a third frequency with the signal frequency. The *mixing* process leads to an interesting result: two new frequencies appear, one equal to the sum of the original two, and one equal to the difference of the original two. These, of course, are in addition to the original two frequencies, which also appear in the output of a mixer. In the superhet receiver, the one we almost always want is the *difference* frequency.

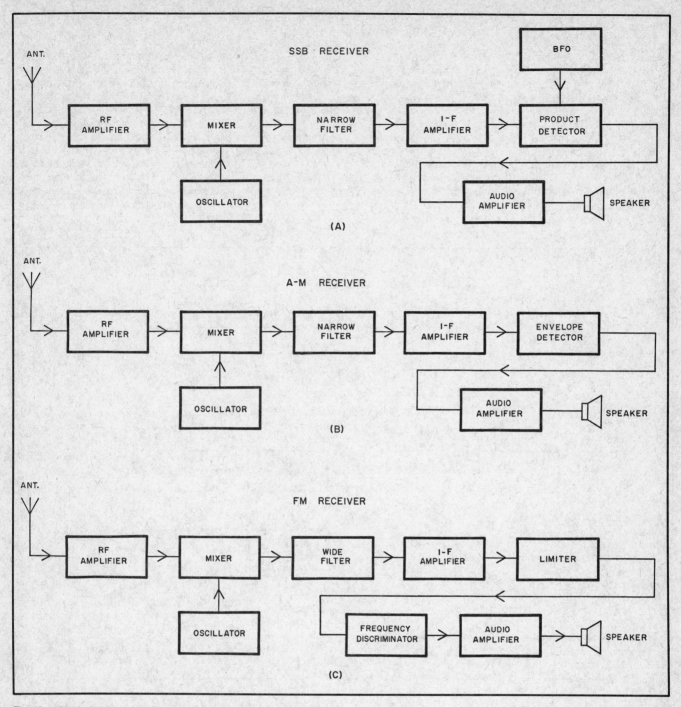

Fig. 40 — Block diagrams of (A) an ssb receiver, (B) an a-m receiver and (C) an fm receiver.

Let's have an example. Our i-f amplifier operates at 455 kHz. There is a signal on 14,150 kHz that we want to convert to 455 kHz, thus 455 kHz will be the difference between 14,150 kHz and a new frequency that we have to introduce in order to make the conversion.

It's easy to see that there are two frequencies — 13,695 kHz and 14,605 kHz — that will meet our needs. Either one is 455 kHz different from the desired frequency. We can use whichever we choose of these two *local-oscillator* frequencies. Do you have any idea why we call them local oscillators? It's because the frequen-

cies are generated by an oscillator in the receiver itself and do not come from outside as the signal does.

Receiver Principles

Block diagrams of ssb, a-m and fm receivers are shown in Fig. 40. By now, you're familiar with the principles used in a standard a-m receiver. An fm receiver normally uses different stages, such as a wider bandwidth filter and a different detector. Most fm receivers have a limiter stage added between the i-f amplifier and the detector (the *frequency discriminator*).

The limiter chops off noise and amplitude modulation from an incoming signal. How does the frequency discriminator work? When the fm signal has no modulation, the discriminator has no output. When audio input to the fm transmitter (when the operator speaks into the microphone) causes a swing in the signal to a higher frequency, for example, the rectified output from the receiver might increase in the negative direction. A signal swing in the other direction would then cause a positive output voltage. In this way, rf signal frequency variations are converted to audio amplitude variations.

The Transmitter

Receivers would be worthless if there were no signals traveling through the air. That's the role of the *transmitter*, which generates radio-frequency signals. Although amateur transmitters are like most things in life, ranging from the simple to the elaborate, they generally have two basic sections, the *oscillator* and the *power amplifier* (PA). The oscillator is what actually produces a radio-frequency signal. On some of the lower-frequency ham bands, a simple oscillator could be used by itself as a transmitter. The power output, though, would be very small. It's much more common to feed the output of the oscillator into one or more amplifiers to increase the power of the signal before you finally *transmit* the signal via the antenna.

A basic beginner's transmitter is shown in block form in Fig. 41A. It consists of a crystal oscillator followed by a power amplifier. A *crystal oscillator* uses a quartz crystal to keep the frequency of the radio signal constant.

Crystal oscillators are not practical in many cases. If an amateur wants to operate on many different frequencies, more crystals are needed. After a while, this activity becomes quite expensive as well as impractical. The solution is to design a circuit or a *variable-frequency oscillator* (VFO). Great care in design and construction of a VFO is necessary if its stability is to compare with that of a crystal oscillator. Stability, by the way, has the same definition in transmitter design as it does in receiver design; it is the property of a transmitter to remain on one frequency.

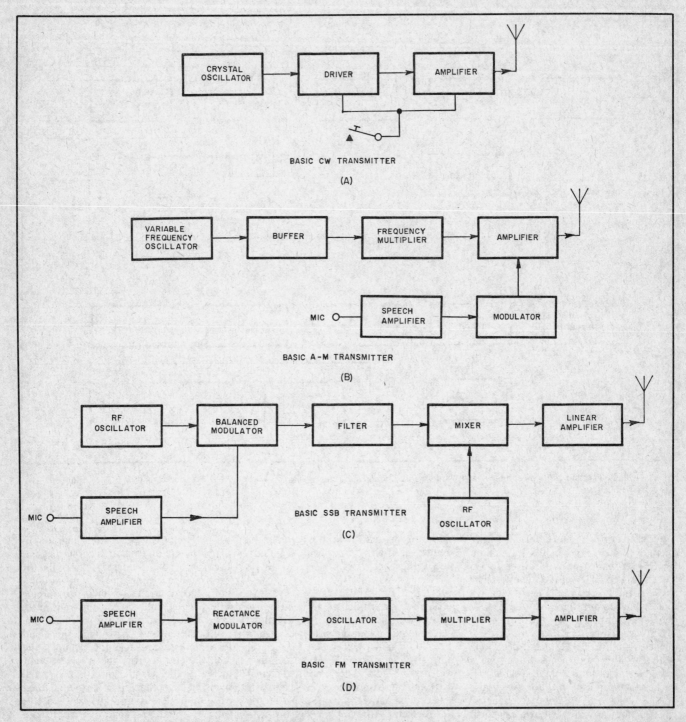

Fig. 41 — Block diagrams of transmitters for the cw, a-m, ssb and fm modes.

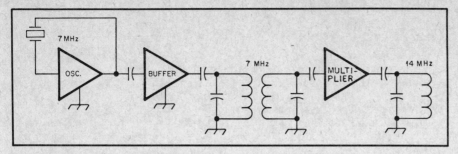

Fig. 42 — Circuit of a typical frequency multiplier.

The block diagram in Fig. 41B is that of a typical a-m transmitter containing a VFO. Immediately following the VFO is a *buffer*, or *buffer amplifier*. Although a buffer is an amplifier, its primary purpose is to isolate two stages (in this diagram, the VFO and the multiplier), rather than increase the power of the signal. Actually, the buffer separates the oscillator from the multiplier in this circuit to maintain the stability of the VFO. Otherwise, the frequency generated by the oscillator is likely to be affected if we change any operating condition of the multiplier. Keying the multiplier, tuning its plate circuit, or adjusting the loading would all react on the oscillator and change the frequency. That's because the load on the oscillator would be changing.

The buffer amplifier is supposed to absorb these reactions and keep a constant load on the oscillator. Occasionally, we use the buffer to amplify the output of the oscillator so that there's enough power to *drive* the power amplifier. Buffer circuits are similar to those used in any amplifier, with emphasis on good isolation between the input (grid or base) and output (plate or collector).

A frequency *multiplier* is actually an amplifier that delivers output at a multiple of the exciting frequency (the frequency delivered to its input). A *doubler* is a multiplier that gives output at twice the exciting frequency; a *tripler* multiplies the exciting frequency by three, and so on.

From the viewpoint of any particular stage in a transmitter, the stage which precedes it is its *driver*. In Fig. 42, the buffer is the driver of the multiplier. The multiplier, in turn, drives the power amplifier.

A transmitting arrangement which is quite popular nowadays is shown in block form in Fig. 41C. The circuit makes use of the conversion principle we discuss in the section on superhet receivers. The signal is first generated at a fixed frequency (usually, but not always, the lowest radio frequency in the transmitter). It is then fed into a mixer, where a variable-frequency

signal from a VFO is combined with it to produce a beat frequency. The output of the mixer stage is then amplified and fed into the antenna.

In transmitters of this type all of the circuits, except for the final amplifer, operate at receiving type power and voltage levels. It is very practical, therefore, to use transistors for these low-level stages. We need to use tubes only in the power-amplifier stage, although new types of transistors can even be used in the PA.

The most significant advantage of this conversion scheme, or heterodyne exciter, is the possibility of using some of the same components and circuits for both transmitting and receiving. A combination transmitting-receiving setup is called a *transceiver (trans*mitter and r*eceiver* in one unit).

The oscillator/multiplier/amplifier type transmitter, as shown in Fig. 41B, has long been popular for transmitting code (cw). However, the heterodyne exciter of Fig. 41C has become increasingly popular for code transmission, despite its slightly more complex circuitry.

A frequency-modulation (fm) transmitter can be modulated only in or following the oscillator stage. An amplitude-modulation (a-m) transmitter can be modulated only in the output stage, unless the modulated stage is followed by a linear amplifier (an amplifier which does not distort the modulation).

Following the generation of a single-sideband (ssb) signal its frequency can be changed only by frequency conversion and not be multiplication. For this reason, the heterodyning exciter shown in Fig. 41C is almost always used in ssb transmitters.

Sideband Techniques

We'll have to confine ourselves to a brief mention of the various aspects of single-sideband transmission in this chapter. Elimination of the carrier from the transmitted signal requires a special circuit called a *balanced modulator*. A balanced

modulator is a special kind of mixer. An ordinary mixer, such as that discussed under "Receivers," produces four output signals: the sum and difference signals, and the two original input signals. In our ssb transmitter these two input signals are the audio signal and the carrier-frequency oscillator. In a balanced modulator these two signals are nearly eliminated at the output. Only the sum and difference signals, which are the two sidebands, are present at the modulator output.

Eliminating one sideband at the transmitter calls for circuits that are more complex than those used in ordinary a-m phone transmission. The two basic ways of doing it are known as the *filter* and the *phasing* methods. The filter method makes use of selective circuits to suppress the unwanted sideband — much the same idea as the ways used for getting selectivity in a receiver. It is shown in block form in Fig. 41C. The phasing method makes use of the properties of the sidebands themselves. By special circuits, it's possible to balance out one sideband and let the other through. With both methods it is customary to start with a balanced modulator so the carrier is eliminated before the "undesired" sideband is suppressed.

Power Amplification

By now, you see that the power amplifier in a transmitter is very important. Without it, the signal reaching the antenna would be much weaker. In addition, the power amplifier cannot, so to speak, drop the ball. There's not much sense in designing a stable oscillator, effective buffer amplifiers, and a reliable multiplier stage, if the power amplifier is going to distort the signal or throw it off its intended frequency. A power-amplifier stage must be efficient (without distortion, in the case of a phone signal) while not affecting the operation of the other stages in the transmitter.

Sometimes an unwanted feedback path that feeds a bit of the output of an amplifier back to its own input occurs. If the amplitude of this feedback is high enough, the feedback signal is in phase with the input signal, the amplifier will oscillate. Feedback such as this that causes oscillation is called *positive* feedback. *Neutralization* is the process of delibelately feeding a portion of the amplifier output back to the input out of phase. (This is called *negative* feedback.) If done correctly, neutralization will cancel any positive feedback that may occur around an amplifier. This will render the stage much more stable and less likely to oscillate.

Sample Study Questions

22) The balanced modulator is used for
A) Removing a sideband from an fm signal
B) Removing a sideband from an a-m signal
C) Removing the carrier from an a-m signal
D) Reinserting the carrier at a receiver

23) Which of the following is not part of a basic radioteletype station?
A) A teleprinter
B) A demodulator
C) A facsimile transmitter
D) A modulator

24) When the total amplitude of a transmitted signal changes each time the station operator speaks into the microphone, the emission type is
A) A-m
B) Afsk
C) Fm
D) Pm

25) What is the principal advantage of the superheterodyne receiver circuit?
A) Constant selectivity
B) High sensitivity
C) Design simplicity
D) Low-power demand

26) In which one of the following would a frequency-discriminator circuit be used?
A) Single-sideband transmitter
B) A-m receiver
C) Fm exciter
D) Fm receiver

27) Below is a block diagram of an a-m receiver. The block that is not identified is the
A) Mixer
B) Filter
C) Rf limiter
D) Second oscillator

28) What is the average power of an a-m signal, modulated 100 percent by a sine wave, when the transmitter output power without modulation is 250 watts?
A) 250 W
B) 305 W
C) 375 W
D) 1000 W

29) What is the approximate bandwidth of an fm signal with a deviation of 100 kHz, where the highest modulating audio frequency is 15 kHz?
A) 100 kHz
B) 115 kHz
C) 215 kHz
D) 230 kHz

30) The primary purpose of neutralization in rf amplifiers is to
A) Prevent oscillation
B) Prevent interference to TV receivers
C) Obtain greater plate efficiency
D) Increase interelectrode capacitance of the tube

31) Which of the following is the primary purpose of a buffer amplifier placed between the oscillator and power amplifier of a transmitter?
A) Increase oscillation
B) Match input and output impedances
C) Isolate the two stages
D) Straight amplification

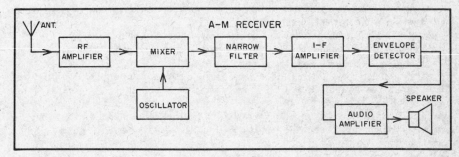

Antennas and Transmission Lines

An antenna system can be considered to include the antenna proper (what is actually supposed to do the radiating of the signal), the transmission line, and any coupling devices or matching networks used for transferring power from the transmitter to the line and from the line to the antenna. Some simple systems may do without the transmission line or one or both of the coupling devices. An applicant for the Technician or General class license should know the basics of transmission lines and of the commonly used types of antennas in Amateur Radio.

The Half-Wave Dipole Antenna

The fundamental amateur antenna is a wire whose total length is approximately equal to half the transmitting wavelength. The antenna is so basic, in fact, that it is the unit from which many more complex forms of antennas are constructed. Amateurs most often call this antenna the half-wave dipole antenna.

The length of a half wave in free space is

$$\text{Length (in meters)} = \frac{150}{\text{frequency (MHz)}}$$
(Eq. 37)

The resonant length of a real-life half-wave antenna will not be exactly equal to the half wave in space, but depends on the thickness of the conductor in relation to the length.

In you have a tape measure and want to cut some wire to build an antenna, the length of an actual half-wavelength wire antenna is approximately

$$\text{Length (in feet)} = \frac{468}{\text{frequency (MHz)}}$$
(Eq. 38)

Current and Voltage Distribution

When power is fed to an antenna, the current and voltage vary along its length. The current is maximum (that is, a *current loop* exists) at the center and nearly zero (that is, a *current node* exists) at the ends, while voltage is just the opposite. Also, the voltage doesn't reach zero at its node

because of the resistance of the antenna, which consists of both the rf resistance of the wire (ohmic losses) and the *radiation resistance*. What about the ohmic losses of an antenna? For a half-wave dipole antenna, they are usually small enough to be neglected for all practical purposes, when compared with the radiation resistance.

The radiation resistance of an infinitely thin half-wave antenna in free space is about 73 ohms. Under practical conditions the value is commonly taken to be between 60 and 70 ohms, although this changes with the height of the antenna above ground. The impedance of the antenna also depends upon the diameter of the conductor in relation to the wavelength. The commonly used term *impedance* refers to the total antenna resistance at resonance — at the frequency the antenna is meant to operate on. If the radiation resistance changes, so does the impedance since impedance is the combination of radiation resistance, ohmic

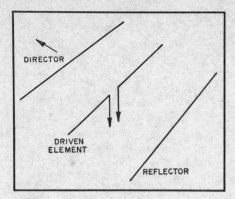

Fig. 43 — Antenna system using a driven element and two parasitic elements, one as a reflector and one as a director.

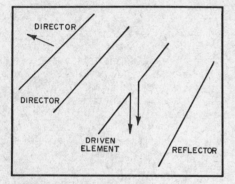

Fig. 44 — A four-element antenna system using two directors and one reflector in conjunction with a driven element.

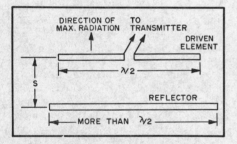

Fig. 45 — A two-element parasitic beam. The lengths in wavelengths shown are electrical rather than physical lengths.

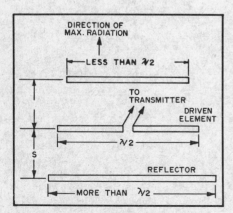

Fig. 46 — The three-element parasitic beam. More parasitic elements — nearly always directors — can be added.

losses (I^2R) and reactance caused by an off-resonance condition.

Radiation Characteristics

The radiation from a dipole antenna is not uniform in all directions. It is strongest in directions perpendicular to the wire and nearly zero along the direction of the wire. The half-wave dipole antenna exhibits excellent directivity when placed at least one-half wavelength above the ground. For example, a 40-meter dipole would require a height above ground of at least 20 meters to take on such directivity. Its directivity is lessened by placing it less than 20 meters above the ground. Despite what might seem like a disadvantage of the half-wave antenna, it is the most common and practical antenna for the 80- and 40-meter bands.

Multiple-Element Arrays

The half-wave dipole antenna mounted over earth is a bidirectional antenna, meaning that it radiates equally well in both horizontal directions perpendicular to it. In other words, a half-wave dipole with its ends at north and south will radiate equally to the east and west. In order for half-wave dipole antennas to have gain (take on unidirectional characteristics), they need additional elements. Antennas with these extra elements are usually referred to by amateurs as *beam antennas*.

Parasitic Excitation

In most of these multiple-element antennas, the additional elements receive power by either induction or radiation from the driven element. They then re-radiate it in the proper phase relationship to achieve directivity or gain over a simple half-wave dipole in free space. These elements are called *parasitic* elements in most amateur beam antennas. They draw power from the *driven* element. The driven element receives its power directly from the transmitter via the transmission line.

There are two types of parasitic elements. A *director* is shorter than the driven element and is located at the "front" of the antenna. A *reflector* is longer than the driven element and is located at the "back" of the antenna. Maximum radiation from a parasitic antenna, therefore, travels from the reflector element through the driven and director elements.

Front-to-Back Ratio

Front-to-back ratio is the ratio between the power radiated in the direction of maximum radiation to the power radiated in the reverse direction. If you point your antenna directly at a receiving station and then turn the antenna 180 degrees, the difference in received signal strength is the front-to-back ratio.

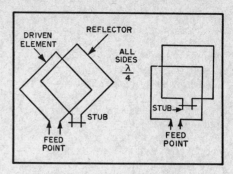

Fig. 47 — The basic two-element quad antenna., with driven loop and reflector loop. The loops are electrically one wavelength in circumference (1/4 wavelength on a side). Both configurations shown give horizontal polarization. For vertical polarization, the driven elements should be fed at one of the side corners in the arrangement at the left, or at the center of a vertical side in the "square" quad at right.

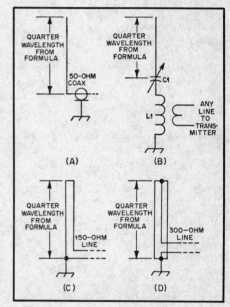

Fig. 48 — A quarter-wavelength antenna can be fed directly with 50-ohm coaxial line (A), with a low standing-wave ratio, or a coupling network can be used (B) that permits a transmission line of any impedance to be used. In (B), L1 and C1 should resonate to the operating frequency, and L1 should be larger than is normally used in a plate tank circuit at the same frequency. By using multiwire antennas, the quarter-wave vertical can be fed with (C) 150- or (D) 300-ohm transmission line.

Gain vs. Spacing

The gain of an antenna with parasitic elements varies with the spacing between the elements and the element length. The maximum front-to-back ratio seldom, if ever, occurs at the same condition that gives maximum forward gain. The impedance of the driven element also changes with the tuning and spacing. Theoretically, an optimum three-element beam antenna (director, driven element and reflector) has a gain over a half-wave antenna in free space of slightly more than 7 dB. *Effective power gain* is the ratio of power required to produce a certain signal strength at a receiving antenna with a *comparison* antenna to the power needed to have as strong a signal with a specific antenna. The comparison antenna is usually our old acquaintance, the half-wave antenna in free space.

We've actually been discussing the *Yagi* antenna, which is a parasitic array usually containing straight, metal tubing for elements. Figs. 45 and 46 show the Yagi. The quad antenna is another type of parasitic array. Its elements are square loops of wire approximately one wavelength in circumference. The quad is shown in Fig. 47.

Driven Arrays

A *driven array* is an antenna with more than two driven elements. The most common form of a driven-array antenna is the *collinear antenna*. The simplest and most popular collinear array uses two elements, each one-half wavelength long. As all collinear arrays are operated with the elements in phase, this setup is usually called "two half-waves in phase."

When more than two collinear elements are used, it is necessary to connect "phasing" stubs between adjacent elements in order to bring the current to all elements in phase. Multiple-element collinear arrays — some using as many as 160 elements and more — are commonly used for DX work on vhf and uhf. The simple two-element collinear array, however, is often used, as it lends itself well to multiband operation.

Vertical Antennas

A vertical quarter-wavelength antenna is often used in the amateur bands to obtain low-angle radiation when a high beam or dipole can't be put up. (*Low-angle radiation* refers to the characteristics of an antenna to emit signals which travel closer to the natural horizon, rather than emitting signals extremely upward. This is advantageous when working DX.) A vertical quarter-wavelength antenna is also used when there isn't enough room for a horizontal antenna. For maximum effectiveness it should be located free of nearby objects and should have a good ground system. An excellent ground connection is necessary for the most effective operation of a vertical antenna (other than the ground-plane type).

The radiation resistance of a theoretical quarter-wavelength vertical antenna over a perfect ground is just under 50 ohms. The feedpoint impedance of real quarter-wavelength verticals varies from 30 to 50 ohms. With a poor ground, the impedance can be as low as 5 to 15 ohms.

Four typical examples of vertical antennas are shown in Fig. 48. The antenna may be wire or tubing supported by wood or insulated guy wires. When tubing is used for the antenna, or when guy wires (broken up at intervals by insulators) are used to reinforce the structure, the length

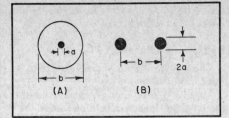

Fig. 49 — Two general types of transmission lines. At A is coaxial cable, and at B is open line. The dimensions represented by a and b are used in the characteristic impedance formulas.

given by the quarter-wavelength formula is likely to be long by a few percent. (The half-wavelength formula can be used by dividing all answers by two).

The Gound-Plane Antenna

A ground-plane antenna is a vertical quarter wavelength antenna using an artificial metallic ground, usually consisting of four metal rods or wires perpendicular or sloping to the antenna and extending outward from its base. Sloping the radials downward raises the feed-point impedance of the antenna. Unlike the quarter-wavelength vertical antennas without an artificial ground, the ground-plane antenna will give low-angle radiation in almost all cases, regardless of the height above *actual* ground.

TRANSMISSION LINES

There are two general types of transmission lines used by amateurs: conductor and cable. Broken down further, there are two kinds of parallel-conductor lines, one in which two wires are separated by insulating rods called spacers, and one that is prefabricated plastic insulation. The latter is commonly used for TV reception and is usually called "twin-lead."

Coaxial cable (or just "coax") consists of one conductor placed in the center of a conducting tube. These two conductors are known as the *center conductor* and the *shield*. The inside surface of the shield and the outside surface of the center conductor form the two conducting surfaces of the line. The most common coaxial cable has either a solid or stranded-wire center conductor surrounded by polyethylene dielectric. Solid pipe or copper braid surrounds the dielectric to form the outer conductor, and a waterproof vinyl covers the shield. With coaxial cable, the fields are entirely inside the tube, because the tube acts as a shield to prevent rf radiation from appearing outside.

Characteristic Impedance

Every transmission line has an apparent "resistance," called its characteristic resistance. A more general term is *characteristic impedance*, indicated in equations by the letter Z_o. Various types of transmission lines have different values of characteristic impedance.

For example, the characteristic impedance of an air-insulated parallel-conductor transmission line is given by the equation

$$Z_o = 276 \log \frac{b}{a} \qquad \text{(Eq. 39)}$$

where

Z_o = characteristic impedance
b = center-to-center distance between conductors
a = radius of conductor (in same units as b)

And the characteristic impedance of an air-insulated coaxial transmission line is given by the equation

$$Z_o = 138 \log \frac{b}{a} \qquad \text{(Eq. 40)}$$

where

Z_o = characteristic impedance
b = inside diameter of outer conductor
a = outside diameter of inner conductor (in same units as b)

Although you don't need to memorize either of these equations, you should know that the characteristic impedance of a transmission line increases as separation between conductors increases, and conductor diameter decreases.

Standing-Wave Ratio

The most common measurement of an antenna system is the *standing-wave ratio* (SWR). Standing waves are variations of current and voltage along a transmission line. These occur when the characteristic impedance of the line is different than the impedance of the antenna at the operating frequency, creating a mismatch.

SWR is the ratio of maximum current to minimum current (or maximum voltage to minimum voltage) along the transmission line. A reflectometer is normally used to measure SWR. The SWR is significant because it's a measure of the mismatch between the antenna and the transmission line. When the line is perfectly matched to the antenna, the SWR is 1:1. The equation for calculating SWR when the line is connected to a purely resistive load is

$$SWR = \frac{Z_R}{Z_o} \text{ or } \frac{Z_o}{Z_R} \qquad \text{(Eq. 41)}$$

where

SWR = standing wave ratio
Z_R = impedance of the load
Z_o = characteristic impedance of the line

Example: A line having a characteristic impedance of 300 ohms is terminated in a resistive load of 50 ohms. The SWR is

$$SWR = \frac{Z_o}{Z_R} = \frac{300}{50} = 6 \text{ to } 1 \qquad \text{(Eq. 42)}$$

The SWR can also be calculated from the equation

$$SWR = \frac{V_f + V_r}{V_f - V_r} \qquad \text{(Eq. 43)}$$

where

V_f = the incident or forward voltage
V_r = the reflected voltage

The Antenna-Matching Network

Most currently manufactured Amateur Radio transmitters are designed to be connected to an antenna system with an impedance of 50 to 75 ohms. Some transmitters with vacuum-tube power amplifiers can be adjusted to match an impedance range somewhat greater than this, but most transmitters with solid-state power amplifiers need to "see" an antenna-system impedance very close to 50 ohms for maximum power transfer.

If you use a quarter-wavelength vertical or half-wavelength dipole antenna *at its resonant frequency*, most likely the antenna feed-point impedance will be at or near 50 to 75 ohms. If you use 50- or 75-ohm transmission line, the transmitter will still see an impedance very near the standard 50 or 75 ohms. When you use such an antenna system at a frequency other than its resonant frequency, the impedance at the transmitter end of the feed line will no longer be the standard value. An SWR rising above 1 indicates a departure from the standard value. If the SWR is much above 2, operational problems may occur with transmitters that have a limited matching range.

A *matching network* changes such a nonstandard value of impedance to a value at or near 50 ohms so that the transmitter is presented with the load it was designed for. Also, practically all transmitter outputs are single-ended or "unbalanced" — one side is grounded to the chassis. This type of output is correct for coaxial-line feed. If you use parallel-conductor transmission line, such as "twin-lead" or open-wire line, a matching network can transform the high-impedance balanced condition to the normal unbalanced 50- or 75-ohm condition.

The easiest way to adjust a matching network is to put a reflectometer (a device for measuring SWR) in the line between the transmitter and the network. Set the reflectometer to read reflected power, and set the sensitivity control to maximum. Key the transmitter with just enough power to give a mid-scale meter deflection. Now adjust the matching-network controls for minimum reflected power. It will probably be necessary to try many different control settings until the optimum point is reached. Increase the transmitter power to get a usable reading as the SWR approaches 1. With persistence, you will find a setting of the controls that will result in no reflected power: The SWR will be 1. It may be helpful to make a chart of matching-network control settings for each band or band segment; this will speed the adjustment procedure when you change bands.

Radio-Wave Propagation

After a signal leaves your antenna, it's beyond your control. It can't do whatever it feels like doing, however. For example, it may want to travel along the ground for 200 miles, but the terrain may not allow it to do that. It may get ideas of heading up toward the ionosphere, a region of charged particles above the earth, and then bouncing off the ionosphere back to earth, thousands of miles away from where it was transmitted. It might just be able to do that, but if the ionosphere has different ideas, the signal may, instead, go straight into outer space, never to return. Or the ionosphere may bounce the signal back to earth, but at a much shorter distance than expected.

Radio waves can't think, of course, and the ionosphere doesn't get any ideas. But the point is still the same: Radio signals are greatly affected by nature. No matter how powerful a radio signal may be, or how good an antenna is, nature is still a big part of communication. Just as most people are interested in the weather, radio amateurs carefully monitor what nature is doing to their signals.

Wave Characteristics

Every radio amateur should have some knowledge of what happens to a radio signal after it leaves his antenna. It would be wasted effort if we all just sent out our signals without having any idea what might happen to them. Of course, this doesn't mean that we know completely what our signals will do at any particular moment. We don't. But we at least try to find out as much as we can about radio phenomena. That way, we can make the most consistent contacts that are possible.

Like other forms of electromagnetic

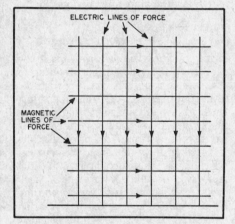

Fig. 50 — Representation of electric and magnetic lines of force in a radio wave. Arrows indicate instantaneous directions of the fields for a wave traveling toward the reader. Reversing the direction of one set of lines would reverse the direction of travel.

radiation such as light, radio waves travel at a speed of about 186,000 miles (300,000 km) per second in free space, and can be reflected, refracted and diffracted. An electromagnetic wave is composed of moving electric and magnetic force. The lines of force in the electric and magnetic fields are at right angles, and both are perpendicular to the direction of travel. A simple representation of a radio wave is shown in Fig. 50. In this drawing the magnetic lines are parallel to the earth's surface and the electric lines are perpendicular, although they could have any position with respect to earth as long as they remain perpendicular to each other (at least with the most common form of wave).

Radio waves don't always travel at the same speed; how fast they go depends on the *medium*, or environment, they're traveling through. When the medium is outer space, the speed is 300 million meters per second. Radio waves travel at almost the same speed as that in air, but move much more slowly in some other substances. What happens when a radio wave meets a good conductor? Actually, a radio wave cannot penetrate a good conductor deeply because the electric lines of force are essentially short circuited by the conductor.

Polarization

Polarization is the direction of the *electric lines* of force of a radio wave. If the electric lines of force are parallel to the earth, we call this a *horizontally polarized* radio wave. A radio wave is *vertically polarized* if its electric lines of force are perpendicular to the earth. For the most part, polarization has a lot to do with what type of transmitting antenna is used. For example, a Yagi antenna with its elements parallel to the earth's surface transmits a horizontally polarized radio wave. On the other hand, an amateur mobile antenna sitting on a car is almost always perpendicular to the earth, or vertical. It puts out a vertically polarized wave. Will the waves, as they travel on the ground, keep their polarization? The longer waves usually do, but the polarization of shorter waves may change during travel, and sometimes will change quite rapidly.

The Inverse Square-Distance Law

In a way, radio waves are like long-distance runners. As a runner travels farther, he loses strength. It's the same with a radio wave. As it travels on the ground or through the atmosphere, it too loses strength. The *inverse square-distance law* explains this. It states that the field intensity of a wave is inversely proportional to the square of the distance from the source. This means that in a uniform medium, if one point is twice as far from the transmitter as another, the field strength at the farther point will be just one-fourth that at the nearer point. This law is based on the assumption that there is nothing in the medium to absorb energy from the wave as it travels. Unfortunately, this isn't the situation in real life, where energy is absorbed as radio waves travel along the gound and through the atmosphere.

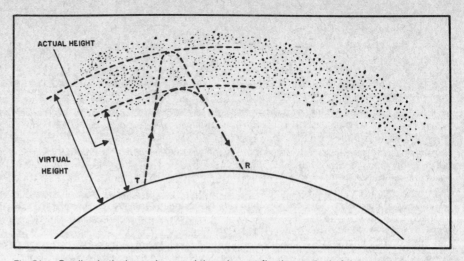

Fig. 51 — Bending in the ionosphere, and the echo or reflection method of determining virtual height.

IONOSPHERIC PROPAGATION IN THE HF AND VHF AMATEUR BANDS

Except for distances of a few miles up to several hundred miles, nearly all amateur communications on frequencies below 30 MHz is by means of *sky waves*. After leaving the transmitting antenna, this wave travels upward from the earth's surface at such an angle that it would continue out into space were its path not bent enough to bring it back to earth. The ionosphere causes this bending. At an altitude of about 60 miles, the ionosphere is a region of the upper atmosphere where there are enough free electrons and ions to have a noticeable effect on radio waves. (An *ion* is a charged atom or molecule.)

Ionization is the process which results in the formation of ions. Ionization of a gas occurs when radiation passes through the gas. In the case of the ionosphere, this radiation comes from the sun. Remember that the ionosphere is not a single region. Instead, it is composed of a series of layers at different heights above the earth. In addition, each layer has a central region where the ionization is dense. Both above and below this central region of a layer, the intensity of ionization tapers off.

Refraction

When a layer of the ionosphere has dense ionization, it bends the path of radio waves drastically. When there's little ionization, the path bends just slightly. This bending, or *refraction*, also depends on the wavelength. The longer the wave, the more the path is bent for a given degree of ionization. This is why low-frequency waves bend more than those of high-frequency. There are times when ionization is so slight that signals in the higher amateur frequencies may not return to earth, because the direction of travel is not bent enough by the ionosphere.

Absorption

In passing through the atmosphere, particularly the ionosphere, a radio wave gives up some of its energy by setting the ionized particles into motion. When the

moving ionized particles collide with each other, this energy is lost. Lower frequencies are more affected by this *absorption* than higher frequencies, because the waves are longer. Absorption also increases with the density of ionization; the more ions, the more absorption occurs.

Virtual Height

Although a layer of the ionosphere is a region of considerable depth, in some cases over 100 miles, it's convenient to assign to it a definite height above the earth's surface. We call this the *virtual height*, which is the height from which a simple reflection would give the same effect as the gradual bending that really takes place during amateur communication. This is illustrated in Fig. 51. The radio wave traveling upward is bent back over a path having quite a large turning radius. And, of course, this large turning process takes time. The virtual height is the height of a triangle having equal sides of a total length proportional to the time taken for the wave to travel from T to R in the illustration.

If we gradually increase the transmitting frequency while taking these height measurements, we'll eventually find a frequency range where the virtual height seems to increase rapidly, until finally the radio wave doesn't come back at all. The highest frequency returned to earth is called the *critical frequency*. If we send a wave with a frequency higher than the critical frequency, it will not return to earth unless we send it so that it strikes the ionosphere at a smaller angle, rather than perpendicular. The higher the frequency, therefore, the smaller the angle a wave needs for refraction to earth. By using very low angles, in fact, long-distance transmission via the F2 layer (we'll discuss this later) is possible at frequencies up to about 3.5 times the critical frequency. You can tell how well the ionosphere is reflecting radio waves by examining the critical frequency.

Since a reflected radio wave acts as though it were reflected from a mirror at the virtual height, the terms "refraction" and "reflection" are commonly interchanged in connection with ionospheric propagation. In most cases, the actual process is refraction. It is possible, however, for true reflection to occur if the boundary of an ionospheric layer is sharply defined and a radio wave strikes it at a small enough angle.

Virtual heights, of course, depend on the height of the ionized region. The critical frequencies vary with the intensity of ionization in the layers, becoming greater as the ionization increases. When the critical frequency is above an amateur band, it's possible to communicate on that band over great distances. For example, if the critical frequency is 15 MHz, it's certainly possible for long-distance contacts to be made on the 20-meter amateur band (14.0 to 14.35 MHz).

Maximum Usable Frequency

There's little doubt that the critical frequency is important to amateur communication. Radio amateurs, however, are more interested in the frequency *range* over which communication can be carried via one or the other of the two reflecting layers. What most amateurs want to know is the *maximum usable frequency* (abbreviated muf) for a particular distance at the time of day at which communication is desired. Why is this so important? Let's give an example. An amateur in Ohio wants to communicate with an amateur in Scotland during the afternoon. If the muf is 18 MHz at that time, he'd do best by trying the 20-meter band, or 14 MHz, as it's the closest frequency to the muf without being higher.

What actually is the muf? It is the highest frequency which allows *one hop* in a multihop transmission to reach whatever is the wave's destination. A multihop transmission occurs when a radio wave bounces back-and-forth between the ionosphere and the earth.

The maximum usable frequency is subject to seasonal changes as well as changes throughout the day. If an amateur is going to use the muf for long-distance communication with the fewest hops, he should usually use an antenna system that radiates well at low vertical angles. In other words, the wave should leave the antenna so that it strikes the ionosphere at the farthest point from the antenna, if at all possible.

The Ionosphere

The ionized layers are designated by letters. The lowest known ionized layer is the *D layer*. It sits about 30 to 55 miles above the earth. The D layer is in a relatively dense part of the atmosphere. For this reason, the atoms broken up into ions by sunlight quickly recombine, so the amount of ionization depends on how much sunlight hits the layer. At noontime, the D layer ionization is maximum, or very close to it. By sunset, any ionization there may have been has disappeared. The

D layer is actually ineffective in bending high-frequency signals back to earth. The major role in amateur long-distance communication of the D layer is as an absorber of energy. The D layer is also responsible for the short daytime communication ranges of the lower amateur frequencies (3.5 and 7 MHz).

The next layer of the ionosphere is the E layer. It appears above the earth at an altitude of about 60 to 70 miles. The atmosphere here is still dense enough so that ions and electrons set free by sunlight do not have to travel far before meeting and recombining to form neutral particles. This makes the E-layer useful for bending radio waves to earth only when it is in sunlight. Like the D layer, the E layer reaches maximum ionization at about midday, and by early evening when the sun is setting, ionization has practically disappeared.

Amateurs should thank another layer of the ionosphere for most of their long-distance communication. This is the F layer, which is about 130 to 260 miles

above the earth, depending on season, latitude, time of day, and where we are in the sunspot cycle. At these heights, the atmosphere is very thin, so the ions and electrons are slow to recombine. Because of this, ionization in the F layer isn't in such a tight relationship with how much sunlight there is, as in the case with the D and E layers. Ionization reaches a maximum shortly after noon local standard time, but tapers off very gradually toward sunset. In fact, the F layer continues to remain ionized throughout the night, reaching a minimum just before sunrise. At sunrise, it increases rapidly and gets to the daytime level in about an hour or so.

During the day, the F-layer splits into two parts, F1 and F2, having heights of about 140 and 200 miles, respectively. They merge again at sunset. The F1 layer actually doesn't have much to do with long-distance communication. It acts more like the E layer. The F2 layer is responsible for almost all long-distance communication on the amateur high-frequency bands.

The Sun and Propagation

By now, you should have the idea that the sun plays a big part in ionization of the different reflective layers of the upper atmosphere. Actually, the sun, ultimate source of life and energy on earth, dominates all radio communication beyond the local range. That means that if we want to communicate by radio over any long-distance at all, we should be aware of what the sun is doing to conditions which will eventually affect our radio signals.

You know about the obvious sun-related cycles on earth, such as the time of day and what season of the year it is. Conditions affecting amateur communication vary with these same cycles. Where you are on earth has a lot to do with how much sunlight you're receiving, so it shouldn't come as any surprise to find out that almost every communications path in the world is unique in some respects. There are also short- and long-term solar cycles that influence propagation in ways which aren't so obvious. The state of the sun at any given moment is also critical to long-distance communication, so it's understandable that predicting what's going to happen to our signals after they leave our transmitting antennas is still a pretty inexact science.

Man's interest in the sun is older than recorded history. *Sunspots*, or dark spots on the sun, were seen and discussed thousands of years ago, and they've been studied since Galileo observed them with the first telescope ever made.

Long before radio propagation forecasting, in fact long before radio, observers of the sun noticed that the number of sunspots increased and decreased in cycles. These *sunspot cycles* influence propagation and average roughly 11 years in length. Some, though, have

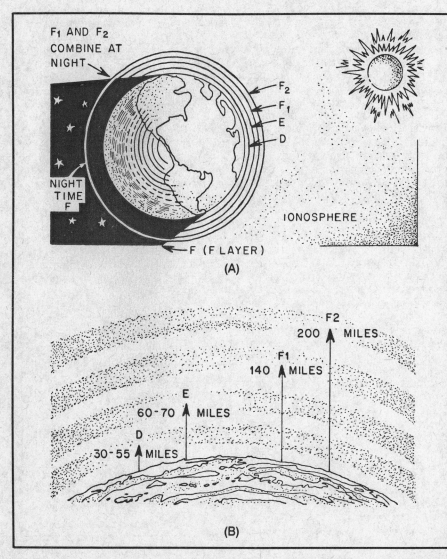

Fig. 52 — The ionosphere is broken up into several layers or regions. By daylight, they take these positions.

been as short as nine and as long as 13 years. The highs and lows of sunspot cycles also vary quite a lot. Cycle 19 peaked in 1958 with a smoothed mean Zurich sunspot number of over 200. That was a "good year" for DX communicating around the world. Cycle 20 was about average and peaked in 1969. It created good, but not the best, conditions for DX. By contrast, one of the lowest, Cycle 14, peaked at only 60 sunspots in 1907.

You shouldn't think of sunspot cycles as having definite patterns. They don't. There can be highs which seem to come out of nowhere during the normally low years. A remarkable example was a run of several days in October 1974, only a few months from the approximate bottom of Cycle 20. The sunspot number during this time reached 98, much greater than the *highs* of certain sunspot cycles on record. Only five months later, the sunspot number had dropped to seven, just about where it should have been.

Although you'll hear amateurs talking about sunspots, there is another useful indication of solar activity, the *solar-flux index*. In fact, solar-flux index is gradually replacing the sunspot number as a means of predicting propagation conditions. Solar flux is noise coming from the sun. But you can't just turn your ear to the sun and expect to eventually hear some noise. It doesn't work that way. It actually requires sophisticated receiving equipment and large antennas turned toward the sun while it is rising or setting. This measurement is taken several times daily in Ottawa on 2800 MHz. This information is transmitted by U.S. Bureau of Standards station, WWV. This is current information, directly related to the sunspot number (see Fig. 54).

Sudden Ionospheric Disturbance

Occasionally, hf sky-wave communications are severely disrupted by solar flares. This is called a sudden ionospheric disturbance (abbreviated SID). Solar flares, heavily laden with ultraviolet and X rays, cause a large increase in ionization of the D layer of the ionosphere. This causes signals to be absorbed by the D layer, instead of passing through it or reflecting from it. During an SID, hf signals suddenly fade out, gradually returning minutes or a few hours later.

The Scatter Modes

All electromagnetic-wave propagation is subject to scattering influences which can cause considerable change in regular patterns. The earth's atmosphere and ionosphere are scattering media, just the same as most objects which intervene in the path of a radio wave. Weak returns of signals are considered resulting from scattering, while strong signal returns are usually thought of as being reflected.

A complex form of scatter is readily

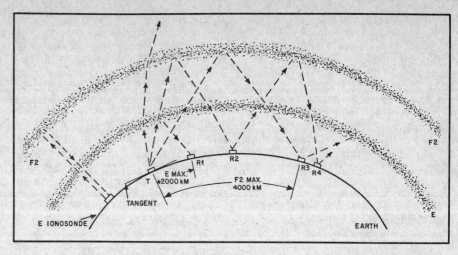

Fig. 53 — Three types of ionospheric propagation. Sounder, left, measures virtual height and critical frequency of the F2 layer. Transmitter T is shown radiating at three different angles. Highest passes through the ionosphere after slight refraction. Lower-angle wave is returned to earth by the E-layer, if frequency is low enough, at a maximum distance of about 2000 km. The F-layer reflection returns a maximum distance of about 4000 km, depending on the radiation angle. It also has a second hop from R2 to R4. The lowest angle wave reaches the maximum practical single-hop distance at R3.

observed when working near the maximum usable frequency for the F layer at the time. The transmitted wave is refracted back to earth at some distant point, which may be an ocean area or a land mass where there is no use for the signal. A small part of the energy is scattered back to the skip zone of the transmitting station (the area between R1 and R2 in Fig. 53) via the ionospheric route.

Backscatter signals are usually rather weak. They're subject to distortion from multipath effects. With excellent equipment, backscatter signals are usable at distances just beyond the local range of the transmitted signal out to several hundred miles.

Tropospheric Bending and Ducting

The troposphere consists of atmospheric layers close to the earth's surface. Although *tropospheric bending* is evident over a wide range of frequencies, it is most useful in the vhf/uhf region, especially at 144 MHz and above. The bending action is caused by a change in the refractive index of adjacent air masses having significantly different temperature, relative humidity or barometric pressure. The boundary layer between these different air masses is the point where the radio wave is bent, much as light is bent when it passes from air into water or from water into air. Normally, this boundary layer is formed within the first few thousand feet above the surface of the earth with a resulting propagation range of from 50 to 400 miles.

Even under normal conditions, *some* bending does take place. The *true* or *geometric horizon* is the most distant point one can see by line of sight and is limited by the height of the observer above ground. Because of the slight bending of radio waves in the troposphere,

however, signals return to earth somewhat beyond the geometric horizon. This *radio-path horizon* is generally about 33 percent farther away than the true horizon.

Under normal conditions, the temperature of the air gradually decreases with increasing height above ground. However, under certain conditions a mass of warm air may actually overrun cold air so that there is an area above the surface of the earth where cold air is covered by a blanket of warm air. This is called a *thermal inversion*. If the two air masses are more or less stationary, waves can become trapped between the air-mass boundary and the earth, and travel great distances with very little attenuation. Sometimes the wave can become trapped between two air-mass boundaries above the surface of the earth. The area between the two boundaries is known as a *duct*. Both the transmitting and receiving antennas must be within the duct if communication is to take place.

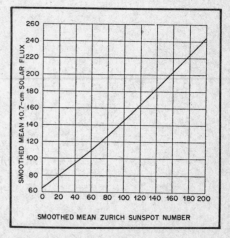

Fig. 54 — Relationship between smoothed mean Zurich sunspot number and the 2800-MHz solar flux.

The manner in which the radio waves are guided along the inversion is very similar to the way microwaves travel through a waveguide. Because of this, radio wave propagation through a duct is called *guided propagation*. Usually ducts form over water, though they can form over land as well. The lowest usable frequency depends on the depth of the duct and the amount the reflective index changes at the boundaries.

Propagation in the Low Bands

The 160-meter amateur band offers reliable communication over distances up to about 25 miles during daylight. On winter nights ranges up to several thousand miles are possible.

The 80-meter band is seldom usable beyond 200 miles in daylight, but long distances are not unusual at night, especially in years of low solar activity. Atmospheric noise tends to be high in the

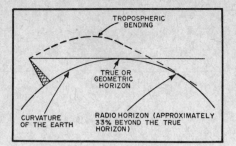

Fig. 55 — Under normal conditions, tropospheric bending causes radio waves to be returned to earth about 33 percent beyond the visual or geometric horizon.

summer months on both the 160- and 80-meter bands.

The 40-meter band has characteristics similar to the 80-meter band, except that greater distances are possible in daylight, and more often at night. In winter dawn and dusk periods, it is possible to work

the other side of the world, as signals follow the darkness path.

The 20-meter band is the most widely used DX band. In the peak years of the sunspot cycle, it is open to distant parts of the world almost continuously. During low solar activity, it is usable mainly in the daylight hours, and is especially good in the dawn and dusk periods. There is almost always a skip zone on this band.

The 15-meter band shows highly variable propagation depending on the level of solar activity. During the peak of the sunspot cycle, it is useful for long-distance work almost around the clock. At intermediate levels, however, it is mainly a daylight DX band.

The 10-meter band is excellent for DX communication in the peak sunspot cycle years, but mostly in the daylight hours. During lows in the sunspot cycle, the band rarely is good for any type of long-distance communication.

Sample Study Questions

32) The characteristic impedance of an air-insulated, parallel-conductor transmission line depends primarily on
A) The type of insulation between conductors
B) The diameter of the conductors and the spacing between them
C) The capacitance of the line
D) The inductance of the line

33) Which of the following conditions would create a 1:1 SWR?
A) A kilowatt dc power input to the transmitter
B) The transmission line exactly equal to one-half wavelength
C) The transmission line and antenna impedances are identical
D) The transmission line runs parallel to the ground

34) The ratio of the total power radiated to the square of the current in the antenna is
A) The radiation resistance
B) The power gain
C) The power density
D) The field strength

35) Which of the following is a characteristic of the half-wave dipole antenna?
A) It radiates equally well in all directions
B) It uses an artificial ground

C) When set up less than one-half wavelength above ground, it exhibits excellent directivity
D) It is the most common and practical antenna for use on the 80- and 40-meter bands

36) The length of a half-wave dipole antenna for use at 14,300 kHz is approximately
A) 18 feet
B) 33 feet
C) 58 feet
D) 92 feet

37) Worldwide communication by way of the ionosphere takes place principally in which of the following portions of the radio spectrum?
A) Hf
B) Vhf
C) Uhf
D) Microwave

38) Which of the following statements characterizes radio-wave propagation for the 20-meter band during the period of maximum sunspot activity?
A) Ionospheric propagation during this period is virtually unknown
B) The band is usually "dead" for long-distance communication at the sunspot cycle peak
C) Good worldwide communication during most of the 24 hours

D) Worldwide communication during the day and almost no communication at night

39) A high sunspot number would most likely be associated with which of the following?
A) A high solar-flux index
B) Poor propagation conditions on the 20-meter band
C) The F-layer of the ionosphere remaining as one layer during the daylight hours
D) Consistent worldwide communication at night on the 80-meter band

40) Which band is excellent for DX communication in the peak sunspot-cycle years during the daylight hours, and is rarely good for any long-distance communication during lows in the sunspot cycle?
A) 160-meter band
B) 40-meter band
C) 20-meter band
D) 10-meter band

41) What is the characteristic impedance of a parallel-conductor transmission line made with conductors 0.064 inch in diameter, spaced 2 inches apart in air?
A) 250 Ω
B) 410 Ω
C) 500 Ω
D) 1700 Ω

Radio Communications Practices

It's easy to form good habits in Amateur Radio. By understanding the fundamentals of radio, you should be able to work and maintain your station so that its operation is in accordance with FCC rules and regulations. In addition, if you're like most amateurs, you'll want to put out the best possible signal. If you know the principles behind the operation of your station, correctly adjust and measure its performance, and take advantage of available test equipment, you should have no problem keeping your station "up to par."

A diagram of a basic Amateur Radio station is shown in Fig. 56. The *receiver* accepts radio signals on the particular frequency to which it is tuned and converts them to audio-frequency signals which in turn are changed to sound waves by the speaker or headphones. The *transmitter* creates and amplifies a radio signal on the particular frequency to which it is set. The *transmission line* carries this signal to the antenna, where it is radiated into the atmosphere and beyond. The *ground rod* is usually of copper and is driven into the ground. It's connected to the cabinets of the transmitter and receiver by heavy wire or braid, which drains off unwanted electrical charges on the equipment. This reduces the danger of the equipment being damaged by lightning strokes.

The *transmit-receive (T-R) switch* connects the antenna to the transmitter during periods of sending and to the receiver during periods of reception. The T-R switch may be mechanical (as shown in Fig. 56), an antenna relay that is switched by the transmitter or receiver, or *electronic*. When an electronic T-R switch is used, the transmitter is continuously connected to the antenna. The receiver antenna connection is via the T-R switch. During transmit periods, the T-R switch prevents large amounts of rf from reaching the receiver by electronically disconnecting the receiver from the antenna and transmitter. Since no mechanical device is involved in the antenna switching, the T-R switch can follow cw keying, making break-in operation practical. The receiver is left operative continuously, and if it can recover from a strong signal quickly enough, it will be sensitive to other signals between the transmitted dits and dahs.

The active device (tube or transistor) that does the switching in a T-R switch may be driven into nonlinearity by the strong signal from the transmitter. For this reason, electronic T-R switches can generate harmonics that can cause TVI. A low-pass filter after the T-R switch may eliminate the TVI, but the low-order harmonics may cause interference to other

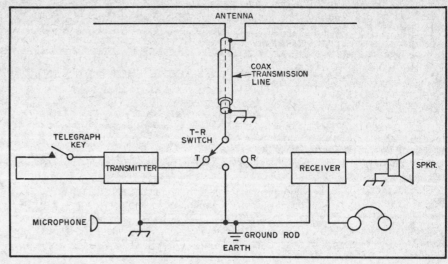

Fig. 56 — A diagram of a basic Amateur Radio station.

communications.

In addition to an electronic T-R switch, an elaborate Amateur Radio station might contain a *speech processor*. The human voice does not have a constant amplitude. When you speak, the amplitude of the sound you create is ever-changing, only occasionally reaching its maximum, or peak, value. Your transmitter is designed to handle this peak voice level, yet most of the time this capability is wasted. The transmitter just loafs along on the softer portions of the speech signal. Fig. 9 on page 5-6 shows a good example of this; the average level of the speech signal shown is much less than the peak level.

The intent of speech processing is to increase the level of the low-amplitude portions of the speech signal while leaving the peak level unchanged. This would tend to fill in the "valleys" between the peaks in Fig. 9, increasing the average power of the transmitted signal. Speech processing can produce improved speech intelligibility at the receiver when propagation conditions are poor or the interference level is high.

From this description, speech processing may sound like a panacea. But it is not. Since speech processing increases the average power of the transmitted signal, the transmitter that it able to handle only unprocessed speech may overheat. Also, processing is by its very nature a distortion of the voice signal. Processing usually results in some loss of fidelity, making the voice sound less "natural" at the receiving end. The distortion products generated during speech processing can increase the bandwidth of your signal and cause splatter.

An *af* speech processor acts on the voice signal while it is still at audio frequencies. This type of processor is usually an external accessory, inserted between the microphone and the transmitter. Such a pro-

cessor often has more gain available than is necessary, so you must be careful not to overdrive the microphone input of your transmitter.

An *rf* speech processor works on the voice signal after it has been converted to rf by the transmitter. This processor is usually built into a transmitter as it is manufactured. Here again, care in adjustment and operation is necessary; you should follow the manufacturer's operating instructions carefully.

Tests, Measurements and Adjustments

The reason an applicant for an Amateur Radio license must be tested on radio theory and electronics is to determine if he or she is qualified to test, measure and adjust equipment, particularly the transmitter.

Transmitter Frequency

Determination of your transmitter frequency is probably the most important measurement in Amateur Radio. It is also one of the most common measurements. What if you didn't make sure that your transmitter was operating on the frequency you thought it was? You might be transmitting on frequencies allocated to other radio services or on parts of amateur bands reserved for different emission types or different class licensees. Without knowing the frequency you're operating on, an amateur might be in violation of FCC rules and regulations.

Most hams check their transmitting frequency with a receiver which they know is accurate. Most receivers nowadays are very accurate thanks to built-in crystal calibrators. These calibrators are themselves aligned with the U.S. Bureau of Standards station, WWV. After inserting the signal from the crystal calibrator into the receiver circuitry, an amateur adjusts the dial on the receiver so that its readings are precise.

Transmitter Tuning

It's become commonplace to see a *dummy load* in a ham shack. A dummy load (or dummy antenna) is simply a resistor that has impedance characteristics which can take the place of a regular antenna system for test purposes. With a dummy antenna connected to the transmitter, an amateur can make tests without having a signal go out over the air. The FCC rules and regulations strictly limit the amount of on-the-air testing that may be done (see Section 97.93). So a dummy load is especially handy for transmitter testing.

For transmitter tests, the dummy antenna must be capable of dissipating safely the entire power output of the transmitter. We want the dummy load to act like a perfectly matched transmission line. That usually means it has a pure resistance of approximately 52 or 75 ohms.

Except for selecting an operating frequency, the most important adjustment of the transmitter that you can make is the tuning and loading of the final amplifier. Most transmitters are tuned with the function switch in the "tune" position. Some without such a position are tuned while the function switch is in the "cw" position. The telegraph key then switches the signal on and off.

Most solid-state transmitters require no tuning; the only adjustment is setting the drive level. Some have a driver tuning control that should be peaked for maximum output.

The tuning procedure for a vacuum-tube transmitter is more complex. These are generalized instructions: Set the *loading control* at minimum loading. You then press the key (or switch the function switch to "tune") for just a second or so. While holding the key down, adjust the *plate tuning control* through its total range. At one point the current will dip to a fairly low value, but it will rise rapidly if you move the knob just slightly to either side. What is this minimum point? It's where you have the tank circuit in resonance with the frequency applied to the grid of the final amplifier tube.

Always keep a final amplifier tuned to resonance. An off-resonance tank circuit is about like a short circuit on a battery; the current is large, but all the power stays in the battery. It is sort of the same with the final amplifier. The input to the plate is high, but the power isn't going anywhere but into the plate of the tube. If this short circuit lasts for more than a few seconds, the tube will overheat. This can easily ruin a final amplifier tube.

Maybe you've already figured out that you now have the tube at resonance, but you're still not done with adjusting the final amplifier. Why not? Although you have the plate current at a minimum point

(indicating resonance), there isn't very much input. And, of course, without much input, there isn't a lot of output heading to the antenna. The tube is operating safely, but it's capable of delivering more power. You need to bring the input power — the plate current at resonance is an indicator of this power — up to normal for the tube and the transmitter. The loading control gives you the means for doing this.

With the key open, advance the loading control a little toward maximum loading. Then, close the key momentarily and again adjust the tuning control for minimum plate current. Changing the loading control detunes the amplifier tank circuit a bit, so the circuit has to be brought back to resonance by the tuning control. If you don't retune the tank circuit, you'll at least partially short-circuit the amplifier, and the efficiency will be low. And low efficiency means that the tube will be unnecessarily hot.

After retuning, you'll notice that the plate current is now somewhat higher than it was when the loading control was at minimum. But it is probably still far below what you're shooting for. Set the loading control a little farther toward maximum and go through the same process again. Keep this up until you reach the recommended value of plate current. Don't forget to readjust the tuning control for minimum plate current after every change in loading.

After you finally reach the recommended value of plate current at resonance, switch the meter to read grid current. The grid current has probably dropped while you were tuning the amplifier. This is quite normal; the higher the plate current the lower the grid current goes (usually). If the grid current is below the recommended value, adjust the drive control on the transmitter to bring it back up. Then read the plate current again. Giving the amplifier its normal drive probably made the plate current go down a little. This shows that the amplifier is operating more efficiently (the output power is now a larger percentage of the input power). You can now touch up the tuning and loading controls to return the input power up to par.

Checking Neutralization of a Screen-Grid Amplifier

Two general procedures are available for indicating neutralization in a screen-grid amplifier stage. If the screen-grid tube is operated with or without grid current, a sensitive output indicator can be used. If the screen-grid tube is operated with grid current, the grid-current reading can be used as an indication of neutralization. When the output indicator is used, both screen and plate voltages must be removed from the tubes, but the dc circuits from the plate and screen to cathode must be completed. If the grid-current

reading is used, the plate voltage may remain on but the screen voltage must be zero, with the dc circuit completed between screen and cathode.

What we're trying to do in the neutralization process is reduce to a minimum the rf driver voltage fed from the input of the amplifier to its output circuit through the grid-plate capacitance of the tube. This is done by adjusting carefully, bit by bit, the neutralizing capacitor or link coils until an rf indicator in the output circuit reads minimum or until the reactance of the unloaded plate-circuit tuning on the grid-current value is minimized.

A *wavemeter* makes a sensitive neutralizing indicator. The wavemeter coil should be coupled to the output tank coil at the low-potential or "ground" point. Care should be taken to make sure that the coupling is loose enough at all times to prevent burning out the meter. The plate-tank capacitor should be readjusted for maximum reading after each change in neutralizing.

When the grid-current meter is used as a neutralizing indicator, the screen should be grounded for rf and dc. The grid current will change as the unloaded plate-tank circuit is tuned through resonance. The neutralizing capacitor (or indicator) should be adjusted until this deflection is brought to a minimum. As a final adjustment, screen voltage should be returned and the neutralizing adjustment continued to the point where minimum plate current, maximum grid current and maximum screen current occur simultaneously. When the plate-tank circuit is tuned slightly on the high-frequency side of resonance, an increase in grid current indicates that the neutralizing capacitance is too small. If the increase is on the low-frequency side, the neutralizing capacitor is too large. When neutralization is complete, there should be a slight decrease in grid current on either side of resonance.

The Oscilloscope

The electrostatically deflected cathode-ray oscilloscope tube, with appropriate associated equipment, is capable of displaying both low-frequency and radio-frequency signals on its fluorescent screen. A television, on the other hand, has a magnetically deflected picture tube not suitable for measurement purposes. In the usual display presentation, the yellowish-green fluorescent spot will move across the screen horizontally at some known rate (called *horizontal deflection* or *horizontal sweep*). At the same time, it will be moved vertically by the signal voltage being examined (*vertical deflection*). The rapidly deflected spot actually appears as one continuous line. So a changing signal voltage makes a pattern appear on the screen.

An oscilloscope is the best instrument generally available to amateurs for adjustment of an a-m transmitter. When a modulated signal is detected in a receiver, the detector output follows the *modulation envelope* (waveform). The stronger the modulation, therefore, the greater is the useful receiver output. Obviously, then, we'd like to make the modulation as strong or "heavy" as possible. There's only one catch: The FCC allows amateurs to use a maximum of 100-percent modulation. There's a good reason for that rule: Overmodulation, or modulation greater than 100 percent, distorts the signal and causes unnecessary interference to other stations on the air.

Specialized oscilloscopes are manufactured for use with Amateur Radio transmitters. These are called monitoring oscilloscopes. They are, as the name suggests, set up for checking the quality of a transmitted signal. Usually all that is required is to connect such an oscilloscope "in the line" between the transmitter and the antenna.

Fig. 57 shows a cw dit from a properly operating transmitter as it would be displayed on a monitoring 'scope. This signal does not have key clicks. The cw signal of Fig. 57B is another story, however. This signal, if transmitted, would certainly result in interference to other amateurs on nearby frequencies.

A monitoring oscilloscope can also be used to check ssb-transmitter performance. When transmitting voice signals, the presence of flattopping can often be easily detected. See Fig. 58.

Two-Tone Tests

Instead of the continuously varying pattern produced by a voice signal, a two-tone test produces a stationary pattern that can be examined for defects. Fig. 58A shows a pattern that is representative of a properly operating ssb transmitter. The pattern of Fig. 58B exhibits two common types of distortion: flattopping and crossover distortion.

The basis of a two-tone test is that you inject two audio signals into the microphone jack of the transmitter from which you should get only two rf signals. No amplifier is ever perfectly linear, so some mixing of the two signals will take place. However, all of the new signals produced should be so weak in comparison with the main output of the transmitter that you cannot detect their presence in an oscilloscope pattern. What you will see is the pattern of two sine-wave signals as they add and subtract, forming peaks and valleys. A two-tone test will show only major defects in a sideband transmitter.

Signal Generators

Radio-frequency oscillators, also known as rf signal generators, are used to align receivers and transmitter filters. Their purpose is to provide a signal at a specific frequency to which the tuned circuits can be set. Usually, the rf oscillator is connected to the input of a circuit and a

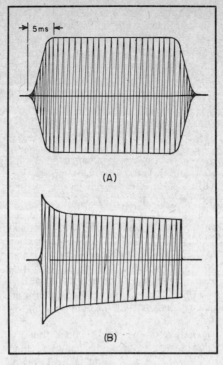

Fig. 57 — At A is the waveform of a single cw dit as seen on a monitoring 'scope. Note the rouded corners and the smooth rise and decay times. Five ms is generally agreed to be the ideal rise and fall time of a cw envelope. The waveform at B is typical of a poorly designed or adjusted transmitter. The sharp rise and decay transitions contain energy at frequencies other than the desired frequency. Also, poor power supply regulation is evidenced by the reduction in overall amplitude during the key-down time.

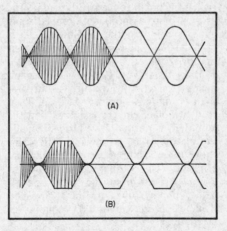

Fig. 58 — The two-tone-test waveform at A is from a properly operating ssb transmitter; note the smooth sinusoidal shape of the curves, especially as they cross the zero axis. At B is the waveform of a two-tone test showing severe flattopping and crossover (zero-axis) distortion.

VTVM or other suitable indicator to the output. The circuit in question is then adjusted to provide minimum or maximum output, depending on circuit function. In some cases, the frequency of the rf oscillator is automatically swept back and forth across a *band* of frequencies. When the sweep signal is used to deflect the

beam of a cathode-ray tube as well, a visual display of the band-pass characteristics of the circuit can be obtained.

The *marker generator* in its simplest form is a high-stability oscillator generating a series of signals which, when detected in the receiver, mark the exact edges of the amateur bands (and subbands in some cases). It does this by oscillating at a low frequency that has harmonics falling on the desired frequencies. Most marker generators put out harmonics at 25-kHz or 100-kHz intervals.

The marker generator is very useful in checking transmitter frequency. How? You first tune in the signal from the transmitter on the receiver. Note the dial setting on the receiver. Then tune in and identify the *nearest* marker frequencies above and below the transmitter signal. The transmitter frequency is obviously between these two known frequencies.

If the marker frequencies are accurate, this is all that needs to be known except that the transmitter frequency must not be so close to a band (or subband) edge that sideband frequencies, especially in phone transmission, will extend over the edge.

If the transmitter signal is "inside" a marker at the edge of an assignment, to the extent that there is no audible beat note with the receiver BFO turned off (if that's possible), normal cw sidebands are safely inside the edge.

When a transceiver is used rather than a transmitter-receiver combination and the transmitting frequency is automatically the same as the frequency the receiver is tuned to, setting the tuning dial to a spot between two known marker frequencies is all that is required.

The Multimeter

The multimeter is a piece of test equipment that most amateurs should know how to use. The simplest kind of multimeter is the VOM. VOM stands for volt-ohm-milliammeter. VOMs use one basic meter movement for all functions; the movement requires a fixed amount of current (often 1 mA) to pass through it for a full-scale reading. A switch selects various ranges of voltage, resistance and current. This switch places high-value dropping resistors in series with the meter movement for voltage measurement, and connects low-value shunt resistors in parallel with the movement for the measurement of current.

When you use a voltmeter or multimeter for voltage measurement, connect the meter terminals *in parallel* with the voltage to be measured. An ideal voltmeter would have an infinite input impedance and would not affect the circuit it is connected to in any way. Real-world voltmeters, however, have a finite value of input impedance. There is a possibility that the voltage to be measured will change because of additional circuit loading when the voltmeter is connected.

If the input impedance of the voltmeter is very high compared to the impedance of the circuit being measured, the current drawn from the circuit by the voltmeter will be negligible, and circuit operation will not be significantly affected. The input impedance of an ordinary voltmeter is on the order of 20 kΩ per volt.

A *vacuum-tube voltmeter* (VTVM) operates in the same manner as an ordinary voltmeter but with one important difference: The indicating meter in a VTVM is isolated from the voltage source by a vacuum-tube dc amplifier. As a result, the voltage source sees only the tube's input impedance, which is very high. The standard VTVM input impedance is 11 MΩ. This is useful for measuring voltages in high-impedance circuits, such as vacuum-tube grid circuits and FET gate circuits.

Voltmeters are manufactured with the indicating meter isolated from the voltage to be measured by an FET, instead of a vacuum tube. These FET-VOMs have an input impedance on the order of several megohms, and are the solid-state equivalent of VTVMs.

When you use an ammeter or multimeter for current measurement, connect the meter terminals *in series* with the current flow to be measured. Most ammeters have very low resistance, but in a low-impedance circuit, there is a chance that the slight additional resistance of the series ammeter will disturb circuit operation.

Other Test Instruments

A *field-strength meter* uses an attached antenna to sample the field of energy generated by a transmitter and provide a relative strength indication on a meter. It can be used to monitor rf output while antenna and transmitter adjustments are optimized. In a mobile installation, it can be used to plot the horizontal radiation pattern around the car.

In measuring standing-wave ratio, we can take advantage of the fact that the voltage on a transmission line consists of two components traveling in opposite directions. The power going from the transmitter to the antenna is represented by one voltage (called *forward* or *incident*), and the power reflected from the antenna is represented by the other (called *reflected*). A bridge circuit separates the incident and reflected voltages for measurement. This is sufficient for determining SWR. Bridges designed for measuring SWR are frequently called *reflectometers* or *VSWR meters*.

A reflectometer is placed in the transmission line between the transmitter and antenna. The closer the meter is to the antenna, the better. This is because we get a more accurate reading of the two voltages, the forward one reaching the antenna and the reflected one coming back from the antenna.

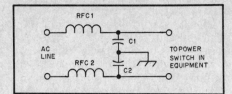

Fig. 59 — A method of ac-line filtering. C1, C2 — 0.01-μF disc ceramic, 1 kV. RFC1, RFC2 — 24 turns of no. 18 AWG enameled wire, close spaced and wound on a 1/4-inch diameter form (such as a pencil).

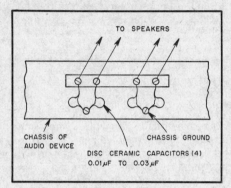

Fig. 60 — When bypassing speaker leads, the disc capacitors should be mounted directly between the speaker terminals and the chassis, keeping the capacitor leads as short as possible.

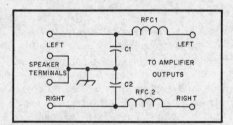

Fig. 61 — A speaker filter for installation inside the chassis of an audio device. C1, C2 — 0.01-μF to 0.03-μF disc ceramic. RFC1, RFC2 — 24 turns of no. 18 AWG enameled wire, close spaced and wound on a 1/4-inch diameter form (such as a pencil).

Another commonly found test instrument is the *wattmeter*. It is a useful instrument for transmitter tuning and testing, measuring rf output power directly in watts. Wattmeters used in Amateur Radio are coaxially fed and calibrated for use with 50-ohm transmission line. Use in a system with characteristic impedance other than 50 ohms would result in incorrect readings. Many wattmeters are directional; they can be switched to read forward power or reflected power. The values of forward and reflected power can be used to calculate SWR with the equation

$$ \text{SWR} = \frac{\sqrt{P_f} + \sqrt{P_r}}{\sqrt{P_f} - \sqrt{P_r}} \qquad \text{(Eq. 44)} $$

where
P_f = forward power and
P_r = reflected power.

You must interpret the forward-power reading of such a wattmeter with care: Whenever the SWR is not equal to 1 (reflected power equal to zero), the forward-power reading is not a true indication of the power delivered to the load. The reflected-power reading must be subtracted from the forward-power reading to obtain the actual load power.

Signal tracing is the process of following the rf, i-f or af signal through a receiver, transmitter or audio amplifier to find the inoperative stage. A *signal tracer* can be any device for detecting rf or af signals. An oscilloscope or ac voltmeter can be used. Most often, however, a signal tracer is a device built specifically for the purpose. Such a device is usually a high-gain audio amplifier with an input probe. Another probe can contain a diode for detecting rf that is modulated by audio frequencies.

Audio Rectification

Even if your transmitter puts out no harmonics or other spurious signals, interference is still an unfortunate possibility. Your rf signal can cause audio interference to a consumer electronic product, such as a radio, television, stereo, electronic organ or intercom. (We'll call these items *audio devices* for the purpose of this discussion.) Your signal must first get into the audio device, and then be detected, or rectified. The resulting audio signal will be amplified by the audio device and produce interference.

The cure involves finding out how the rf is entering the audio device, and "closing the door" with bypassing and filtering to keep it out. Possible points of entry are the ac-line cord, an antenna connection (if any), speaker wires, interconnecting cables (as in a component stereo system), or direct radiation into the circuitry of the audio device itself (usually through the wooden or plastic case).

Experience has shown that most times rf gets in via the speaker leads or the ac line. A simple ac-line filter, as shown in Fig. 59, can be built from readily available parts and installed inside the audio device. The preferred location for the filter is inside the chassis of the audio device, at the point where the ac-line cord enters. If rf is entering through external speaker wires, simply bypassing the wires to the chassis at the terminals is usually effective. See Fig. 60. In stubborn cases it might be necessary to install the filter shown in Fig. 61 inside the chassis of the audio device.

Your amateur transmitter should be effectively grounded to a metallic cold-water pipe or a ground rod driven into the ground at least 8 feet. The ground lead should be at least no. 10 wire or copper ribbon. Just remember, the greater the surface area of the ground lead, the more effective it will be. Also, the ground lead should be as short as possible.

Also keep in mind that amateurs may use only the amount of power necessary to establish the desired communication. Operating with excessive power is likely to cause audio rectification problems.

Safety

Your station equipment not only makes use of ac line voltage, which is dangerous in itself — it probably generates additional lethal potentials of its own. For your own safety and that of others who may come in contact with your equipment, you should be familiar with some basic precautions.

All dangerous voltages in equipment should be made inaccessible. A good way to ensure this is to enclose all equipment in metal so that no "hot" spots can be reached. Don't forget any component shafts that may protrude through the front panel; if hot, these may be protected from contact by means of an insulating knob.

Each metal enclosure should be connected to a good earth ground, such as a ground rod or a cold-water pipe. Thus, if a failure occurs inside a piece of equipment, the metal case will never present a shock hazard; the fuse will blow instead.

It's also a good idea to make it impossible for anyone to energize your equipment when you're not present. A key-operated main switch is a good way to accomplish this. Another means is to wire a female ac receptacle in series with the hot side of the main power line in your equipment. An ordinary line plug with a shorting wire between the two pins will energize the station. When the plug is removed, a stranger or child isn't likely to spot or suspect the empty receptacle.

Rules and Regulations

Besides learning about the technical aspects and operating procedures of Amateur Radio, the FCC expects every amateur to know and abide by its rules. Therefore, it should not be surprising to find a list of rules to be learned in the FCC's General class study outline. Every General class license applicant can expect to be tested on the rules found in this section. The numbers in parentheses reference the section of Part 97 of the Commission's Rules. Part 97 is printed in its entirety in Chapter 9 of this *License Manual.*

Control Point (§97.3[p])

Control point is defined in the rules as "The operating position of an amateur radio station where the control operator function is performed." Under most circumstances, this will be at the operating desk in your ham shack. However, it is possible to have a control point at a position that is removed from the transmitter site. For example, a control operator may be able to shut down a repeater station via a telephone line. This is *remote control,* where the *control point* (operating position) is located at a point removed from the transmitter.

Emergency Communications (§97.3[w] and 97.107)

Emergency communications is defined in the rules as "Any amateur radio communication directly relating to the immediate safety of life of individuals or the immediate protection of property." Section 97.107 of the rules deals with amateur operation in emergencies. If an emergency strikes a widespread area, disrupting the normal lines of communication, the FCC engineer-in-charge of the area may designate certain frequencies for use by station assisting the stricken area only. All amateur transmissions with, or within, the designated area conducted on the FCC-designated emergency frequencies must pertain directly to relief work, emergency service or the establishment and maintenance of efficient networks for handling emergency traffic. Also, the Commission may designate certain amateur stations to police the emergency frequencies, warning noncomplying stations operating there. The emergency conditions imposed by the FCC under Section 97.107 of its rules can be lifted only by the FCC or its authorized representative. Amateurs desiring a declaration of a communication emergency should contact the FCC engineer-in-charge of the area concerned.

Amateur Radio Transmitter Power Limitations (§97.67)

In all circumstances, an amateur station should use the minimum amount of power necessary to carry out the desired communication. While operating in the Novice subbands, however, no amateur station may exceed 250 watts input power to the final amplifying stage supplying radio-frequency energy to the antenna. (This does not include power used to heat tube cathodes.) The Novice frequency bands are: 3700-3750 kHz, 7100-7150 kHz (7050-7075 kHz when the terrestrial location is not within Region 2 — the Americas), 21,100-21,200 kHz and 28,100-28,200 kHz.

Under *no* circumstances may an Amateur Radio transmitter be operated with a power input exceeding one kilowatt (1000 watts). If an amateur transmitter is operated with a power input exceeding 900 watts, the operator must have an accurate means for measuring the power input.

Also, the maximum allowable effective radiated power (erp) of an Amateur Radio station in repeater operation depends on the antenna's height above average terrain (HAAT) and the frequency band being used. Section 97.67(c) has a chart giving the erp limitations for repeater HAAT.

Station Identification Requirements (§97.84[b], [f], [g] and 97.79[c])

Amateur Radio operators are required to give their call signs at the beginning and end of each transmission or exchange of emergency traffic. Also, the Commission transmissions and at intervals not to exceed 10 minutes while on the air. Additionally, when signing off, the operator must give the call sign (or a network identifier) for at least one of the stations with which contact was made, followed by his own call sign.[1]

Under no circumstances may an amateur exceed the mode and frequency privileges of his or her own operator's license, even if he or she is operating a station (and using the call sign) licensed to a holder of a higher-class license. (§97.79[c])

Suppose Maureen, KA1DYZ, a Novice licensee, visits Jim, K1UJ, an Amateur Extra Class licensee. May Maureen operate on phone in the Extra Class portion of 80 meters if she uses Jim's call? Certainly not! Her operator privileges are Novice, and she may not exceed these privileges no matter what call sign she has permission to use.

What if, on the other hand, Jim visits Maureen and guest operates at her station? Is Jim, an Extra Class operator, restricted from using his Extra Class privileges at Maureen's station? No. If an FCC monitor were to hear KA1DYZ operating on phone in the Extra Class subbands, however, poor Maureen would be cited with a violation. The FCC would have no way of knowing that the station was being operated by Jim if it heard Maureen's call only. Therefore, the FCC has adopted a special identification procedure to be used when a guest operator, whose license class exceeds the station licensee's, operates beyond the host's privileges. In our example where Jim, K1UJ, an Extra Class operator, is visiting Maureen, KA1DYZ, a Novice, and Jim operates beyond Novice privileges, he would say, "This is KA1DYZ with K1UJ controlling." If the identification were in

---

[1]As this book went to press, FCC had proposed a rule change in Docket 80-136 that would delete the requirement of giving the other station's call sign unless the contact involved international third-party traffic.

telegraphy, Jim would sign KA1DYZ/KIUJ. Note: If Jim were operating Maureen's station in the Novice subbands, he *would not* have to sign his call after Maureen's. The special identification procedure is required only while the higher-license-class operator is operating in a manner that exceeds the host's privileges.

Third-Party Participation in Amateur Radio Communications (§97.77[d])

One of the joys of Amateur Radio is allowing an unlicensed friend to participate in Amateur Radio communication. It is important to use the word "participate" in this context because an unlicensed person may not *operate* an amateur station. An amateur station must be operated by a licensed *control operator*. The control operator is the first party to the amateur communication, and the control operator of the other station (the one you're in contact with) is the second party. Any other person participating in the communications is a *third party*.

An amateur operator may permit a third party to participate in communications from his station only when he or she (the control operator) is present and continuously monitors and supervises the radio communication to ensure compliance with the rules.

Domestic and International Third-Party Traffic (§97.114; Appendix 2, Article 41, Section 2)

The United States permits its radio amateurs to conduct radio communications on behalf of third parties; however, there are restrictions that *must* be observed. Third-party traffic involving material compensation, either tangible or intangible, direct or indirect, to a third party, a station licensee, a control operator or any other person is *strictly prohibited*. And except for emergency communication, business communication on behalf of any party *is not allowed*. Business communication is defined as any transmission or communication the purpose of which is to facilitate the regular business or commercial affairs of any party.

Even if a third-party communication does not violate any of the aforementioned provisions, most countries do not permit third-party traffic under *any* circumstances. Article 41, Section 2 of the *Radio Regulations* of the International Telecommunication Union states: "(1) When transmissions between amateur stations of different countries are permitted, they shall be made in plain language and shall be limited to messages of a technical nature relating to tests and to remarks of a personal character for which, by reason of their unimportance, recourse to the public telecommunications service is not justified. It is absolutely forbidden for amateur stations to be used for transmitting international communications on

behalf of third parties. (2) The preceding provisions may be modified by special arrangements between the administration of the countries concerned."

Because the U.S. is a signatory to the ITU *Radio Regulations*, its provisions apply to U.S. amateurs. U.S. amateurs may conduct third-party communications with the countries listed in Table 3 of chapter 8 only. You will not have to memorize the list for the examination if you remember that most countries permitting third-party traffic with the U.S. are located in Central and South America. Other countries currently allowing third-party traffic with the U.S. are Canada, Ghana, Israel, Jordan and Liberia. Also, third-party traffic is permitted with 4U1ITU, the Amateur Radio club station at ITU headquarters in Geneva, Switzerland.

Permissible One-Way Transmissions (§97.91)

Amateurs generally conduct two-way communications with other amateur stations. Broadcasting is not allowed. To clarify its position on broadcasting by amateurs, however, the Commission has listed in §97.91 of its rules four types of one-way transmissions that *are* permitted and that it will not construe as broadcasting. These are: (1) Emergency communications, including bona fide emergency drill practice transmissions; (2) information bulletins consisting solely of subject matter having direct interest to the Amateur Radio Service; (3) round-table discussions or net-type operations where more than two amateur stations are in communication, each station taking a turn at transmitting to other station(s) of the group; and (4) code practice transmissions intended for persons learning or improving proficiency in the international Morse code.

Additionally, §97.91 of the rules refers to another type of one-way transmission. Section 97.89 of the rules permits amateur stations to be used for measuring radio emissions, propagation studies, controlling remote objects (such as model airplanes), and other experimental purposes. Amateur Radio beacon stations, which are used to learn if a band is open, is another example of a permissible one-way communication.

Frequency Bands Available To Technician Class (§97.7[d])

Even if your intent is to take the exam for the General class license, since the written portion is the same for both the Technician and the General class licenses, you will be expected to know the frequencies both classes are allowed. Refer to the frequency chart.

The Technician class licensee is permitted Novice privileges on the high frequency (hf) bands. Above 50 MHz, Technicians are permitted *all* amateur frequen-

cies and privileges.

Frequency Bands Available to General Class (§97.7[b])

General class operators are permitted all amateur frequencies and privileges above 28 MHz. This class is also allowed to use the 160-meter band, as long as the operators comply with the frequency and power limitations for their areas. You won't have to remember all the frequency and power limitations for 160 meters, but take a look at §97.61(b) in the rules chapter of this book to get the general idea of what's involved in 160-meter operation.

Perhaps a good way to remember the frequencies permitted to General class amateurs is to memorize those frequencies *not permitted*. Again, refer to the frequency chart on page 8-4. On the hf bands 80 through 15 meters, the General class is not permitted on the lower 25 kHz of the bands. Also, the General class is not permitted on the following:
3775-3890 kHz
7150-7225 kHz
14,200-14,275 kHz
21,250-21,350 kHz

Limitations on the Use of Amateur Radio Frequencies (§97.61)

Amateurs are permitted to use a large variety of emission types. Some of these are: amplitude-modulated voice, frequency-modulated voice, slow-scan television, radioteleprinter and continuous-wave telegraphy. Generally, on the more heavily used frequency bands (80, 40, 20 and 15 meters, for example) the types of emissions requiring relatively more bandwidth, such as fast-scan television, are not permitted. Section 97.61 of the rules, which can be found in the rules chapter in this book, lists all the amateur frequencies and the emissions permitted. The reader should turn to §97.61 and give it more study. Note, for example, that 160-meter operation (1800 to 2000 kHz) requires reduced power levels during nighttime hours. Also, only A1 and A3 emissions are permitted on 160-meter frequencies.

A1 emission, which is continuous-wave telegraphy, is, without exception, permitted on every amateur frequency band. The reader should also note under §97.61(c) and (d) the frequencies on which stations in repeater and auxiliary operation must operate. If there are any terms in this section of the rules you do not understand, check §97.3 and the appendices to Part 97 for definitions.

Radio-Controlled Model Crafts and Vehicles (§97.65[a] and 97.99)

Amateur Radio is a mixed bag of many interests. There are traffic handlers, satellite users, vhfers, and so on. This section is about radio remote control of model craft and other objects. A0 emission type, which is the FCC's designation for unmodulated carrier, can be used for remote control of models. By looking at §97.61 of the rules, we see that A∅ is not authorized below 50 MHz. Upon closer examination of the rules, however, we see that under §97.65(a) A∅ may be used for short periods where required for remote control even where it is not specifically designated. Above 50 MHz, A∅ is permitted on all bands.

To make life for the radio remote-control enthusiast a little easier, the FCC has simplified logging and identification. If the mean output power of the transmitter controlling the model craft does not exceed 1 watt and the transmitter has affixed to it a transmitter-identification card (either FCC form 452-C or a durable, home made card with the station's call sign and licensee's name and address), on-the-air identification and logging are not required. Also, the signals will not be construed as codes or ciphers, which are prohibited under other circumstances. See §97.99 for details.

Radioteleprinter Emissions (§97.69)

There are two standard codes for amateur radioteleprinter operation: the International Telegraphic Alphabet No. 2 (also known as the Baudot Code) and the American Standard Code for Information Interchange (ASCII). Aside from radioteleprinter operations, these codes may be use for controlling Amateur Radio stations, models and other objects, transfer of computer programs or direct computer-to-computer communications, and for various types of data networks (including so-called "packet switching" systems). Transmitting speeds depend on the frequency band being used. The faster the transmitting speed, the more bandwidth occupied by the signal. Section 97.69 of the rules gives the *maximum* rates of transmitting speeds for the frequency band being used.

PROHIBITED PRACTICES

Broadcasting (§97.113)

No amateur station may be used for broadcasting. This means that you may not direct your transmissions to the general public. It is also illegal to retransmit automatically the radio signals from a broadcast station, a weather station or any other class of station other than amateur. An amateur may allow a broadcast station to retransmit his amateur transmissions, however, provided the amateur transmissions contain no reference to the rebroadcast.

Music (§97.115)

The transmission of music by an amateur station is forbidden.

Codes and Ciphers (§97.117)

All amateur transmissions, regardless of the types of emission used, must be in plain language. Codes or ciphers used to obscure the meaning of any amateur transmission is forbidden. Abbreviations may be used, but they must be of the type generally recognized to facilitate communications.

Obscenity, Indecency, Profanity (§97.119)

No licensed radio operator or other person shall transmit communications containing obscene, indecent or profane words, language or meaning.

OPERATING PROCEDURES

Nothing says more about you, the individual radio amateur than the way you conduct yourself on the air. With a growing amateur population, it is especially important to know the proper means of operating your station. The ultimate goal is to make your amateur experience more pleasant and efficient—for you and your on-the-air contacts.

Radiotelephony

Speech is the stuff of which voice communications are made. To be effective, it must be clearly enunciated, delivered directly into the microphone at a speed suitable for the purpose at hand. To be effective, the operator must use the microphone and other speech equipment to its best advantage.

Microphones vary in design and purpose, but generally it is best to speak close to the mike, an inch or less away and across the face of its windscreen rather than directly into it. Close speaking improves the signal-to-noise ratio by making the voice much louder than any background noises from the kids and the TV set. Close speaking is especially important when using VOX (*voice-operated xmitter*) since it permits the microphone gain and VOX sensitivity to be sharply reduced. This prevents random noises from tripping the VOX accidentally. Likewise in high-noise situations, as when mobiling, close speaking permits the voice to override the background. Speaking into the windscreen, however, can result in strong sibilants and popping sounds.

Automatic level controls (alc) help, but operator care is also needed to maintain speech levels relatively constant. On single sideband, keep "talk power" up but avoid flattopping. In any mode (ssb, fm and even a-m) pay attention to your mike technique to keep average speech levels high without overdoing it.

When band conditions are not good, use phonetics when signing your call. Standard phonetics work best, as they are nearly universally understood. ITU-recommended phonetics are:

A — Alpha	F — Foxtrot	K — Kilo	S — Sierra
B — Bravo	G — Golf	L — Lima	T — Tango
C — Charlie	H — Hotel	M — Mike	U — Uniform
D — Delta	I — India	N — November	V — Victor
E — Echo	J — Juliette	O — Oscar	W — Whiskey
		P — Papa	X — X-Ray
		Q — Quebec	Y — Yankee
		R — Romeo	Z — Zulu

Vox

Voice-operated break-in (VOX) is a method of keying a transmitter with audio signals from a microphone. When the operator speaks into the microphone, the VOX circuit turns on the transmitter. Careful adjustment of the VOX circuit is necessary so audio from the speaker and stray noises don't accidentally key the transmitter. VOX control can be a helpful operating aid. It can speed traffic handling and contest operation because it allows the operator to keep both hands free and to listen to the receiver during pauses.

Radio Teleprinting

Radio teleprinting (RTTY) operation involves specialized communications techniques and practices. You should be familiar with the unique aspects of this mode before getting on the air and communicating via the "green keys." By gentlemen's agreement, RTTY is centered in certain portions of each high-frequency (hf) band. Along with the growth of 2-meter activity there has been a parallel growth of RTTY on this band. Some repeaters are devoted to RTTY; these often operate on the 146.10/.70-MHz frequency pair. Two-meter simplex frequencies are also popular for RTTY.

Once you have a station set up and have done enough listening around RTTY to be confident that you know how to operate the equipment, your next move will probably be to pick a frequency and call CQ. High frequency (hf) frequency shift-keying (F1 emission type) is okay anywhere in the cw-exclusive bands, although it is not legal on 160 meters.

Calling CQ on RTTY is quite similar to cw procedure, except that most RTTYers use a CQ tape to lessen wear and tear on the fingers. After listening first to make sure the frequency is not in use, you might send your CQ something like this:

(cw identification)
CQ CQ CQ DE W1AW W1AW W1AW
CQ CQ CQ DE W1AW W1AW W1AW
CQ CQ CQ DE W1AW W1AW W1AW
THIS IS W1AW CHUCK IN NEWINGTON CT K
(cw identification)

Note the cw identification. FCC regulations require i-d by voice or code at the beginning and end of each QSO and at least once every 10 minutes in between, no matter what mode you are using. You don't have to send the other station's call sign when operating RTTY, but it is common practice to send both calls on the keyboard so that anyone copying will know who is on the frequency.

If, after scanning the bands, you hear a RTTY CQ, how do you answer? After the CQer finishes the cw i-d, give him or her a short call:

W1AW W1AW W1AW DE N5TC N5TC N5TC K (cw i-d)

Sending his call three times gives your contact time to get his or her receiver tuned in, and sending your call gives three chances to copy it through noise or interference that might be on frequency.

If you want to break into an ongoing QSO, do it with care so as not to "step on anybody's toes." Wait until one station finishes transmitting and sends his cw i-d. Then *quickly* send BK DE N5TC followed by your cw identification. If it is acknowledged, make a short transmission and pass it along to the next station in the group. More information about operating procedures for RTTY can be found in the *ARRL Operating Manual.*

Use of Repeaters

A repeater is a device that receives a signal on one frequency and simultaneously transmits (repeats) the received signal on another frequency. Often located atop a tall building or high mountain, repeaters greatly extend the operating coverage of amateurs using mobile and hand-held transceivers.

To use a repeater, you must have a transceiver with the capability of transmitting on the repeater's input frequency — the frequency the repeater listens on — and receiving on the repeater's output frequency — the frequency the repeater transmits on. This capability can be acquired by installing the correct crystals in your transceiver or, if you have a synthesized rig, by dialing the correct frequency and selecting the proper offset (frequency difference between input and output).

When you have the frequency capability, all that you need to do is key the microphone button and you will access the repeater. Some repeaters have limited access by requiring the transmission of a subaudible tone or series of tones or bursts to gain access. Most repeaters briefly transmit a carrier after a user has stopped transmitting to inform the user that he/she is actually accessing the machine.

After acquiring the ability to access a repeater, you should become acquainted with the operating practices that are inherent in the unique mode:

(1) Monitor the repeater to become familiar with any peculiarities in its operation.

(2) To initiate a contact, simply indicate that you are on the frequency. Various geographical areas have different practices of making yourself heard, but generally, "This is WA3NLO monitoring" will suffice. Do not call CQ through a repeater.

(3) Identify legally; you must transmit

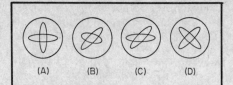

Fig. 62 — Tuning indicator oscilloscope patterns. Figure A shows a properly tuned in RTTY signal. At B the receiver is slightly off frequency. The fsk signal displayed at C has a different frequency shift than the demodulator. The mark (horizontal) line is normal, but the space line is tilted and smaller in amplitude indicating that this tone is coming in at the wrong frequency.

your call sign at the beginning and end of each contact and every 10 minutes in between. At the end, you must also identify the station you were in QSO with (per current FCC regulations). It is illegal to key a repeater without identification.

(4) Pause between transmissions. This allows other hams to use the repeater (someone may have an emergency). On most repeaters, a pause is necessary to reset the timer.

(5) Keep transmissions short and thoughtful. Your monologue may prevent someone in an emergency situation from using the repeater.

(6) Use simplex whenever possible. If you can complete your QSO on a direct frequency, there is no need to tie up the repeater and prevent others from using it.

(7) Use the minimum amount of power necessary to maintain communications. This FCC regulation minimizes the possibility of accessing distant repeaters on the same frequency.

(8) Don't break into a contact unless you have something to add. Interrupting is no more polite on the air than it is in person.

(9) FCC forbids using *autopatch* (facilities that connect the repeater to the telephone system) for anything that could be construed as business communication. Nor should an autopatch be used to avoid a toll call. Do not use an autopatch where regular telephone service is available.

(10) All repeaters are assembled and maintained at considerable expense and effort. Usually, an individual or group is responsible and it behooves those who are regular users of a machine to support the effort of keeping it on the air.

Full Break-In Telegraphy

Break-in (QSK) telegraphy is a system of radiotelegraph transmission in which the station receiver is sensitive to other signals between transmitted key pulses. This capability is very important to traffic handlers, but can be used to great advantage in general operating as well. Break-in gives cw communication the dimension of more natural conversation.

Most commercially manufactured

transceivers feature a "semi break-in" mode in which the first key closure actuates the VOX relay. The VOX controls are usually adjusted to hold the relay closed between letters. With proper VOX adjustment, it is possible for the other operator to break your transmission between words, but this system is a poor substitute for true break-in.

The simplest way to implement full break-in is to use separate antennas for receiving and transmitting. If the transmitter power is low (below 50 watts or so) and the isolation between transmitting and receiving antennas is good, this method can be satisfactory. Best isolation is obtained by mounting the antennas as far apart as possible and at right angles. Smooth break-in involves protecting the receiver from permanent damage by the transmitter power and ensuring that the receiver will recover fast enough to be sensitive between keying pulses.

Orienting an Antenna

One problem with a multiple-element directional array, such as a Yagi antenna, is deciding where to point it. One way, of course, is to rotate the antenna until the desired signal peaks in the receiver. But what if the ham on the other end is making short transmissions, or you haven't heard any stations in the area you want to contact? Clearly, some sort of list or chart showing beam headings is in order. An azimuthal (or great circle) map shows true bearings for all parts of the world from any single point. Once the desired target area has been determined, a quick glance at the map provides the proper beam heading in degrees. Several advertisers in *QST* and other publications offer customized azimuthal maps centered on any exact location.

Another method of determining proper beam headings is to use a chart, arranged alphabetically by country and centered on a specific location. For example, if you live in the first call area and want to contact a station in Japan, the beam heading chart would list approximately 330° as the direction for that country. Again, several vendors offer custom beam heading data centered on any requested location.

Emergency-Preparedness Drills

Tens of thousands of amateurs are involved with public service communication. ARRL sponsors a field organization comprised of two divisions: The Amateur Radio Emergency Service (ARES) and the National Traffic System (NTS). ARES is an emergency-preparedness group of approximately 70,000 amateurs who have voluntarily signed up to keep Amateur Radio in the forefront of public service operating. NTS functions as a message-handling network operating 365 days a year for the systematic handling of formal third-party traffic. The Radio Amateur Civil Emergency Service (RACES) is under the auspices of the Federal Emergency Management Agency, as a subpart of the Amateur Service serving civil preparedness. Where possible, ARRL advocates dual membership between ARES and RACES groups.

ARES activities provide emergency preparedness training and primarily tactical communication at the city or county level. Each group is headed by an ARRL emergency coordinator. Most drill activities occur on the 2-meter band, usually on fm. The use of battery-powered vhf gear is advantageous; however, one does not need equipment to join the local ARES. All one needs is the interest to serve the community through Amateur Radio and the time to participate in the periodic training tests. These drills run the gamut from the serious simulated emergencies (including the annual ARRL Simulated Emergency Test), to providing communications for parades and walkathons, or conducting a message-traffic exhibition at a shopping mall during the Christmas season. Also, numerous groups have trained with the National Weather Service to become tornado and storm spotters. These types of drills are important so that when a flood or ice storm disrupts the community, experienced hams will know exactly what to do.

The bulk of typical local emergency communication, as already mentioned, has been handled on vhf, usually involving repeater operation. Repeaters can be accessed with low-cost, portable equipment, hand-held or mobile. They provide clear, reliable communications up to 100 miles or so. Many repeaters have emergency-power capabilities as well, making them the mainstay in any widespread emergency.

ARRL's other public service "arm," NTS, serves a dual purpose: (a) the rapid movement of long-haul traffic from origin to destination; and (b) the training of amateurs in the handling of formal radiogram traffic in efficient, directed nets. In essence, NTS conducts emergency training on a daily basis. NTS can be thought of as a pony express of the airwaves, with assigned amateurs to carry message traffic to and from the next higher or lower echelon in the system. NTS operations are concentrated mainly on the hf segments, but local nets on 2-meter fm are becoming more and more popular as the ideal place to distribute traffic for delivery after a long, often transcontinental journey.

Operating Courtesy

Amateur Radio operators are privileged to have a large variety of frequencies and modes to choose from. However, congestion in many parts of the amateur spectrum requires judicious choice of operating frequencies, power and, above all, operating courtesy. A good operator *always* listens before transmitting so as not to interfere with stations already using that frequency. If the frequency is occupied, he or she should move to another frequency far enough away to prevent QRM. Know how much bandwidth your signal occupies for each mode of emission and act accordingly.

A good amateur transmits only what is necessary to accomplish his or her purpose and keeps the contents of the transmission within the bounds of propriety and good taste. And a good operator always reduces power to the minimum necessary to carry out the desired communications. (Not only is this operating courtesy, it's an FCC rule! See Section 97.67[b].)

It is inexcusably bad manners to QRM a station thousands of miles away because you are talking to a buddy across town on a DX band. Judicious selection of a band is important for reducing unintentional QRM. Also, testing and "loading up" a transmitter should be done on a *dummy antenna* without putting any signal on the air. On-the-air tests should be made only when necessary and kept as brief as necessary to carry out the test. You can contribute to the Amateur Radio Service's image as a self-disciplined, self policing service of high standards: Always be more courteous than the other person!

International Communications

One of the basic purposes of the Amateur Radio Service is stated in Section 97.1 of the rules: "Continuation and extension of the amateur's unique ability to enhance international good will."

Whenever you operate your station and contact an amateur in a foreign country, you are acting as an ambassador of your own country. Respect for the rules of the foreign amateur's country and the rules of the International Telecommunication Union (ITU) is necessary to carry out the important role Amateur Radio plays in the international community.

According to Section 2 of Article 41 of the ITU Radio Regulations,

"(1) When transmissions between amateur stations of different countries are permitted, they shall be made in plain language and shall be limited to messages of a technical nature relating to tests and to remarks of a personal character for which, by reason of their unimportance, recourse to the public telecommunications service is not justified. It is absolutely forbidden for amateur stations to be used for transmitting international communications on behalf of third parties.

(2) The preceding provisions may be modified by special arrangements between the administrations of the countries concerned."

The list of countries with which third-party traffic is permitted is shown in Chapter 8 of this *License Manual*. If you are asked to conduct third-party traffic with a country that has not signed a third-party agreement, you should politely decline to handle the message.

Sample Study Questions

42) A General class amateur licensee may operate in the Advanced class phone bands when
A) Using an Advanced class station and call sign
B) Signing his or her call sign followed by an Advanced class call sign
C) Operating using A1 emission only
D) A General class amateur may not operate in the Advanced class phone bands

43) An amateur licensed by the FCC may conduct third-party traffic with amateurs in

A) Countries which have a reciprocal operating agreement with the United States
B) France
C) Israel
D) United Kingdom

44) An Amateur Radio operator must identify his station at least every
A) 5 minutes
B) 10 minutes
C) 3 minutes
D) only when signing on the air

45) A tuning indicator oscilloscope pattern for a properly tuned in RTTY signal is shown at

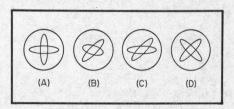

46) Most Amateur Radio transmitters are designed to operate with an antenna system impedance of

A) 300 ohms
B) 600 ohms
C) 50 ohms
D) 432 ohms

47) A reflectometer (VSWR meter) should be placed
A) Between the transmitter and amplifier
B) Between the transmitter and dummy load
C) Between the transmitter and frequency counter
D) Between the transmitter and antenna

48) One-way communications are permitted in the amateur bands for:
A) Rebroadcast of NOAA weather forecast transmissions
B) Radio signals emanating from broadcast stations provided permission has been obtained from the broadcast station
C) Code practice transmissions.
D) Emergencies only

49) On which frequency would a General class operator be operating illegally?
A) 3880 kHz
B) 7250 kHz
C) 14,280 kHz
D) 435-438 MHz

50) Joel, WA1ZUY, visits Dale, WA3NLO, and operates Dale's station using the call sign WA3NLO. Joel
A) is a third party
B) must contact only those countries which have a third-party agreement with the United States
C) is a control operator
D) must log each contact

51) Above 50 MHz, a Technician class operator may operate
A) On all amateur frequency bands except the lower 25 kHz of each band
B) A1 emission only
C) On any amateur frequency
D) On any frequency except those reserved for Advanced and Extra Class amateurs

52) On-the-air identification and logging are
A) Not required for transmitters operating less than 1 watt when used to control model craft.
B) Not required for portable operation
C) Not required for mobile operation
D) Always required

53) A station in repeater operation may be operated in the 2-meter band with an effective radiated power (erp)
A) Not exceeding 800 watts
B) Not exceeding 100 watts
C) Not exceeding 1000 watts
D) Not exceeding 200 watts

54) A station in repeater operation may be operated at
A) 431-433 MHz
B) 435-438 MHz
C) 144.5-145.5 MHz
D) 51-52 MHz

55) The best aid for orienting a beam antenna is a
A) Topographical map
B) Azimuthal map
C) Mercator map
D) Land-relief map

56) If, after scanning the bands, you hear a RTTY CQ, how do you answer?

A) Send the other station's call three times and your own call three times using A1 emission.
B) Send the other station's call once and your own call once using A1 emission.
C) Send your own station's call sign once using A1 emission.
D) Send your own station's call sign many times using the RTTY keyboard.

57) A test instrument used to sample the field of energy generated by a transmitter and provide a relative strength indication on a meter is
A) A reflectometer
B) A multimeter
C) A field strength meter
D) A VTVM

58) The best conductor for grounding an amateur transmitter is
A) No. 10 wire or copper ribbon
B) No. 18 aluminum wire
C) The third conductor of the power plug
D) Piano wire

59) A final amplifier circuit should be
A) Always tuned to resonance
B) Always tuned to off-resonance
C) Be tuned while being driven with full power
D) Dissipating most energy in the form of heat

60) Automatic operation is permitted under the rules for
A) Beacon stations
B) Repeater stations
C) Stations used to control model craft
D) RTTY bulletin stations

Chapter 6

The Advanced Class License

When you upgrade from the General to the Advanced class license, you will greatly increase the number of hf frequencies on which you can operate voice modes. As you might expect, these additional privileges must be earned by demonstrating a more comprehensive understanding of radio and electrical theory and practice. While many questions contained in the Advanced class examination will deal with subjects related to these additional privileges, you can expect to be questioned on any subject covered in the FCC Advanced class outline.

If you are already familiar with the subjects covered here and plan to use this book mainly for review purposes, then no outside materials should be necessary to prepare for the test. If much of this material is new to you, however, you may benefit by obtaining outside reference material to supplement the information contained herein. A copy of ARRL's *The Radio Amateur's Handbook* will be particularly useful, and other League publications such as the *Antenna Book, Understanding Amateur Radio* and *A Course in Radio Fundamentals* can be an invaluable aid by providing alternative explanations of subjects on which you are still unclear after reading this book.

Federal Communications Commission Study Outline

Advanced Class Amateur Radio Operator License Examination

(Element 4A Syllabus)

A. Rules and Regulations

1) Frequency bands available to the Advanced class Amateur Radio operator and limitations on use §97.7(a); §97.61.
2) Automatic retransmission of Amateur Radio signals and signals from other radio services §97.3(x); §97.113; §97.126
3) Amateur Radio stations in repeater operation §97.3(l); §97.85; §97.61(c)
4) Amateur Radio stations in auxiliary operation §97.3(l); §97.86; §97.61(d)
5) Remote control of Amateur Radio stations §97.3(m)(2); §97.88
6) Automatic control of Amateur Radio stations §97.3(m)(3)
7) Control link §97.3(n)
8) System network diagram §97.3(u)
9) Station identification §97.84(c), (d), (e)
10) Station log requirements §97.103(c), (d), (e), (f), (g)
11) Height limitations for Amateur Radio station antenna structures, including FAA notification criteria, and calculation of height above average terrain §97.45; §97.67(c); Appendix 5

B. Operating Procedures

1) Facsimile transmission
2) Slow-scan television transmission

C. Radio Wave Propagation

1) Sporadic-E
2) Selective fading
3) Auroral propagation
4) Radio-path horizon

D. Amateur Radio Practice

Use of test equipment:

1) Frequency measurement devices
2) Grid-dip meter; solid-state dip meter
3) Performance limitations of oscilloscopes, meters, frequency counters; accuracy, frequency response, stability

Electromagnetic compatibility:

4) Intermodulation interference
5) Receiver desensitizing
6) Cross-modulation interference
7) Capture effect

E. Electrical Principles

Concepts:

1) Reactive power
2) Series and parallel resonance
3) Skin effect
4) Fields, energy storage, electrostatic, electromagnetic

Mathematical relationships:

5) Resonant frequency, bandwidth, and "Q" of R-L-C circuits, given component values
6) Phase angle between voltage and current, given resistance and reactance
7) Power factor, given phase angle
8) Effective radiated power, given system gains and losses
9) Replacement of voltage source and resistive voltage divider with equivalent circuit consisting of a voltage source and one resistor (an application of Thevenin's Theorem, used to predict the current supplied by a voltage divider to a known load)

F. Circuit Components

Physical appearance, types, characteristics, applicants, and schematic symbols for the following:

1) Diodes; zener, tunnel, varactor, hot-carrier, junction, point contact, PIN
2) Transistors; npn, pnp, junction, unijunction, power, germanium, silicon
3) Silicon-controlled rectifier, triac
4) Light-emitting diode, neon lamp
5) Crystal-lattice ssb filters

G. Practical Circuits

1) Voltage-regulator circuits; discrete and integrated
2) Amplifiers; Class A, AB, B, C; characteristics of each type
3) Impedance-matching-networks; PI, L, PI-L
4) Filters; constant K, M-derived, band-stop, notch, modern-network-theory, PI-section, T-section, L-section (not necessary to memorize design equations; know general description, characteristics, responses, and applications of these filters)
5) Oscillators; various types and their applications; stability

Transmitter and receiver circuits — know purpose of each, and how, basically, each functions:

6) Modulators; a-m, fm, balanced
7) Transmitter final amplifiers
8) Detectors, mixer stages
9) Rf and i-f amplifier stages

Calculation of voltages, currents, and power in common Amateur Radio oriented circuits:
10) Common emitter class A transistor amplifier; bias network, signal gain, input and output impedances
11) Common collector class A transistor amplifier; bias network, signal gain input and output impedances

Circuit design; selection of circuit component values:
12) Voltage regulator with pass transistor

and Zener diode to produce given output voltage
13) Select coil and capacitor to resonate at given frequency

H. Signals and Emissions
1) Emission types A4, A5, F4, F5
2) Modulation methods
3) Deviation ratio
4) Modulation index
5) Electromagnetic radiation
6) Wave polarization
7) Sine, square, sawtooth waveforms
8) Root-mean-square value
9) Peak-envelope power

relative to average
10) Signal-to-noise ratio

I. Antennas and feedlines
1) Antenna gain, beamwidth
2) Trap antennas
3) Parasitic elements
4) Radiation resistance
5) Driven elements
6) Efficiency of antenna
7) Folded, multiple wire dipoles
8) Velocity factor
9) Electrical length of a feedline
10) Voltage and current nodes
11) Mobile antennas
12) Loading coil; base, center top

Electrical Principles

The Advanced class examination will emphasize ac circuits. You will be expected to have a good working knowledge of impedance calculations, phase angle and resonance.

Stored Energy

If you were to carry a stone to an upper floor of your house and place it on a window sill, you'd be storing energy in the stone. What kind of energy? Potential energy. The energy stored in the stone is equal to the work you did in carrying it up. If you then push the stone off the sill, its stored energy is released, carrying it rapidly back to the ground.

Electrical energy can be stored, too. If you send a direct current through a conductor, a *magnetic field* is created. This field contains stored energy. If you then open the circuit, all the stored energy would come back the very instant you open the switch since the current could no longer be maintained. If the returning energy is large, it will make itself visible by a fat spark at the switch contacts in trying to keep the current flowing.

Magnetic Energy

Putting energy into a magnetic field also takes work. Work consists of overcoming an opposing force — gravity, inertia, friction or what-have-you, in the case of mechanical work. In storing energy in a magnetic field, the work done consists in overcoming a force generated in the inductance by the very fact that energy is being stored. This opposition takes the form of an *induced voltage* which bucks the applied voltage. Its value depends not on the actual value of current but on the rate at which the current *changes*. The current changes in value rapidly at the instant that voltage is applied to an inductance, so at this moment the induced voltage is almost equal to the applied voltage. Then the rate of current change becomes slower and slower, and eventually there is no change that can be measured. At this time the work is com-

plete; the maximum energy is stored in the field, there is no induced voltage, and from then on the resistance of the circuit governs the current flow. Ohm's Law is finally victorious.

Electric-Field Storage

You can store energy in a capacitor too. In this case, the storehouse is an *electric field*, not a magnetic field. If you apply a dc voltage to a capacitor, there will be an instantaneous rush of current into the capacitor to charge it. The only thing that limits the current at the instant of closing the switch is whatever resistance there may be in the circuit. The capacitor itself acts like a short-circuit, at that instant, and all the voltage appears across the resistance. Then as the capacitor "fills up" with electricity — meaning that one set of plates is getting an excess of electrons while the other is being robbed of the same number — the voltage across it rises. Eventually, the voltage at the capacitor terminals is equal to the source voltage, and the current flow stops. If the source of voltage is

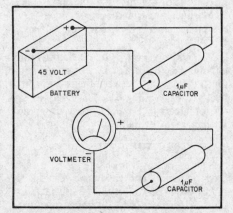

Fig. 1 — Current flows from a dc source into a capacitor until the capacitor is "charged" (has a voltage equal to the source). The capacitor retains its charge until it is discharged by an external or internal resistance. Good capacitors will hold a charge for minutes; "leaky" ones have low internal resistance and discharge in a few seconds.

disconnected, the capacitor will remain charged to that voltage. The charge will stay there just as long as there is no path by which electrons can travel from one set of plates to the other. A capacitor with very low *leakage* will hold a charge for days on end.

If you connect a resistance to the charged capacitor, the energy will leave, or be dissipated, in heating the resistor. If the capacitance and resistance are both large, it may take a long time for its voltage to disappear entirely from the capacitor terminals. However, the capacitor can be discharged rapidly into a low resistance or a short circuit (an electrical path with virtually no resistance). If you touch a wire to the terminals of a capacitor of several microfarads charged to a few hundred volts, you'll get quite a spark. (If you touch the terminals yourself, you'll get quite a jolt! To avoid this danger, capacitors used in power supplies of amateur equipment have *bleeder resistors* connected across them to drain the charge.)

Reactance

In working with dc circuits, inductors are considered to have negligible resistance, and capacitors are considered to be insulators. The only elements that enter into calculations are resistors. In a pure resistor, the value to resistance is constant for all frequencies. The current flowing through a resistance is the result of the instantaneous voltage present across that resistance as calculated by Ohm's Law.

Ac circuits are more complex. Inductors and capacitors both exhibit reactance that varies in value with changes in frequency. You can think of *reactance* as being similar to resistance, since both are a measure of the amount that a component hinders the flow of current. Both quantities are measured in ohms, and the relationship between the current and voltage across a coil or capacitor satisfies Ohm's Law; $E = IX$, $I = E/X$, and $X = E/I$, where X is the reactance of the coil or capacitor, E is the voltage and I is the current.

To calculate the value of inductive reactance (X_L), solve

$$X_L = 2\pi fL \qquad \text{(Eq. 1)}$$

where
f = frequency in hertz
L = inductance in henrys.
π = 3.14159
Capacitive reactance (X_C) is given by

$$X_C = \frac{1}{2\pi fC} \qquad \text{(Eq. 2)}$$

where
f = frequency in hertz
C = capacitance in farads
π = 3.14159

Phase Shift

As you can see from these equations, the value of X_L increases while the value of X_C decreases as the frequency goes up. However, another phenomenon also occurs when an ac voltage is applied to an inductor or capacitor: The currents which flow through the component are out of phase with the applied voltage. In the case of a perfect inductor, the current lags behind the applied voltage by 90 degrees. In a perfect capacitor, the current leads the voltage by 90 degrees. A convenient mnemonic device to remember this is to think of "ELI the ICE man." Voltage (E) in an inductor (L) leads the current (I). Current (I) in a capacitor (C) leads the voltage (E).

Coil and capacitor reactances in a series circuit subtract, that is, the total reactance is the difference between the reactance of the coil and capacitor. Why? In a series circuit, the current flowing through each component must be identical to that flowing in every other component. It is impossible to have current leading in one part and lagging in another part of a series circuit. If the current in an inductor lags the applied voltage by 90 degrees, it is just as true that the voltage leads the current by 90 degrees. In a capacitor, the voltage *lags* the current by 90 degrees. Thus the

voltages across a coil and capacitor in series are 180 degrees out of phase. For this reason, if the voltages across each component have the same amplitude, they will exactly cancel and there will be zero voltage across the series combination. This is the case in a series-resonant circuit. Because the impedance of a circuit is the voltage divided by the current through it, the impedance of a series-tuned circuit is zero. (Actually, practical coils have some series resistance, depending on their Q factor. For this reason, the impedance of a real-life, series-tuned circuit is not exactly zero.) Another way of saying this is that if a coil and capacitor connected in series have the same reactance, their reactances will cancel.

In the case of a parallel-resonant circuit, the *voltage* across each component must be the same. Thus it is the *currents* that are 180 degrees out of phase. If the amplitudes of the currents through each component are identical, they cancel, so that the total current through the parallel tuned circuit is zero. In this case the impedance at resonance is infinite. (Again, since real coils do not have infinite Q, the actual impedance will not be exactly infinity. If coil Q is high, however, impedance will also be quite high.)

The reactance or resistance of each component in a series circuit affects the phase relationships in the circuit as a whole. Since the voltage across a resistor is in phase with the current through it, resistive impedance is considered to have zero phase. Capacitive reactance is considered to lag resistance by 90 degrees, and inductive reactance leads resistance by 90 degrees. Using these conventions, the three types of impedance can be plotted as in Fig. 2.

Resistance is plotted as an arrow pointing to the right. Inductive and capacitive reactances are plotted as arrows pointing up and down, respectively. The length of each arrow corresponds to the magnitude of the impedance it represents. These lines are called vectors since they represent both magnitude (ohms) and direction (degrees).

You add two vectors by placing the tail of one on the head of the other and plotting the result between the two unconnected ends as in Fig. 1D. The length of Z, the total reactance, can be found using the Pythagorean theorem

$$Z = \sqrt{X_L^2 + R^2} \qquad \text{(Eq. 3)}$$

Since inductive and capacitive reactances are of opposite polarity, they subtract, so that the formula for total impedance in a series circuit is

$$Z = \sqrt{(X_L - X_C)^2 + R^2} \qquad \text{(Eq. 4)}$$

Let's solve an example; see Fig. 3. The procedure is as follows: (1) Solve for any components in parallel. The resistance of

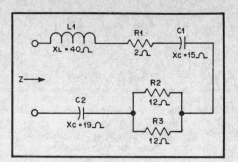

Fig. 3 — Impedance is a combination of reactance and resistance. See text for a method of calculating it.

R2 and R3 in parallel is

$$R = \frac{R2 \times R3}{R2 + R3} \qquad \text{(Eq. 5)}$$

or 144/24 = 6 ohms. (2) Add like reactances and add like resistances. Total resistance is 6 + 2 = 8 ohms. Total capacitive reactance is 15 + 19 = 34 ohms. (3) Subtract capacitive from inductive reactance: 40 − 34 = 6 ohms. (4) Use Pythagoras' theorem

$$Z = \sqrt{X_t^2 + R^2}$$

where $X_t = X_L - X_C$ $\qquad$ (Eq. 6)

$$Z = \sqrt{6^2 + 8^2} = \sqrt{36 + 64}$$

$$= \sqrt{100} = 10 \text{ ohms} \qquad \text{(Eq. 7)}$$

If component values were given for the coils and capacitors rather than reactances, then the first step would be to convert all inductances and capacitances into reactances. See equations 1 and 2.

Once you've solved for total circuit impedance, you can also calculate either the voltage across the circuit, given the current through it, or the current, given the voltage. Just substitute impedance (Z) for resistance (R) into Ohm's Law: E = IZ, I = E/Z and Z = E/I. Note that the simple sum of the magnitude of the voltage drop across each component will not always equal the total voltage across the entire series circuit. As mentioned before, this is because voltages of the capacitors and inductors are out of phase and thus partially or completely cancel.

In Fig. 4, the *phase angle* between the voltage and the current is indicated by the angle between the resistance and impedance vectors. If the impedance vector is *above* the resistance on the diagram (Fig. 5B), the phase angle is *positive* (meaning the voltage leads the current), and if the impedance vector is below the resistance (Fig. 5C), the phase angle is *negative* (meaning the voltage lags the current). The phase angle will always be between plus and minus 90 degrees since the resistance is never negative. If you are familiar with trigonometry, you can see

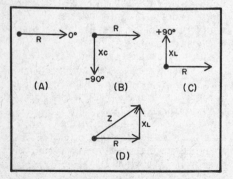

Fig. 2 — The phase relationships between resistance (R) inductive and capacitive reactance (X_L and X_C) and impedance (Z).

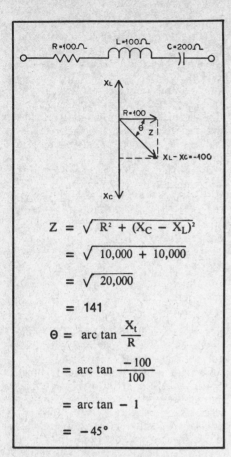

Fig. 4 — By the Pythagorean Theorem, total impedance is the square root of the sum of the squares of the resistance and reactance.

$$Z = \sqrt{R^2 + (X_C - X_L)^2}$$
$$= \sqrt{10,000 + 10,000}$$
$$= \sqrt{20,000}$$
$$= 141$$
$$\Theta = \text{arc tan } \frac{X_t}{R}$$
$$= \text{arc tan } \frac{-100}{100}$$
$$= \text{arc tan } -1$$
$$= -45°$$

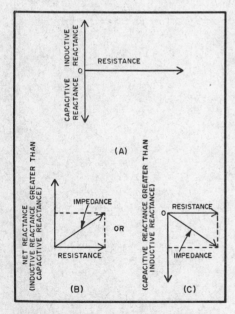

Fig. 5 — Conventional method of representing resistance and inductive and capacitive reactance on an impedance diagram (A). Impedance is the vector sum of reactance and resistance (B, C). (See text.)

that the phase angle, θ, between the voltage and current is given by

$$\tan\theta = \frac{X_t}{R} \qquad \text{(Eq. 8)}$$

where

$$X_t = \text{the total reactance } (X_L - X_C)$$

so

$$\theta = \text{arc tan } \frac{X_t}{R} \qquad \text{(Eq. 9)}$$

Reactive and Apparent Power

We've seen that energy is stored in the magnetic field when current increases through an inductor, and in the electric field when the voltage across a capacitor increases. If the current through the inductance is made to decrease, energy will come back into the circuit. The induced voltage will tend to keep current flowing in the same direction as the original current. By the same token, if the voltage applied to the capacitor is made to decrease, the capacitor will discharge into the circuit, giving back stored energy.

An alternating voltage or current not only is one which reverses its direction periodically, but also is one in which the *value* of the voltage or current is continually changing. Because of this continual change, energy will at times be stored in the magnetic field and shortly thereafter returned to the circuit, if the circuit contains inductance. A similar event takes place with the electric field and capacitance.

In other words, inductance and capacitance take energy (or power) from the power source only to hand all of it back again. A "pure" inductance or capacitance (one without resistance) uses no power. Nevertheless, current does flow in the circuit when voltage is applied. If we multiply the voltage by the current, the same as we do to find power in dc circuits, we get a number which seems to represent power. It only *seems* to do so, because no real work is done unless there is resistance. This power is called *reactive power* or *wattless power*. To distinguish it from real power, a different unit than the watt is used — a *volt-ampere*. One volt-ampere is the same as one watt — except that it doesn't do any work, while a real watt does. If a circuit or a load contained *both* reactance and resistance, and you multiplied the measured current by the voltage in the load, you would get a quantity called *apparent power*, which contains both the reactive power in the reactance and the true power dissipated in the resistance.

You're probably curious as to how there can be a voltage and current but no power. This has to do with *phase*, which means the time interval between the instant when one thing occurs and the instant when a second related thing takes place. The later event is said to *lag* the earlier, while the one that occurs first is said to *lead*. Since each ac cycle occupies exactly the same amount of time as every other cycle of the same frequency, we can use this cycle itself as the time unit. Using the cycle as the time unit makes the

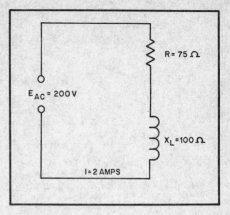

Fig. 6 — Only the resistance actually consumes power. The power consumed in the resistance is $P = I^2R = (2)^2 \times 75 = 300$ watts.

measurement of phase independent of the frequency of the current, so long as we're using only one frequency at a time.

The time interval or "phase difference" which we'll be considering usually will be less than one cycle. Phase difference could be measured in decimal parts of a cycle, but it's a lot easier if we divide the cycle into 360 parts or *degrees*. A phase degree is, therefore, 1/360 of a cycle.

Power Factor

To convert apparent power to real power, multiply it by the *power factor*, which is the cosine of the phase angle between voltage and current. For example, refer to Fig. 6. In the circuit, an applied emf of 250 volts results in a current of 2 amperes, giving an apparent power of $250 \times 2 = 500$ watts. However, only the resistance actually consumes power. If you are given the phase angle between the voltage and current as being 53.1°, use the following equation to find the power factor:

$$\text{Power factor} = \cos \theta$$
$$= \cos 53.1°$$
$$= 0.6 \qquad \text{(Eq. 10)}$$

You can also figure the power factor of the circuit by determining the ratio of the power consumed to the apparent power:

$$\text{Power factor} = \frac{R}{Z}$$

where

R = real power in watts
Z = apparent power in volt-amperes.

In the example given in Fig. 6, the power factor would be $300/500 = 0.6$. Power factor is frequently expressed as a percentage; in this case, it would be 60 percent.

Remember, "real" or dissipated power is measured in watts; apparent power, to distinguish it from real power, is measured in volt-amperes and has no direct relationship to the power actually used or dissipated unless the power factor

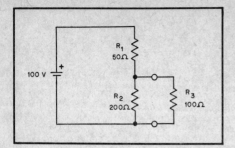

Fig. 7 — We could use Ohm's Law to calculate the total current in this circuit and then use the current divider relationship to calculate the current going through R3. However, Thevenin's Theorem simplifies this problem considerably. See text.

of the circuit is known. The power factor of a purely resistive circuit is 100 percent or 1, while the power factor of a pure reactance is zero. In the example in Fig. 6, the reactive power is

$$VAR = I^2X = (2)^2 \times 100$$
$$= 400 \text{ volt-amperes (Eq. 11)}$$

If you multiply the *apparent* power by the power factor, you should get the real power.

$$500 \times 0.6 = 300 \text{ watts} \qquad \text{(Eq. 12)}$$

Average Power

If you apply 1-volt dc across a 1-ohm resistor, 1 watt of power will be dissipated. If, on the other hand, you apply a 1-volt peak-ac signal (that is, it varies between plus 1 volt and minus 1 volt) across the 1-ohm resistor, *less* than 1 watt of *average power* will be dissipated. This is because the ac wave reaches 1 volt only on peaks of the sine wave. The rest of the time it is less than 1 volt, so while the *peak power* is 1 watt, the average power is less. An ac voltage that will cause an average power of 1 watt to be dissipated in a 1-ohm resistor is said to be 1-volt *rms* (root-mean-square). The peak voltage of an ac-sine wave is $\sqrt{2}$ or 1.414 times the rms value. Thus the *peak power* in an ac circuit is $(\sqrt{2})^2$ or two times the average (rms) power.

When speaking of rf amplifiers, the peak power is rarely mentioned. When we speak of a 100-watt transmitter, we mean it runs 100 watts rms. However, linear amplifiers designed for single sideband use do not operate at their maximum power level continuously. The rms power of the ssb-output signal varies at an audio rate, reaching its maximum only on peaks. For this reason, we speak of the *peak-envelope power* (PEP), which is the maximum rms power of a single-sideband signal. The same term may be used for amplitude modulation (a-m). The peak-envelope power of a 100-percent-modulated a-m transmission is four times the average carrier power. Unfortunately,

you will sometimes hear people use the term "peak power" to refer to PEP, but you should remember that they are talking about the maximum rms power of the signal, not the peak power of the rf wave.

Thevenin's Theorem

A useful tool for simplifying complex networks of resistors (or other components) is *Thevenin's Theorem*. We'll limit its scope to resistors (no reactive components) for this discussion. The theorem states that any two-terminal network of resistors and voltage sources, no matter how complex, can be replaced by a circuit consisting of a single voltage source and a single series resistor. Doing this can simplify complex network calculations.

To apply Thevenin's Theorem, first remove the load from the network to be simplified. The new Thevenin-equivalent voltage source has a voltage equal to the open-circuit (no-load) voltage at the load terminals. In the original network, replace the voltage source with its "internal resistance." (Most voltage sources can be assumed to have an internal resistance of zero ohms, so we'll use a piece of wire in place of the voltage source.) The Thevenin equivalent series resistor has a resistance equal to that which an ohmmeter would see "looking back" into the network from the load terminals.

A voltage source and a resistive voltage divider (R1 and R2) are shown connected

to a load resistor (R3) in Fig. 7. To find the current supplied to the load resistor by the voltage divider, we could first calculate the resistance of the parallel combination of R2 and R3. To this we could add the resistance of R1 to get the total resistance. We could use Ohm's Law to calculate the total current in the circuit, and then use the current-divider relationship to determine the current passing through the load, R3.

Using Thevenin's Theorem simplifies the solution to this problem considerably. First, remove the load resistor (Fig. 8A). Then use the voltage-divider principle to calculate the open-circuit voltage at the load terminals:

$$V = E \frac{R2}{R1 + R2}$$
$$= 100 \frac{200}{50 + 200} = 80 \text{ V} \quad \text{(Eq. 13)}$$

This is the voltage of the Thevenin-equivalent voltage source. When we replace the original network voltage source with its internal resistance (a direct short), we get the circuit of Fig. 8B. The Thevenin-equivalent resistance is simply R1 and R2 in parallel, 40 ohms.

Now we can replace the original voltage-divider network with our new *Thevenin equivalent circuit*, consisting of an 80-volt source in series with a 40-ohm resistor. Adding the load resistor, as in

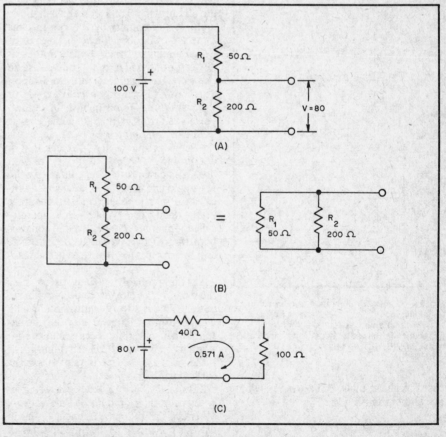

Fig. 8 — Step-by-step explanation of Thevenin's Theorem. See text.

Fig. 8C, enables us to calculate the load current easily:

$$I = E/(R1 + R2) = 80 \text{ V}/140 \text{ } \Omega$$
$$= 0.571 \text{ A} \qquad \text{(Eq. 14)}$$

Reactances Combined

We've already seen that inductive reactance and capacitive reactance have opposite effects: In an alternating voltage, capacitive reactance "pushes" the current ahead of the voltage, and inductive reactance "pulls" it behind the voltage. So what happens if we connect a coil and a capacitor in series in a circuit? One tends to undo what the other is trying to do. That's a lot different from placing two *resistors* in series, as they work together fighting the flow of current. The total resistance is the sum of the two resistors.

But if we put inductive and capacitive reactance in series, the total reactance is the *difference*. We traditionally call capacitive reactance "positive." This means that if we have a series circuit with an inductive reactance of "plus" 15 ohms and a capacitive reactance of "minus" 10 ohms, the total reactance would be only 5 ohms (15 − 10).

Reactances of the *same* kind, however, add up just as resistors do. That is, an inductive reactance of 15 ohms placed in series with one of 8 ohms will result in a total of 23 ohms. The same would be true if we had two capacitors in series. Their total reactance would be the sum of their individual reactances, except that the sign would be negative.

You're probably already wondering what happens when reactances are combined in parallel. When the reactances are the *same* (all capacitive or all inductive), we use the same rules we use for resistances. But as you might expect, reactances of *opposite* kind in parallel are a much different story. In fact, it's a complicated story, one which we won't go into here. Most radio amateurs don't need this knowledge, but there is one special case where different reactances are combined in parallel which we need to discuss: the resonant circuit.

Resonant Circuits

What have we learned already about reactance? We've learned that when we increase the frequency of an alternating voltage entering an inductor, its reactance goes *up*. And when we increase the frequency of an alternating voltage entering a capacitor, its reactance goes *down*. What just might happen if we connect a capacitor and an inductor in series? We may find a frequency where the two reactances, capacitive and inductive, are *equal*. Actually, they can never be equal; one will always be negative and the other positive. But they can have the same *value*. In other words, the capacitor can have a reactance of −8 ohms, while the inductor has a reactance of +8 ohms.

And if you put them end-to-end (a series circuit), what's the total reactance? Zero, that's what! It wouldn't be right if we didn't give this frequency a special name of its own, so we called it the *resonant* frequency of the circuit.

If we change the circuit by adding a different inductor or capacitor, will the resonant frequency of the circuit change? It sure will. Remember that the resonant frequency of a circuit depends on the values of the different components in that circuit, so it's rare when any two circuits, by pure coincidence, have identical resonant frequencies.

The resonant frequency of a series or parallel circuit is given by the equation

$$f_r = \frac{1}{2\pi\sqrt{LC}} \qquad \text{(Eq. 15)}$$

where

f_r = the resonant frequency
L = the inductance in henrys
C = the capacitance in farads, and
π = 3.14

We're hardly ever able to ignore resonance in radio-frequency circuits. It's important because at the resonant frequency, the inductive reactance is balanced by the capacitive reactance. This leaves us only with resistance operating in the circuit. There's more to it than just cancellation of reactive effects, though, as we shall see.

Series Resonance

The coil and capacitor used in a resonant circuit may either be connected in series or parallel. If we have a source of voltage at the resonant frequency and the two are in series, the current will cause a voltage to exist across each reactance. Strange as it may seem, they can be many, many times larger than the source voltage. In fact, they are sometimes at least 10 times as large, and may be as much as a few hundred times as large.

This happens because the two reactances cancel each other's effects, since they are equal at resonance. So around the circuit there is zero reactance. There is nothing, then, to limit the flow of current except the resistance in the circuit. There is always some resistance in a circuit, because no components operate without at least a little power loss. But if the total resistance is small, the current will be large, by Ohm's Law. And a large current will result in large, but equal, voltage drops across each reactance. The phase of these voltages causes the voltage across the coil to have its *positive* maximum at the same time that the voltage across the capacitor has its *negative* maximum. The two voltages always add up to zero.

We can look at this another way, which may make it seem more reasonable: These mutually large voltages can develop because of energy stored in the reactances. The energy going into the magnetic field

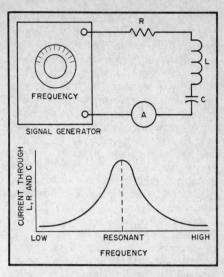

Fig. 9 — A series-connected LC or RLC circuit behaves like a very low resistance at the resonant frequency. Therefore, at resonance the value of the current passing through the components reaches a peak.

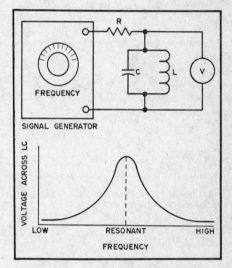

Fig. 10 — A parallel-connected LC or RLC circuit behaves like a very high resistance at the resonant frequency. Therefore, the value of the voltage measured across a parallel-connected LC circuit reaches a peak at the resonant frequency.

of the inductance is energy coming out of the electric field of the capacitor during one part of a cycle. Then, when it's all been stored in the magnetic field, it starts coming back into the circuit and goes into the electric field. This means that a lot of energy can be handed back and forth between L and C without making it necessary for the source to supply any. Of course, the energy "bank account" came from the source. But after an initial surge, the source has only to supply the actual power used up in resistance.

Parallel Resonance

We have a different state of affairs when a coil and capacitor are connected in parallel. Here, there are two current paths with the same voltage applied to both. The two branch currents, the one going through the capacitor and the one going through the coil, depend only on the same Ohm's Law equation for a reactive circuit. If the reactance is small and the voltage is large, each branch current will be large. But the same *voltage* is applied to both reactances (in the series circuit both had the same current). So in this case, the currents add up to zero around the circuit. Their phase is such that they cancel each other in the part of the circuit outside the coil and capacitor. In this case, then, there is no current flowing around the circuit as a whole.

A parallel-resonant circuit "looks like" an open circuit to the voltage source. Compare this with the series circuit, which "looked like" a short circuit. The reason for this behavior of the parallel circuit is the same as in the series case — stored energy is tossed back and forth between the inductance and capacitance.

These ideas of "short circuit" and "open circuit" must be taken with cau-

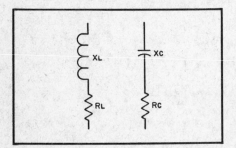

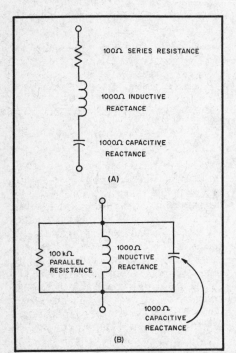

Fig. 11 — The Q of a component is the ratio of its reactance to its resistance.

Fig. 12 — Finding Q in a series resonant circuit at A and a parallel resonant circuit at B. At resonance, capacitive reactance equals inductive reactance.

tion. They would be literally true if we could have coils and capacitors without any losses. But these components always do have losses. If the losses are very small, the series circuit is *approximately* a short circuit, and the parallel circuit is *approximately* an open circuit. Losses mean that the voltages in the series circuit don't quite balance each other, and the currents in the parallel circuits don't quite cancel each other. Some of the energy is lost each time it's handed back and forth. This lost energy has to be supplied continuously by the source, in order to keep things going at an even rate. The source, therefore, "sees" a resistance — a very small one in the case of the series circuit, and a very large one in the case of the parallel circuit.

Q — The Shorthand Number

Another thing you'll hear and read a lot about is Q, the merit or quality factor. It is a number tacked on to coils and capacitors, and circuits formed from them. It gives some idea of the characteristics of these components and circuits. With its help, and with some simplifying assumptions, a good deal of calculation can be saved in planning the operation of circuits.

One definition of Q is that it's the ratio of reactance to resistance. This means that in Fig. 11 the Q of the combination of X_L and R_L is equal to X_L divided by R_L. R_L may be a separate resistor, as shown. On the other hand, it may be the resistance of the coil itself. This internal resistance can't be separated from the coil, of course, but it acts just the same as though it were in series with a lossless coil.

The Q of a capacitor is found in the same way — that is, the Q is equal to the reactance, X_C, divided by the resistance, R_C. Internal resistance here acts the same as in the case of the coil.

When both an internal and external resistance are present, the internal and external resistances have to be added together to find the value of R that's going to be used in the Q equation. Since added external resistance can only raise the total resistance, the Q always goes down when resistance is added in series. There's no way to lower the internal resistance of a coil or capacitor and, therefore, raise the Q except by building a better component.

We've talked about a series circuit containing both reactance and resistance, but what happens when the resistance and reactance are in parallel? That's a whole new ball game. In that case, in a parallel circuit containing reactance (and, of course, resistance), Q is equal to the resistance of the circuit divided by the reactance of the circuit, R_L/X_L.

The Q of a series-resonant R-L-C circuit is equal to the reactance of either the inductor or the capacitor (they're the same at resonance) divided by the series resistance in the circuit. For example, in

the circuit of Fig. 12A. Q = 1000/100 = 10.

The Q of a parallel-resonant circuit is equal to the parallel resistance in the circuit divided by the reactance of either the inductor or the capacitor. In the circuit of Fig. 12B, Q = 100 k/1000 = 100.

It can be useful to know how to predict the bandwidth of a resonant circuit. Bandwidth here refers to the frequency spread between the half-power points on the response curve. The half-power points are, as the name suggests, the points at which the response of the circuit is down 3 dB from the peak value. Also, at the half-power points the voltage and current are each reduced by a factor of 0.707 from their peak values. The half-power points are called f_1 and f_2; Δf is the difference between the two frequencies f_1 and f_2. The bandwidth of a resonant circuit is given by the equation

$$\Delta f = \frac{f_r}{Q} \qquad \text{(Eq. 16)}$$

where
Δf = the half-power bandwidth
f_r = the resonant frequency of the circuit,
Q = the Q of the circuit
For example, if the circuit of Fig. 12B were resonant at 1 MHz, its bandwidth would be equal to 1 MHz/100 = 10 kHz.

Diodes

To qualify for the Advanced class license, the FCC will expect you to be familiar with some specialized types of diodes.

Switching Diodes

High-speed switching diodes must have excellent high-frequency characteristics. Among these is low capacitance. The ordinary *junction diode* has a relatively large surface area at the junction and therefore a high capacitance. Point-contact diodes have a much smaller junction surface and

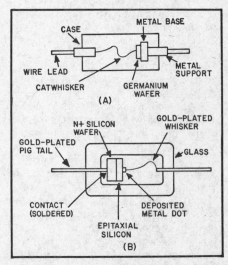

Fig. 13 — Construction of point-contact (A) and hot-carrier (B) diodes.

a correspondingly smaller capacitance, usually on the order of one picofarad or less. Another diode with good high-frequency characteristics is the *hot-carrier diode*. This device is very similar in construction to the point-contact diode, but with an important difference. Whereas the point-contact device employs a metal whisker to make contact with the active element, a hot-carrier diode is physically attached by means of a metal dot deposited on the element. The construction of both the point contact and hot-carrier diodes is given in Fig. 13. The construction of the hot-carrier type provides improved power-handling characteristics, lower contact resistance, lower device noise and improved immunity to burnout caused by transient-noise pulses.

Voltage-Variable Capacitors (Varicaps)

As mentioned above, any junction diode has an appreciable capacitance between its two terminals. When a reverse bias is applied to the junction, this capacitance is reduced because the current carriers (holes and electrons) on either side of the junction are drawn apart. These devices are specially manufactured to be capable of exhibiting a wide range of capacitances. A typical varicap can provide capacitance changes over a 10:1 range with bias voltages in the 0- to 100-volt range. These devies are used in frequency multipliers, remotely tuned circuits and simple frequency modulators. The varicap symbol and typical circuits are given in Fig. 14.

PIN Diodes

In between the p-type layer and the n-type layer of a PIN diode is sandwiched a layer of *intrinsic* material. It's called intrinsic because the concentration of charge carriers is characteristic of the material itself, rather than of the impurity materials that are added to other semiconductors in the doping process.

PIN diodes are commonly used as switches and variable attenuators. They are useful as series elements for obtaining agc (automatic gain control) action in receivers. A simple switch circuit using a PIN diode is shown in Fig. 15. The generator signal is switched to the load only when forward bias is applied to the diode. As the forward bias current in the diode varies, the rf insertion loss of the diode will vary, being lowest when the bias current is greatest.

Tunnel Diodes

The tunnel diode is an extremely specialized type of diode that, when properly biased, possesses an unusual property: *negative resistance*. Negative resistance means that when the voltage across the diode increases, the current *decreases*. This property makes this type of diode useful in microwave oscillators and amplifiers. The tunnel diode is seldom

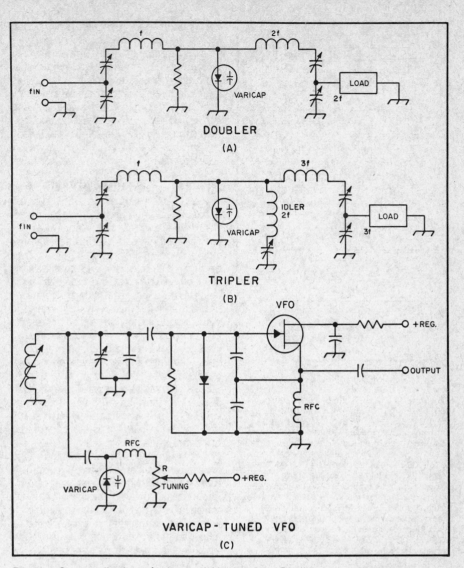

Fig. 14 — Some applications of voltage-variable capacitors. These devices make excellent frequency multipliers as in the circuits at A and B. At C, an adjustable bias voltage is used to tune the VFO frequency.

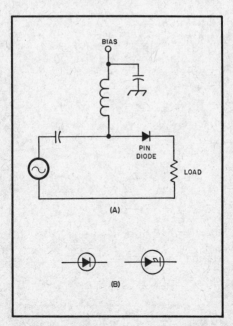

Fig. 15 — (A) A PIN diode used as a variable attenuator. (B) At times, you may see a PIN diode represented by either of these symbols.

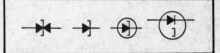

Fig. 16 — The tunnel diode may be represented any one of these four ways.

used today, however, having been replaced by more modern devices that offer higher performance. The schematic symbols for the tunnel diode are shown in Fig. 16.

Zener Diodes

If a reverse voltage applied to a semiconductor diode is gradually increased from zero, we'll find that at first the current (leakage current) is very small and changes very little with increasing reverse voltage. There will be a point, however, where the current suddenly rises. And beyond this point, the current increases very rapidly for a small increase in voltage. The diode is said to *avalanche*

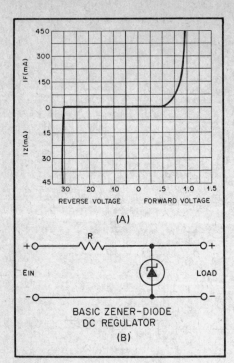

(A)

BASIC ZENER-DIODE
DC REGULATOR
(B)

Fig. 17 — At A is a graph of the voltage versus current characteristics of a semiconductor diode. Note that the voltage (horizontal) scale on the graph is different for forward and reverse voltages. This is because very little forward bias voltage is required to cause current flow, but no significant reverse current flows until the Zener-avalanche voltage (here about 30 volts) is reached. The Zener-diode regulator at B takes advantage of the fact that reverse-bias voltage across the device will be nearly constant so long as a nonzero current flows through the device. To ensure that at least some current flows through the diode at all times, resistor R is chosen so that current flow (voltage drop divided by resistance) is greater than the maximum load current.

at this point. *Zener voltage* is the voltage necessary to cause avalanche.

Since the current in the avalanche region can change over a wide range while the voltage stays practically constant. This kind of diode can be used as a voltage regulator. The voltage at which avalanche occurs can be precisely controlled in the manufacturing process. Diodes calibrated in terms of avalanche voltage are called *Zener diodes*.

Electronic Voltage Regulation Principles

Fig. 17 shows the most basic type of voltage-regulator circuit, using just a Zener diode and a bias resistor. *Electronic voltage regulation* is a technique of providing a very steady power-supply voltage by means of a *pass transistor* in series with the unregulated voltage source. The conduction of the pass transistor is controlled in such a way that a nearly constant voltage appears at the output no matter how much load current is drawn. In the voltage-regulator circuit of Fig. 18A, the output voltage at the transistor emitter closely follows the voltage at its base. Since the voltage across the Zener diode is nearly constant, so will be the output voltage. R_s provides operating current for the Zener diode and bias current for the transistor.

Just as in a diode, there is a voltage drop across the base-emitter junction of a transistor. The drop is about 0.6 volt in a silicon transistor; 0.2 volt is a germanium transistor. Say you were designing a voltage regulator using a silicon pass transistor, and you wanted an output of 12.6 V. A Zener diode rated at about 12.0 V

will, when the 0.6-V base-emitter potential is added, produce the output voltage you desire. R_s sets the Zener-diode bias current. R_s must be low enough in value to ensure that the Zener diode operates in breakdown, yet not so low that the maximum power dissipation rating of the diode is exceeded. To select a value for R_s in Fig. 18A, you must know the expected voltage at the positive output of the bridge rectifier. Let's say that it's 18 V. You must also know the desired Zener-diode current. This information can be obtained from manufacturer's data sheets. Let's say the 12-V Zener diode we're using requires a current of 5 mA. The value for R_s is given by the equation

$$R_s = \frac{E_{out} - E_Z}{I_Z} \qquad \text{(Eq. 17)}$$

where

E_{out} = the output voltage of the bridge rectifier

E_Z = the Zener-diode voltage, and

I_Z = the Zener-diode current

Using the values we've assumed above, R_s = (18 V − 12 V)/5 mA = 1200 Ω.

Integrated-circuit voltage regulators can take the place of the pass transistor, bias resistor and Zener diode in Fig. 18A. These "three-terminal" IC regulators contain a voltage reference, all on one chip. They are available in a wide range of output voltages and power-dissipation ratings. An important specification is the range of unregulated input voltages allowed. Your power supply must provide a voltage within this range of values for all load currents. The schematic diagram of a power supply using an IC regulator is shown in Fig. 18B.

Light-Emitting Diodes (LEDs)

Light-emitting diodes are designed to emit light when current passes through their pn junctions. They are operated in a forward-biased condition. LEDs are available in plastic cases or metal cases with a transparent end. Available LED colors are red, green and yellow. LEDs are useful as replacements for incandescent panel and indicator lamps. In this application they offer long life, low current drain and small size. But one of their most important applications is in numeric displays, where LEDs are arranged to provide illuminated segments which form the numbers. Schematic symbols for the LED are shown in Fig. 19.

A typical red LED has a voltage drop of 1.6 V. Amber and green LEDs have higher voltage drops (2 V for amber and 4 V for green). To use an LED it is necessary to forward bias it and limit the current to a safe value. The manufacturer usually specifies this value. As with other diodes, varying the current through the diode can be accomplished by using resistors in series. Varying the current through an LED will affect its intensity;

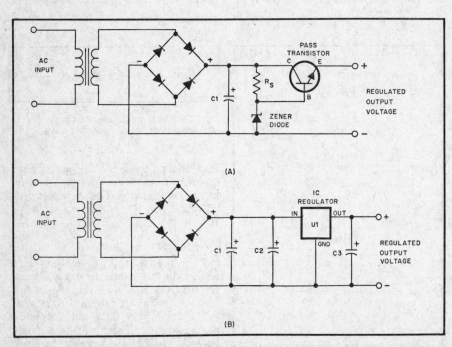

(A)

(B)

Fig. 18 — (A) The circuit of a simple electronic voltage regulator, using discrete components. See the text for a design example. (B) A voltage regulator using a three-terminal regulator IC. C2 and C3 are bypass capacitors; for stability, it is important to bypass the input and output of these regulators close to the case.

Fig. 19 — Schematic symbols for the LED.

the voltage drop will remain fairly constant, however.

The Thyristor

Also known as the silicon-controlled rectifier (SCR), the *thyristor* is a diode whose forward conduction from cathode to anode is controlled by a third terminal, the gate. Specifically, the diode will not conduct until the voltage exceeds the forward-breakdown voltage, a value that is determined by the gate current. Once the rectifier begins to conduct, the gate no longer has any control, and the device behaves as a low-forward-resistance diode. This condition persists until the voltage drops to zero again at which time the forward-breakdown voltage barrier is re-established, and the gate regains control.

A *triac* is a type of bidirectional SCR. Electrically, a triac is equivalent to two reverse-connected (anode-to-cathode) SCRs with their gates tied together. The gate voltage of an SCR or triac can be set so that it conducts only part of an ac voltage. Varying the gate voltage varies the amount of the ac voltage that passes through. SCRs and triacs can control the current flow to ac-operated devices, and find common application as light dimmers and motor speed controls. The schematic symbols for the SCR and the triac are shown in Fig. 20.

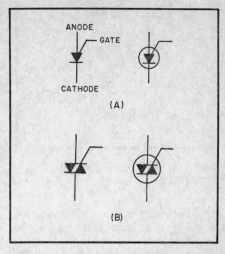

Fig. 20 — Two schematic symbols for the SCR are shown at A. Two triac symbols are shown at B.

Transistors

The transistor is a type of three-terminal, solid-state device. It is made up of a thin base layer of doped semiconductor crystal sandwiched between two layers of material with the opposite type of doping. If the outer layers are p-type material, we call the device a pnp transistor, and if n-type, it is known as an npn transistor.

The three layers of the transistor sandwich are called the emitter, base and collector. These are functionally analogous to the cathode, grid and plate of a vacuum tube. A diagram of the construction of a typical pnp transistor is given in Fig. 21. As shown in the diagram, forward bias voltage across the emitter-base section of the sandwich causes electrons to flow through it from the base to the emitter. As the free electrons from the n-type material flow into the holes of the p-type material, the holes in effect travel into the base. Some of the holes will be neutralized in the base by free electrons, but because the base layer is so thin, some will move right on through into the p-type material in the collector. As shown, the collector is connected to a negative voltage with respect to the base. Normally, no current will flow because the base-collector junction is reverse biased. However, the collector now contains an excess of holes because of those from the emitter that overshot the base. Since the voltage source connected to the collector produces a negative charge, the holes from the emitter will be attracted to the power-supply connection. The amount of emitter-collector current flow is approximately proportional to the base-emitter current. Because of the construction of a transistor, however, the current flowing through the collector will be considerably larger than that flowing through the base. The ratio of collector current to base current is the current gain,

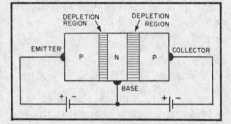

Fig. 21 — A bipolar transistor contains two p-n junctions. Even under no-bias conditions some electrons from the n-material cross over to fill nearby holes in the p-material. Thus, an area called the *depletion region* is created on each side of the junction in which few majority carriers are present. When sufficient forward bias voltage is applied, this lack of current carriers is overcome and current flow is sustained.

or *beta*. If a base current of 2 mA causes a collector current of 100 mA, then the beta is

$$\beta = \frac{I_c}{I_b} \qquad \text{(Eq. 18)}$$

where
I_c is the collector current
I_b is the base current
Thus, beta is

$$\beta = \frac{100}{2} = 50$$

Biasing

For normal operation, a bipolar transistor must be provided with a forward bias current through the base-emitter junction. To determine the proper bias current, divide the desired collector current by the beta current gain. For example, if the transistor current gain is 100 and you want 10 mA of collector current, the base current should be 10 ÷ 100 or

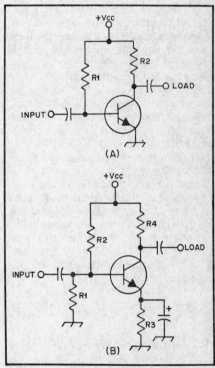

Fig. 22 — Two methods of biasing bipolar transistors. Collector current at A equals transistor beta times the base current which is approximately equal to the supply voltage divided by R1. Since beta changes with variations in temperature, this circuit is subject to thermal instability. The source resistor in the circuit at B introduces considerable negative dc feedback so that operation of this circuit is relatively independent of temperature.

0.1 mA. In the circuit of Fig. 22A, the base bias current is determined by R1. By Ohm's Law, R1 should equal the supply voltage (less the base-emitter voltage drop) divided by the desired base current.

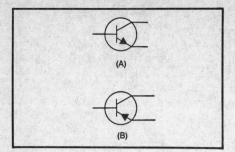

Fig. 23 — (A) NPN transistor. (B) PNP transistor.

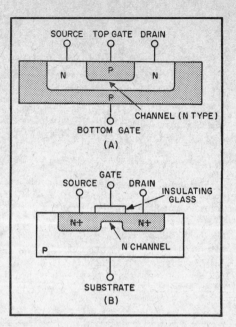

Fig. 24 — Construction of a junction field-effect transistor (A) and metal-oxide semiconductor FET (B).

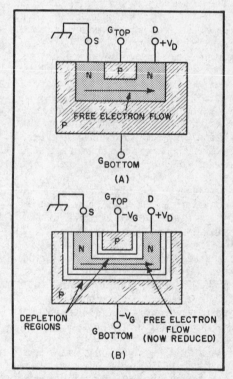

Fig. 25 — Operation of a junction field-effect transistor. When a reverse bias is applied between the gate and source-drain channel, current flow is constricted to the center of the channel, which increases the source-drain resistance. For this reason, a small gate voltage is capable of controlling a large source-drain current.

The circuit at Fig. 22B is less susceptible to changes in transistor parameters because of temperature variations. Normally, voltage-divider resistors R2 and R1 have high enough values that base current through them can be ignored. Emitter voltage will equal base voltage minus base-emitter voltage drop (about 0.7 volt for silicon transistors). This is because if the emitter voltage starts to fall below this value, more current will flow through R3 which brings the voltage back up. If emitter voltage starts to rise, base current will fall, reducing the collector current so that the voltage across R3 will be brought back down. We say that the emitter voltage *follows* the base voltage.

Since collector-emitter current is approximately equal to current through R3 (base-emitter current is usually small enough to ignore), the desired emitter voltage is equal to (from Ohm's Law) collector current times R3. Choose R2 and R1 to give this voltage (plus the base-emitter voltage) at the base connection.

The *alpha* (*a*) of a transistor is the ratio of the collector current to the emitter current. The smaller the base current, the closer the collector current comes to being equal to the emitter current and the closer alpha comes to being 1. In our example, we know that the emitter current is the sum of the two other currents, or 100.

$$a = \frac{I_c}{I_e} \qquad \text{(Eq. 19)}$$

where
  I_c is the collector current
  I_e is the emitter current
Thus, alpha is

$$a = \frac{98}{100} \text{ or } 0.98$$

Because transistors are used not only with direct current but also with alternating current, anyone designing a circuit should know that transistors have frequency characteristics. Symbol f_T is the *gain bandwidth product* (common-emitter) of the transistor. At this frequency, the gain of the transistor is equal to one.

Transit time is the period of time required for the current to flow from emitter to collector, through the semiconductor base material. The thicker the base material, the greater the transit time. This means that there's more chance of a phase shift of a signal passing through a thick base material than through a thin one. In fact, at frequencies near and above the gain bandwidth product, we might get partial or complete phase shift.

Gain Bandwidths

At radio frequencies, beta is not an accurate measurement of ac current gain. Two additional parameters are used to specify transistor operation at high frequencies.

The grounded-base cutoff frequency or *alpha cutoff frequency* is the frequency at which the grounded-base current gain is down 3 dB from its low-frequency value. That is, it is where the gain in the grounded-base configuration is 0.707 times the value it has at low frequency (usually measured at 1000 Hz). For example, if a base current of 2 mA causes a collector current of 100 mA, then the emitter current is 102 mA, and the grounded-base current gain (collector current divided by emitter current) is 0.98. At the alpha cutoff frequency, the current gain would be 0.707 × 0.98, or 0.693.

Gain-bandwidth product, or f_T, is a more useful figure of merit. It is the frequency at which the beta of the device drops at 1 (or zero dB gain). As the frequency of operation approaches f_T, the usefulness of the transistor becomes less and less. The gain is roughly inversely proportional to the frequency. For example, if the frequency being amplified is half of the f_T, the gain is about 2; if a 10th the f_T, the gain is ten. (The gain will never exceed the dc beta, however.) To be useful, transistors are usually selected so that the f_T is many times higher than the frequency of operation.

Field-Effect Transistors

Field-effect transistors (FET) exhibit considerably higher input impedance than do bipolar transistors and thus behave more like vacuum tubes. There are two basic types of FET, the *junction FET* (JFET) and the *metal-oxide semiconductor FET* (MOSFET), sometimes called an *insulated-gate FET* (IGFET). The construction of typical JFET and MOSFET devices is given in Fig. 24. As you can see, two of the terminals, the source and the drain, are connected to the same layer of semiconductor material.

JFET operation is diagramed in Fig. 25. Under no-bias conditions, electrons can flow freely from the source terminal through the FET to the drain terminal. When the bias voltage (which can be modulated by the signal) is applied to the gate terminals, a depletion region is formed which reduces the area through which source-to-drain current can flow. This is, in effect, an increase in the internal resistance. The result is that large changes in source-to-drain current can be achieved by making small changes in the gate voltage. The measure of gain in an FET is the same parameter used with vacuum tubes — *transconductance*. It is the change in output drain current divided by the corresponding change in input gate voltage.

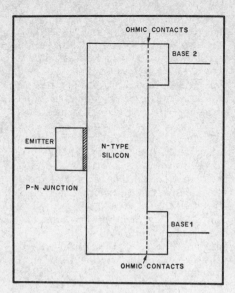

Fig. 26 — Unijunction transistor.

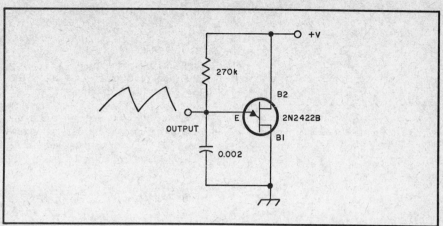

Fig. 27 — A relaxation oscillator based on a unijunction transistor. The frequency of oscillation is approximately 1500 Hz.

The MOSFET also operates on the principle of constricting the source-to-drain current channel by the application of a voltage across the gate and substrate terminals. The gate, however, is insulated from the source-drain channel by a thin dielectric layer. Since there is very little current flow through this dielectric, the input impedance is very high (in the megohm range) and approximates the grid circuit of a vacuum tube.

Unijunction Transistors

Another three-terminal semiconductor device is the *unijunction transistor* (UJT), sometimes called a *double-base diode*. The elements of a UJT are base 1, base 2 and emitter. The single rectifying junction is between the emitter and the silicon substrate. The base terminals are ohmic contacts; the current is a linear function of the applied voltage. Current flowing between the bases sets up a voltage gradient along the substrate. In operation, the direction of flow causes the emitter junction to be reverse biased. The relaxation oscillator circuit (the most common UJT application) of Fig. 27 illustrates the function of the UJT. When the circuit is energized, the capacitor charges through the resistor until the emitter voltage overcomes the reverse bias. As soon as current flows in the emitter, the resistance of the base 1 region decreases dramatically, discharging the capacitor. The decreased base 1 resistance alters the voltage distribution along the substrate, establishing a new bias point for the emitter junction. As more and more emitter current flows, the majority carrier injection builds a space charge in the base 1 region, which causes the emitter current to cease. Current is again available to charge the capacitor and the cycle repeats. If the resistor were replaced by a constant-current source, the output waveform would be a linear ramp instead of a sawtooth. The UJT schematic symbol resembles that of an n-channel JFET — the angled emitter distinguishes the unijunction transistor.

Practical Circuits

Voltage Stabilization Circuits

In a previous section we dealt with some of the circuit components that can be used to regulate voltages and currents. In this section we are going to learn a little more about the actual circuits using these components.

Gaseous Regulator Tubes

There is frequent need for maintaining the voltage applied to a low-voltage low-current circuit at a practically constant value, regardless of the voltage regulation of the power supply or variations in load current. In such applications, gaseous regulator tubes (0B2/VR105, 0A2/VR150, etc.) can be used to good advantage. The voltage drop across such tubes is constant over a moderately wide current range. Tubes are available for regulated voltages near 150, 105, 90 and 75 volts.

A typical VR tube circuit is shown in Fig. 28. Let's see how the tube operates. Suppose that the load wants 150 volts, regulated, at a current of 25 mA, and that the unregulated dc input voltage is 250

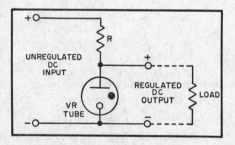

Fig. 28 — Voltage-regulator tube circuit for maintaining a constant output voltage.

volts. Allowing 5 mA (the minimum current for stable operation) for the current through the 150-volt VR tube, the total current through the resistor is 5 + 25 = 30 mA. The resistor must drop 250 volts to 150 volts; that is, the drop in R must be 100 volts. Using Ohm's Law, the resistance is

$$\frac{100}{0.03} \qquad \text{(Eq. 20)}$$

which is approximately 3300 ohms.

Now if the input voltage rises to, say, 300 volts, the drop of R must increase to 300 − 150 = 150 volts to keep the output voltage constant at 150 volts. The current through R must then be

$$\frac{150}{3300} = 45 \text{ mA} \qquad \text{(Eq. 21)}$$

The load is still drawing 25 mA, since the voltage across it hasn't changed, so the additional current, 45 − 25 or 20 mA, must flow through the VR tube. In other words, the VR tube regulates the voltage by drawing more current when the input voltage tends to rise and by drawing less when it tends to decrease.

There are two points to remember when using a VR tube. The *maximum current* through a VR tube should not be allowed to exceed the tube rating. Also, the unregulated input voltage must always be higher than the *striking voltage* — that is, the voltage required to ionize or "break down" the special gas in the tube. After breakdown, the *maintaining voltage* (the voltage at which the tube regulates) keeps

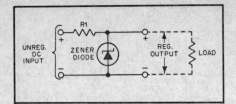

Fig. 29 — Voltage-regulator circuit using a Zener diode. Principle of operation is similar to that of the VR tube circuit of Fig. 28.

the gas ionized. The striking voltage is usually about 25 percent higher than the maintaining voltage.

Zener Diode Regulation

A Zener diode can be used to stabilize a voltage source in much the same way as when the gaseous regulator tube is used. A basic circuit is shown in Fig. 29. Note that the cathode side of the diode is connected to the positive side of the supply.

Zener diodes are available in a wide variety of voltages and power ratings. The voltages range from less than two to a few hundred, while the power ratings (power the diode can dissipate) run from less than 0.25 watt to 50 watts. The ability of the Zener diode to stabilize a voltage is dependent upon the conducting impedance of the diode, which can be as low as one ohm or less in a low-voltage, high-power diode to as high as a thousand ohms in a low-power, high-voltage diode.

Diode Power Dissipation

Unlike gaseous regulator tubes, Zener diodes of a particular voltage rating have varied maximum current capabilities, depending upon the power ratings of each of the diodes. The power dissipated in a diode is the product of the voltage across it and the current through it. Conversely, the maximum current a particular diode may safely conduct equals its power rating divided by its voltage rating. Thus, a 10-V, 50-W Zener diode, if operated at its maximum dissipating rating, would conduct 5 amperes of current. A 10-V, 1-W diode, on the other hand, could safely conduct no more than 0.1A, or 100 mA. The conducting impedance of a diode is its voltage rating divided by the current flowing through it, and in the above examples would be 2 ohms for the 50-W diode, and 100 ohms for the 1-W diode. Disregarding small voltage changes which may occur, the conducting impedance of a given diode is a function of the current flowing through it, varying in inverse proportion.

The power-handling capability of most Zener diodes is rated at 25° C, or approximately room temperature. If the diode is operated in a higher ambient temperature, its power capability must be derated. A

typical 1-watt diode can safely dissipate only 1/2 watt at 100° C.

Limiting Resistance

The value of R1 in Fig. 29 is determined by the load requirements. If R1 is too large the diode will be unable to regulate at large values of I_L, the current through the load. If R1 is too small, the diode dissipation rating may be exceeded at low values of I_L. The optimum value for R1 can be calculated by

$$R1 = \frac{E_{DC(min)} - E_Z}{1.1\, I_{L(max)}} \qquad \text{(Eq. 20)}$$

When R1 is known, the maximum dissipation of the diode, P_D, may be determined by

$$P_D = \left[\frac{E_{DC(max)} - E_Z}{R1} - I_{L(min)} \right] E_Z$$

$$\text{(Eq. 21)}$$

In the first equation, conditions are set up for the Zener diode to draw 1/10 the maximum load current. This ensures diode regulation under maximum load.

Example: A 12-volt source is to supply a circuit requiring 9 volts. The load current varies between 200 and 350 mA.

E_Z = 9.1 V (nearest available value)

$$R1 = \frac{12 - 9.1}{1.1 \times 0.35} = \frac{2.9}{0.385}$$

$$= 7.5 \text{ ohms}$$

$$P_D = \left[\frac{12 - 9.1}{7.5} - 0.2 \right] 9.1$$

$$= 0.185 \times 9.1 = 1.7\,\text{W} \qquad \text{(Eq. 22)}$$

The nearest available dissipation rating above 1.7 W is 5; therefore, a 9.1-V, 5-W Zener diode should be used. Such a rating, it may be noted, will cause the diode to be in the safe dissipation range even though the load is completely disconnected [I_L (min) = 0].

Electronic Voltage Regulation

Several circuits have been developed for electronically regulating the voltage output of a power supply. While more complicated than the VR-tube and Zener-diode circuits, they will handle higher voltage and current variations, and the output voltage may be varied continuously over a wide range.

Voltage regulators fall into two basic types. In the type most commonly used by amateurs, the dc supply delivers a voltage higher than that which is available at the output of the regulator, and the regulated voltage is obtained by dropping the voltage down to a lower value through a dropping "resistor." Regulation is accomplished by varying either the current

through a fixed dropping resistance as changes in input voltage or load currents occur (as in the VR-tube and Zener-diode regulator circuits), or by varying the equivalent resistive value of the dropping element with such changes. This latter technique is used in electronic regulators where the voltage-dropping element is a vacuum tube or a transistor, rather than an actual resistor. By varying the dc voltage at the grid or current at the base of these elements, the conductivity of the device may be varied as necessary to hold the output voltage constant. In solid-state regulators the series-dropping element is called a *pass transistor*. Power transistors are available which will handle several amperes of current at several hundred volts, but solid-state regulators of this type are usually operated at potentials below 100 volts.

The second type of regulator is a switching type, where the voltage from the dc source is rapidly switched on and off (electronically). The average dc voltage available from the regulator is proportional to the duty cycle of the switching wave form, or the ratio of the on time to the total period of the switching cycle. Switching frequencies of several kilohertz are normally used to avoid the need for extensive filtering to smooth the switching frequency from the dc output.

Discrete Component Regulators

The previous section outlines some of the limitations when using Zener diodes as regulators. Greater current amounts can be accommodated if the Zener diode is used as a reference at low current, permitting the bulk of the load current to flow through a series pass transistor (Q1 of Fig. 30). An added benefit in using a pass transistor is that of reduced ripple on the output waveform. This technique is commonly referred to as "electronic filtering."

Q1 of Fig. 30 can be thought of as a simple emitter-follower dc amplifier. It increases the load resistance seen by the Zener diode by a factor of beta (β). In this circuit arrangement D1 is required to supply only the base current for Q1. The net result is that the load regulation and ripple characteristics are improved by a factor of beta. Addition of C2 reduces the ripple even more, although many simple supplies such as this do not make use of a capacitor in that part of the circuit.

The primary limitation of this circuit is that Q1 can be destroyed almost immediately if a severe overload occurs at R_L. The fuse cannot blow fast enough to protect Q1. In order to protect Q1 in case of an accidental short at the output, a current limiting circuit is required. An example of a suitable circuit is shown in Fig. 31.

It should be mentioned that the greater the value of transformer secondary voltage, the higher the power dissipation in Q1. This not only reduces the overall efficiency of the power supply, but re-

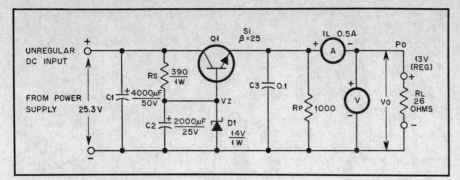

Fig. 30 — Illustration of a power supply regulator. A pass transistor, Q1, is used to extend the range of the Zener diode.

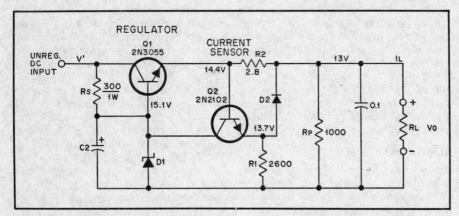

Fig. 31 — Overload protection for a regulated supply can be effected by addition of a current-overload protective circuit.

quires stringent heat sinking at Q1.

Design Example

To calculate the value of R_S in Fig. 30, the base current of Q1 must be known. The base current is approximately equal to the emitter current of Q1 in amperes divided by beta. The transistor beta can be found in the manufacturer's data sheet, or measured with simple test equipment (beta = I_c/I_b). Since the beta spread for a particular type of transistor — 2N3055 for example, where it is specified as 25 to 70 — is a fairly unknown quantity, more precise calculations for Fig. 30 will result if the transistor beta is tested before the calculations are done. A conservative approach is to design for beta minimum of the transistor used. Calculating I_b

$$I_b = \frac{0.5}{25} = 0.02A = 20 \text{ mA} \quad \text{(Eq. 23)}$$

As pointed out earlier, for D1 to regulate properly it is necessary that a fair portion of the current flowing through R_S should be drawn by D1. The resistor will have 0.02 A flowing through it as calculated above (base current of Q1). A conservative amount of 10 mA will be used for the Zener diode current, bringing the total current through R_S to 0.03 A or

30 mA. From this, the value of R_S can be calculated as follows

$$R_S = \frac{(V' - V_Z)}{I_{R_S}} = \frac{(25.3 - 14)}{0.03}$$

$$= 376 \text{ ohms} \quad \text{(Eq. 24)}$$

The nearest standard ohmic value for R_s is 390. The wattage ratings for R_s and D1 can be obtained with the aid of the formulas given earlier for Zener-diode regulators.

The power rating for Q1 will be calculated next. The power dissipating of Q1 is equal to the emitter current times the collector-to-emitter voltage. Calculate as follows:

$$P_{Q1} = I_E \times V_{CE} \quad \text{(Eq. 25)}$$

where

V_{CE} = the desired $V' - (V_Z - V_{BE})$, and V_{BE} is approximately 0.7 V for a silicon transistor.
Therefore:

$$P_{Q1} = 0.5 \text{ A} \times 12 \text{ V} = 6 \text{ watts}$$

It is a good idea to choose a transistor for Q1 that has at least twice the rating calculated. In this example a transistor

with a power dissipation rating 12 watts or more would be used.

Current Limiting for Discrete-Component Regulators

Damage to Q1 of Fig. 30 can occur when the load current exceeds the safe amount. Fig. 31 illustrates a simple current-limiter circuit that will protect Q1. All of the load current is routed through R2. A voltage difference will exist across R2, the amount being dependent upon the exact load current at a given time. When the load current exceeds a predetermined safe value, the voltage drop across R2 will forward bias Q2 and cause it to conduct. Since D2 is a silicon diode, and because Q2 is a silicon transistor, the combined voltage drops through them (roughly 0.7 V each) will be 1.4 V. Therefore, the voltage drop across R2 must exceed 1.4 V before Q2 can turn on. This being the case, R2 is chosen for a value that provides a drop of 1.4 V when the maximum safe load current is drawn. In this instance 1.4 volts will be seen when I_L reaches 0.5 A.

When Q2 turns on, some of the current through R_S flows through Q2, thereby depriving Q1 of some of its base current. This action, depending upon the amount of Q1 base current at a precise moment, cuts off Q1 conduction to some degree, thus limiting the flow of current through it.

Fixed-Voltage IC Regulators

The modern trend in regulators is toward the use of three-terminal devices commonly referred to as three-terminal regulators. Inside each regulator is a reference, a high-gain error amplifier, sensing resistors and transistors, and a pass element. Some of the more sophisticated units have thermal shutdown, overvoltage protection and current foldback. Many of the regulators currently on the market are virtually destruction-proof.

Three-terminal regulators (a connection for unregulated dc input, regulated dc output and ground) are available in a wide range of voltage and current ratings. Fairchild, National and Motorola are perhaps the three largest suppliers of these regulators at present. It is easy to see why regulators of this sort are so popular when one considers the low price and the number of individual components they can replace. The regulators are available in several different package styles — TO-3, TO-39, TO-66, TO-220 and dual in-line (DIP), to name just a few.

Three-terminal regulators are available as positive or negative types. In most cases, a positive regulator is used to regulate a positive voltage and a negative regulator a negative voltage. However, depending on the systems ground requirements, each regulator type may be used to regulate the "opposite" voltage.

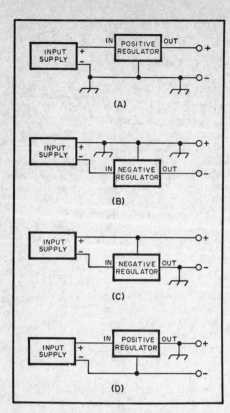

Fig. 32 — A and B illustrate the conventional manner in which three-terminal regulators are used. C and D show how one polarity regulator can be used to regulate the opposite polarity voltage.

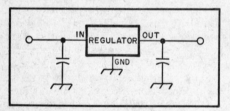

Fig. 33 — Three-terminal regulators require careful bypassing directly at the case. Here, both the input and output leads are bypassed.

Figs. 32A and B illustrate how the regulators are used in the conventional mode. Several regulators can be used with a common-input supply to deliver several voltages with a common ground. Negative regulators may be used in the same manner. If no other common supplies operate off the input supply to the regulator, the circuits of Figs. 32C and D may be used to regulate positive voltages with a negative regulator and vice versa. In these configurations the input supply is floated; neither side of the input is tied to the system ground.

When choosing a three-terminal regulator for a given application the important specifications to look for are maximum output current, maximum output voltage, minimum and maximum in-

put voltage, line regulation, load regulation and power dissipation.

In use, these regulators require an adequate heat sink since they may be called on to dissipate a fair amount of power. Also, since the chip contains a high-gain error amplifier, bypassing of the input and output leads is essential to stable operation (see Fig. 33). Most manufacturers recommend bypassing the input and output directly at the leads where they protrude through the heat sink. Tantalum capacitors are usually recommended because of their excellent bypass capabilities up into the vhf range.

Adjustable-Voltage IC Regulators

Relatively new on the electronic scene are high-current, adjustable voltage regulators. These ICs require little more than an external potentiometer for an adjustable voltage range from 5 to 24 volts at up to 5 amperes. The same precautions should be taken with these types of regulators as with the fixed-voltage units. Proper heat sinking and lead bypassing is essential for proper circuit operation.

Modulation Circuits

Modulation is really a mixing process; any mixer or converter circuit could be used for generating a phone signal. Instead of introducing two *radio* frequencies into a mixer circuit we simply introduce one radio frequency (the carrier frequency) and the voice band of audio frequencies.

Mixer circuits used in receivers are designed to handle a small signal and a large local-oscillator voltage. This means that the percentage of modulation is low. In a transmitter we want to get as close as possible to 100-percent modulation, and we also want more power output. For these reasons modulator circuits differ in detail from receiving mixers, although much the same in principle.

The Filter Method

To have an ssb signal, we must remove the carrier and one of the sidebands from an ordinary a-m signal. The block diagram shown in Fig. 34 shows how it is done. The rf oscillator generates a carrier wave which is injected into the balanced

modulator. Audio information, after it is amplified by the speech amplifier, is also applied to the modulator. It is the job of the balanced modulator to take these two inputs and supply as its output both sidebands minus the carrier. This meets the first requirement for the generation of an ssb signal — removal of the carrier.

Let's see how the balanced modulator accomplished this. There are many different types of balanced modulators and it would be impossible to show them all here. One of the more popular types is illustrated in Fig. 35. This particular circuit is called a diode-ring balanced modulator. Audio information is coupled into the circuit through transformer T1. The carrier is injected through coils L5-L6 and the double sideband suppressed-carrier output is taken through L3-L4. To better understand the circuit operation, let's first analyze the circuit with only the carrier applied. The polarity of voltage shown across L5 will cause current to flow in the direction indicated by the arrows. CR1 and CR4 will conduct. The current that flows through each half of L3 is equal and opposite causing a cancelling effect. Output at L4 will be zero. During the next half cycle, the polarity of voltage across L5 will reverse, CR2 and CR3 will conduct, and again the output at L4 will be zero.

Now for a moment, let's remove the carrier signal and connect an audio source to the terminals marked audio. During one half of the audio cycle CR2 and CR4 will conduct and the output will be zero. On the other half cycle of the audio signal, CR1 and CR3 will conduct and again the output at L4 will be zero. We can see that if either the carrier or the audio is applied without the other, there will be no output.

Both signals must be applied if the circuit is to work as intended. In practice, the carrier level is made much larger than the audio input. Conduction of the diodes is, therefore, determined by the carrier. There are basically four conditions that can exist as far as the polarity of voltage of the carrier and audio signals are concerned. We must keep in mind that the carrier is going through many, many cycles while the audio sine wave goes

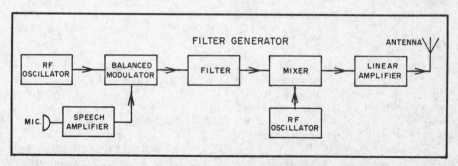

Fig. 34 — A basic system for generating a single-sideband suppressed carrier signal.

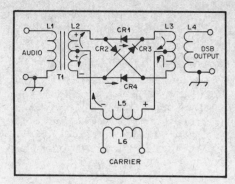

Fig. 35 — A diode-ring balanced modulator. Arrows indicate the direction of current flow with only the carrier applied and with the polarity shown across L5.

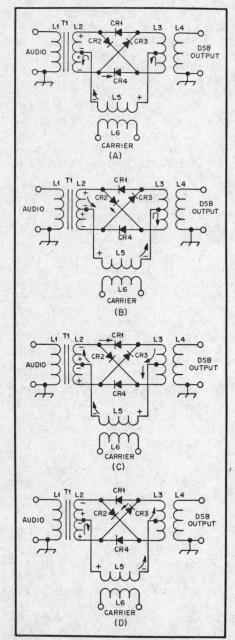

Fig. 36 — Shown here are the four possibilities of polarities of voltages of the modulating source and carrier. Arrows indicate the direction of maximum current flow.

through only one. Let's look at the drawing at Fig. 36. With the polarities indicated, the major current flow will be through CR4 since the audio and carrier voltages are aiding (adding together) in this path. Since the balance through L3 has been upset (the bottom half of L3 has more current flowing through it than does the top half), there will be an output present at L4. At B, the polarity of the carrier has reversed while the audio polarity has remained the same. This is the order in which the polarities would change since the carrier is reversing polarity at a much quicker rate than the audio signal. At C, the carrier polarity is back to what it was at A; however, now the audio is on the negative portion of its sine wave and so its polarity is reversed. Maximum current flow under these conditions is through CR1 and again an output signal appears at L4. The fourth condition that will exist is shown at D. The audio signal polarity is the same as in C, but the carrier is reversed. This time, diode CR3 will be the main path for current flow. As you have probably guessed, there is output at L4 under these conditions.

Fig. 37 shows a composite drawing of the audio and carrier waveforms. The shaded-in areas represent the double sideband suppressed-carrier output from the balanced modulator.

Another type of balanced modulator is shown in Fig. 38. Two balancing controls are provided so that the circuit can be adjusted for optimum carrier suppression (50 dB is a practical amount). The principle of operation in this circuit is the same as that of the one we previously discussed. With either the audio or carrier applied separately, the circuit is balanced and there will be no output. With both the audio and carrier applied, the balance is upset and output will be present at T1. We

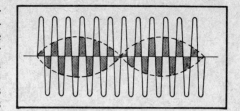

Fig. 37 — Superimposed audio and rf waveform. The shaded-in area represents the double-sideband suppressed-carrier output from the balanced modulator.

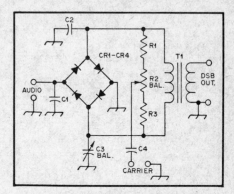

Fig. 38 — Here is another common form of balanced modulator. C3 and R2 are adjusted for maximum carrier suppression.

won't go into the detail that we did in the previous circuit. The reader can determine which diodes are conducting for the different polarities of voltage presented by the audio and carrier signals.

The two circuits that we have just examined can be classified as passive balanced modulators. That is, they do not provide gain (amplify) but actually cause a small amount of signal loss (insertion loss). Balanced modulators can be built using active devices. One such modulator is shown in Fig. 39. This circuit makes use

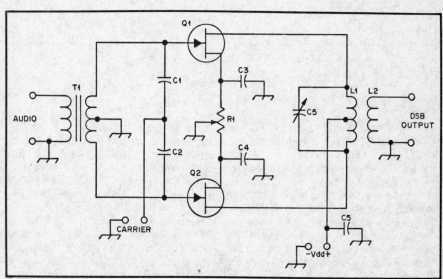

Fig. 39 — This circuit is an active balanced modulator using two FET devices. R1 is adjusted for maximum carrier suppression and C5 is adjusted for maximum double-sideband output.

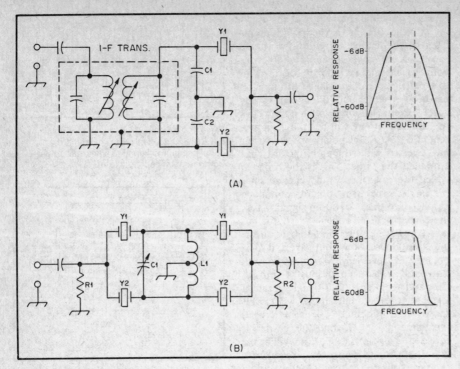

Fig. 40 — A half-lattice band-pass filter at A; B shows two half-lattice filters in cascade.

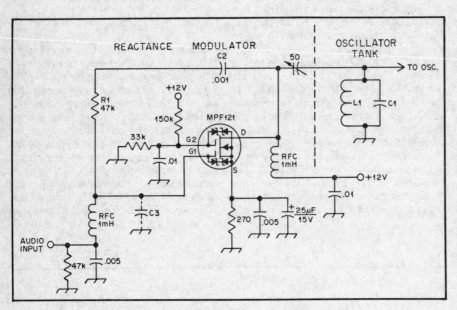

Fig. 41 — Reactance modulator using a high-transconductance MOSFET.

Sum and difference frequencies are developed at the output (double-sideband suppressed carrier).

Removing the Unwanted Sideband

We now have a signal that contains both the upper and lower sidebands of what was an a-m signal. The next step in generating our ssb signal is to remove one of the sidebands. Looking back at Fig. 34, we see that the next stage after the balanced modulator is the *filter*. This circuit does just as its name suggests — it filters out one of the sidebands.

An example of a simple *crystal filter* is shown in Fig. 40. The two crystals would be separated by approximately 2 kHz to provide a bandwidth suitable for passing one sideband and not the other. More elaborate filters using four and six crystals will give reduced bandwidths farther down the slopes of the response without affecting the bandwidth near the top of the response. The curves to the right of the filters show this. As we can see, the filter with more crystals has a narrower response at the −60 dB point. The filter at B has better "skirt selectivity" than that at A. Two half-lattice filters of the type shown at A are connected back to back to form the filter at B. Crystal-lattice filters of this type are available commercially for frequencies up to 40 MHz or so.

Amplification for the Modulator

The last stage shown in the block diagram in Fig. 34 is the linear amplifier. Since the modulation process occurs at low power levels in a conventional transmitter, it is necessary that all of the amplifiers following the balanced modulator be linear. At the low-power level stages of the transmitter, high voltage gain and maximum linearity are quite a bit more important than efficiency. Class A amplifiers are normally used. At the higher power levels it would be nice to be able to use Class C amplifiers for improved efficiency. The distortion level, unfortunately, is rather high. Distortion is in the form of odd-order intermodulation products that are close to the desired frequency and cannot be filtered out by the resonant tank circuit. This results in an increase of transmitted signal bandwidth either side of the normal signal. Since linearity is very important, high power amplifiers are normally run Class AB or B.

Generating an FM Signal

Most methods of producing fm will fall into two general categories. They are *direct fm and indirect fm*. As you might expect, each has its advantages and disadvantages. Let's look at the direct-fm method first.

Direct FM

A simple and satisfactory device for producing fm in the amateur transmitter is

of two FETs as the active devices. As was true with the two other modulators, the circuit is in a balanced condition if either the audio or carrier are applied separately. In this circuit the tuned output network (C5/L1) is adjusted for resonance at the rf (carrier) frequency. At audio this circuit represents a very low impedance allowing no audio to appear at the output. Consider the carrier input for a moment. Injection voltage is supplied to each gate in a parallel fashion. Since the input to each gate is of equal amplitude and of the same phase and the output circuit is connected

for push-pull operation, the currents flowing through each half of the tank are equal and opposite. The signals will effectively cancel and the output will be zero.

Let's analyze the circuit with both the audio and carrier energy applied. Since we have a push-pull input arrangement for the audio information, the bias for the FETs varies at an audio rate. The audio signal applied to one gate is 180 degrees out of phase with the other. While one of the devices is forward biased, the other is reverse biased. The input to each device is the audio signal plus the carrier signal.

the reactance modulator. This is a vacuum tube or transistor connected to the rf tank circuit of an oscillator in such a way as to act as a variable inductance or capacitance.

Fig. 41 is a representative circuit. Gate 1 of the modulator MOSFET is connected across the oscillator tank circuit, C1L1, through resistor R1 and blocking capacitor C2. C3 represents the input capacitance of the modulator transistor. The resistance of R1 is made large compared to the reactance of C3, so the rf current through R1C3 will be practically in phase with the rf voltage appearing at the terminals of the tank circuit. However, the voltage across C3 will lag the current by 90 degrees. The rf current in the drain circuit of the modulator will be in phase with the gate voltage, and consequently is 90 degrees behind the current through C3, or 90 degrees behind the rf tank circuit. This lagging current is drawn through the oscillator tank, giving the same effect as though an inductance were connected across the tank. The frequency increases in proportion to the amplitude of the lagging plate current of the modulator. The audio voltage, introduced through a radio-frequency-choke, varies the transconductance of the transistor and thereby varies the rf drain current.

The modulated oscillator usually is operated on a relatively low frequency, so that a high order of carrier stability can be secured. Frequency multipliers are used to raise the frequency to the final frequency desired.

A reactance modulator can be connected to a crystal oscillator as well as to the self-controlled type as shown in Fig. 42. However, the resulting signal will be more phase-modulated than it is frequency-modulated, since the frequency deviation that can be secured by varying the frequency of a crystal oscillator is quite small.

The sensitivity of the modulator (frequency change per unit change in grid voltage) depends on the transconductance of the modulator transistor. It increases when R1 is made smaller in comparison with C3. It also increases with an increase in L/C ratio in the oscillator tank circuit. However, for highest carrier stability it is desirable to use the largest tank capacitance that will permit the desired deviation to be secured while keeping within the limits of linear operation.

A change in *any* of the voltages on the modulator transistor will cause a change in rf drain current, and consequently a frequency change. Therefore, it is advisable to use a regulated power supply for both modulator and oscillator.

The circuit shown in Fig. 43 consists of a reactance modulator which shifts the frequency of an oscillator to generate an fm signal directly. Successive multiplier stages provide output on the desired frequency, which is amplified by a PA stage.

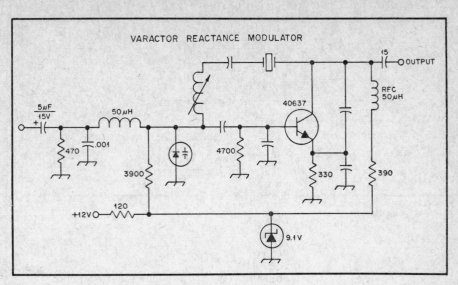

Fig. 42 — Reactance modulator using a varactor diode.

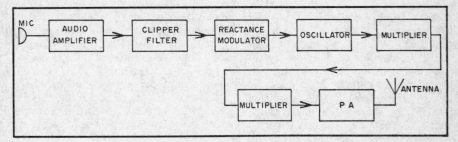

Fig. 43 — Block diagram of a direct-fm transmitter.

This system has a disadvantage in that, if the oscillator is free running, it is difficult to achieve sufficient stability for vhf use. If a crystal-controlled oscillator is employed, unless the amount that the crystal frequency is changed is kept small, it is difficult to achieve equal amounts of frequency swing.

Indirect FM

The same type of reactance-tube circuit that is used to vary the tuning of the oscillator tank in fm can be used to vary the tuning of an amplifier tank and thus vary the phase of the tank current for pm. Hence, the modulator circuit of Fig. 41 or 44 can be used for pm if the reactance transistor or tube works on an amplifier tank instead of directly on a self-controlled oscillator. If audio shaping is used in the speech amplifier, as described above, fm instead of pm will be generated by the phase modulator.

The phase shift that occurs when a circuit is detuned from resonance depends on the amount of detuning and the Q of the circuit. The higher the Q, the smaller the amount of detuning needed to secure a given number of degrees of phase shift. If the Q is at least 10, the relationship between phase shift and detuning (in kHz either side of the resonant frequency) will

be substantially linear over a phase-shift range of about 25 degrees. From the standpoint of modulator sensitivity, the Q of the tuned circuit on which the modulator operates should be as high as possible. On the other hand, the effective Q of the circuit will not be very high if the amplifier is delivering power to a load since the load resistance reduces the Q. There must, therefore, be a compromise between modulator sensitivity and rf power output from the modulated amplifier. An optimum figure for Q appears to

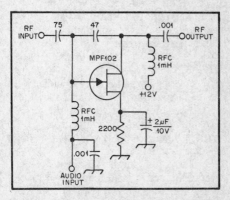

Fig. 44 — Phase modulator using an MPF 102 JFET.

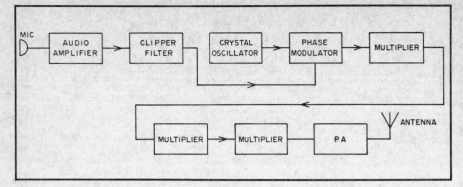

Fig. 46 — Block diagram of an indirect-fm transmitter.

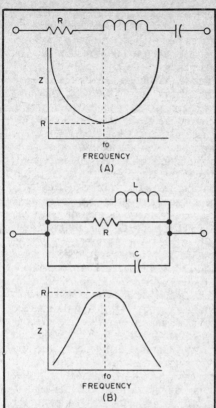

Fig. 47 — Impedance of a series-resonant circuit (A) is minimum at resonance while the impedance of a parallel-resonant circuit (B) is maximum at resonance.

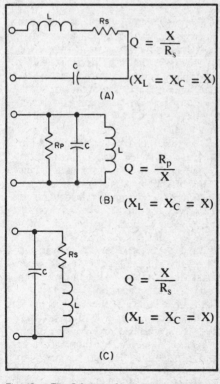

Fig. 48 — The Q-factor of a tuned circuit is a measure of how much it is affected by resistance. The higher the Q, the sharper the selectivity (i.e., the narrower the bandwidth). X is the reactance of either the coil or capacitor at resonance, Rs is the series resistance, and Rp is the parallel resistance.

be about 20; this allows reasonable loading of the modulated amplifier and the necessary tuning variation can be secured from a reactance modulator without difficulty. It is advisable to modulate at a low power level.

Reactance modulation of an amplifier stage usually results in simultaneous amplitude modulation because the modulated stage is detuned from resonance as the phase is shifted. This must be eliminated by feeding the modulated signal through an amplitude limiter or one or more "saturating" stages; that is, amplifiers that are operated Class C and driven hard enough so that variations in the amplitude of the input excitation produce no appreciable variations in the output amplitude.

For the same type of reactance modulator, the speech-amplifier gain required is the same for pm as for fm. However, as pointed out earlier, the fact that the actual frequency deviation increases with the modulating audio frequency in pm makes it necessary to cut off the frequencies above about 3000 Hz before modulation takes place. If this is not done, unnecessary sidebands will be generated at frequencies considerably away from the carrier.

The indirect method of generating fm shown in Fig. 46 is currently popular. Shaped audio is applied to a phase modulator to generate fm. As the amount of deviation produced is very small, a large number of multiplier stages is necessary to achieve wide-band deviation at the operating frequency.

Resonant Circuits

In a series-*resonant* circuit, inductive and capacitive reactances cancel so that total impedance is just equal to the series resistance of the circuit. Impedance of a series-resonant circuit is *minimum* at the resonant frequency.

Similarly, in a parallel-resonant circuit, inverse inductive and capacitive reactances are equal ($B_C = B_L$) so that the total inverse reactance (susceptance) is zero ($B_t = B_C - B_L = 0$). Total admit-

tance is just the inverse resistance (conductance)

$$Y = \sqrt{0 + G^2} \qquad \text{(Eq. 26)}$$

so that the impedance is equal to the total resistance in parallel with the tuned circuit ($Z = 1/Y = 1/G = R$). Total impedance of a parallel-resonant circuit is *maximum* at the resonant frequency.

Since in either a series- or parallel-resonant circuit resonance occurs when the capacitive and inductive reactances are equal, the following relationship holds.

$$X_L = 2\pi fL = X_C = \frac{1}{2\pi fC}$$

$$1 = \frac{1}{(2\pi fL)(2\pi fC)}$$

$$f^2 = \frac{1}{(2\pi)^2 LC}$$

$$f = \frac{1}{2\pi \sqrt{LC}} \qquad \text{(Eq. 27)}$$

Note that since inductive and capacitive reactance (or inverse reactance) change in opposite directions as the frequency is changed, there will be only *one* frequency at which a coil and capacitor will have the same reactance. In other words, a tuned circuit is resonant on only one frequency.

The more a resonant circuit is affected by resistance, the higher its Q factor. A series-resonant circuit with zero series resistance or a parallel-resonant circuit with infinite parallel resistance (zero resistive admittance) has infinite Q. More exactly, in a *series*-resonant circuit:

$$Q = \frac{X}{R_s} \qquad \text{(Eq. 28)}$$

and in a parallel-resonant circuit:

$$Q = \frac{R_p}{X} \qquad \text{(Eq. 29)}$$

where

X = the reactance at resonance of either the coil or capacitor
R_s = the series resistance
R_p = the parallel resistance
Thus the Q-factor of a tuned circuit is a

measure of how much it is affected by resistance (Fig. 48A and B).

Just to complicate matters a little, we should also point out that in a *parallel-resonant* circuit, resistance in series with either the coil or capacitor can also lower the Q (Fig. 48). The *unloaded* Q of a resonant circuit is its Q when it is not connected to anything and is determined by the series resistance of the inductor. (Usually the capacitor's series resistance is negligible.) The *loaded* Q is the Q of a tuned circuit when it is loaded down by the resistance of the circuit in which it is used.

It is often convenient to speak of the unloaded Q of a coil even when it is not being used in a tuned circuit. The formula is $Q = X_L/R_S$ where X_L is the reactance of the coil and R_S is its series resistance. Since inductive reactance is proportional to frequency ($X_L = 2\pi fL$), the Q of a coil also increases proportional to frequency. This assumes that the series resistance is the same at all frequencies. Actually, however, at high frequencies, the series resistance increases due to skin effect and losses in the core material (if any). At very high frequencies, the resistive losses increase faster than the coil reactance and the Q begins to decrease with increasing frequency (see Fig. 49).

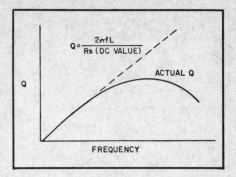

Fig. 49 — For low frequencies, the Q of an inductor is proportional to frequency. At high frequencies, increased losses in the coil cause the Q to decrease.

Low- and High-Pass Filters

The function of a *filter* is to transmit a desired band of frequencies without attenuation and to suppress all other frequencies. The resonant circuits discussed in previous sections all do this. However, the term "filter" is frequently reserved for those networks that transmit a desired band with little variation in output, and in which the transition from the "pass" band to the "stop" band is more rapid than is the case with simple resonant circuits.

The term *attenuation* refers to the ratio of the voltage applied to the filter's input terminals to the voltage that appears across its output terminals. Attenuation is usually expressed in decibels, which measure a power ratio rather than a voltage ratio.

Although the use of decibels may seem to imply that more real power enters the filter than reaches the *terminating resistance* connected to the output terminals — in other words, that the attenuated power is dissipated in the filter — this is not the case. The attenuation in decibels expresses the ratio of the power that would have been dissipated in the terminating resistance had the filter not been there, to the power that actually reaches the terminating resistance through the filter.

Classification of Filters

Filters are classified into three groups. A low-pass filter is one in which all frequencies below a specified frequency called the *cut-off frequency* are passed without attenuation. Above the cut-off frequency there is attenuation which changes with frequency in a way that is determined by the network design. A *high-pass* filter is just the opposite: in it there is no attenuation *above* the cut-off frequency, but attenuation does occur *below* cut-off.

The third type is the *band-pass* filter. In this type there are two cut-off frequencies, one at the upper-frequency edge of the

band to be transmitted and one at the lower edge. Frequencies on both sides of the pass band are attenuated. An overcoupled pair of resonant circuits, both independently tuned to the same frequency, is an example of a simple band-pass circuit, although its design differs from that of a filter made according to the general principles described in this section.

Pi and T Network Filter Sections

A *filter section* is either a π- or T-type network in which the series and shunt reactances are of opposite types, as in Fig. 50. Unlike the π and T networks described in the section on antenna couplers, these sections are not designed for transforming a given value of load resistance into a *different* value that will be suitable for the source of power. Instead, the design is such that the load resistance on the output side of the section will also be seen looking into the input side.

To do this the values of L and C in the section must be chosen so that the section itself will have a *characteristic* or *image impedance* (in the pass band) that equals the load resistance. When this is so, power is transferred from the source to the load without attenuation. Another consequence of the repetitive nature of the load and input impedances is that one loaded section may be used as the load for another; i.e., sections may be cascaded with no change in the input impedance shown to the source of power in the pass band.

The advantage in cascading filter sections is that in the *stop band* — the range of frequencies in which attenuation occurs — the attenuation increases with the number of filter sections while remaining zero in the pass band. If the attenuation of a section at a given frequency is expressed in decibels, each similar section that is added to a filter also adds the same number of decibels to the overall attenuation at the same frequency. The basis on which filters are designed is the *half sec-*

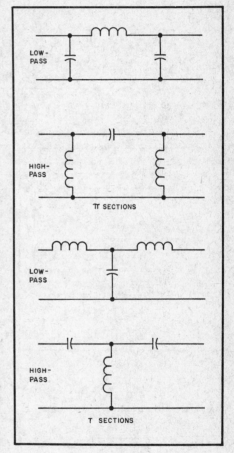

Fig. 50

tion, shown in Fig. 51. The inductance and capacitance, usually designated L_k and C_k, in the half section are related to a desired value of resistance, R, which is the termination or load for the output side of the filter.

Looking into the half section from the series end shows the beginning of a T section, and looking into it from the opposite side, the shunt end, shows the beginning of a π section. The full sections are

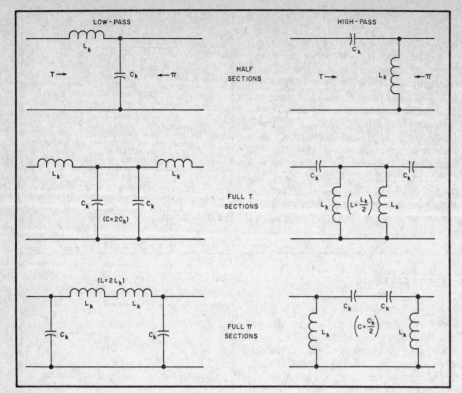

Fig. 51

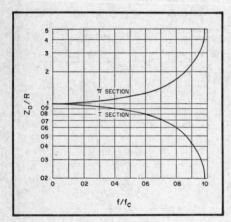

Fig. 52

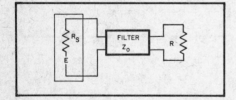

Fig. 53

formed by connecting two half sections together as shown in Fig. 51. When two reactances are in parallel, as in the shunt arm of the full T sections, they may be combined into a single physical element. Similarly, where two are in series they may be combined into a single element having a value equal to the two in series, as in the full π sections. However, series elements separated by a shunt arm cannot be combined, nor is any coupling between elements permitted, other than the combinations just mentioned.

Image Impedance

Unfortunately, the image impedance of a given filter section is not constant at all frequencies in the passband, nor are the image impedances alike for π and T sections using the same L_k and C_k. The terminating impedance R is therefore a "nominal" value. The variation in image impedance in the passband, expressed as a ratio of the image impedance, Z_o, to the nominal impedance, R, is shown in Fig. 52 as a function of the applied frequency, f, and the cut-off frequency, f_c.

In a practical circuit, Fig. 53, using a source of power having an internal resistance R_S, the terminating resistance will be chosen either to match R_S (for maximum available power) or to match some optimum value of load impedance for the source. Since the filter's image impedance, Z_o, does not match R perfectly in most of the passband, the impedance looking into the filter from the power source will not be either R or Z_o. The input impedance that results from the mismatch cannot be determined from R and Z_o alone, but can be found for any selected frequency by analyzing the actual circuit.

In any event, the mismatch loss is entirely between the source and the input im-

pedance of the filter. There is no loss of power in the filter itself. Since the filter contains only pure reactances any power that enters it is either delivered to the terminating resistance R or returned to the source. If there is an adjustable impedance-matching network between the power source and the filter the mismatch loss can be overcome. This is usually the case when the filter follows a transmitting power amplifier.

Attenuation in the Stop Band

In the stop band the impedances are deliberately mismatched to prevent transfer of power to the load. In this band the attenuation, with the type of filter section so far considered, increases progressively as the applied frequency is moved away from the cut-off frequency. Fig. 54 shows the theoretical attenuation of a single filter section, either π or T, high-pass or low-pass. The curves are based on the assumption that the load impedance equals the image impedance of the filter, a condition that cannot be fulfilled in practice because there is no way to construct a load whose impedance would vary in the ways shown in Fig. 52. However, the curve is reasonably accurate if the actual load is a resistance having the nominal value, R.

Note that the transition from the passband to the stop band is rather abrupt. With an actual filter section terminated in R there will be variations in attenuation in the stop band near the cut-off frequency, and the sharp transition will be smoothed off. At frequencies somewhat removed from cut-off the real curve becomes free from these variations and approaches the theoretical curve. Beyond about twice the cut-off frequency in the low-pass case, and about half the cut-off frequency in the high-pass case, the attenuation increases uniformly at 12 dB per octave. (An octave is equal to a frequency ratio of 2 to 1.)

Again there is no loss of power in the filter itself. The loss is a mismatch loss between the source of power and the input impedance of the filter; i.e., the filter simply refuses to accept power from the source.

Constant-K Filter Design

Filter sections of the type considered so far are known as constant-k sections. Constant-k filters are easily built up from the basic sections. The values of the components can be found by calculation or by using reactance charts. However, it is not necessary to know design equations for the examination.

The construction of a complete filter is shown in Fig. 55A and the final component arrangement is shown at B. Such a filter would be suitable for suppressing the harmonic output of a transmitter operating well below the cut-off frequency. The most important harmonic, the second, would be attenuated about 30 dB by the two sections, as shown in Fig. 54.

M-Derived Half Sections

When it is necessary to have additional attenuation at some particular frequency in the stop band, *m-derived* half sections or full sections can be used instead of the constant-k type. There are two general types of m-derived sections. In the *series m-derived* type additional reactance is introduced in series in the shunt arm to form a circuit that is series-resonant at the frequency to be suppressed. This short-circuits the output at that frequency and (theoretically) the attenuation is infinite. In the *shunt m-derived* type a series arm of the half section contains a circuit that is parallel-resonant at the frequency to be suppressed. As such a circuit has theoretically infinite impedance, the undesired frequency is prevented from reaching the output end of the filter.

The basic low- and high-pass m-derived sections are shown in Fig. 56. The π and T relationships are the same as for the constant-k half sections already discussed. Full sections, as well as multisection filters, can be formed by cascading sections as before. Also, m-derived and constant-k sections can be used in the same filter.

The *image impedance* of an m-derived section is not constant over the pass band. In this it resembles the constant-k section; in fact, the variation in image impedance of a series m-derived T section is exactly the same as that of a constant-k T section for all values of m, if L_k and C_k are the same in both cases. Thus series m-derived and constant-k T sections will match at all frequencies when connected together.

This identity of impedances is not true of series m-derived π sections. In these, depending on the value of m, the image impedance tends to stay closer to the nominal value, R, over much more of the passband. In the particular case where m = 0.6, the image impedance is essentially equal to R for all passband frequencies except those within about 10% of the cut-off frequency.

As explained earlier, if the half section is viewed in one direction it is the beginning of a T section, and viewed from the other direction it is the beginning of a π section. The T direction can be used for maintaining a match to other full T sections that may be used in the filter, and the benefits of the smaller variation in image impedance can be obtained if the half section is viewed from the π direction from *outside* the filter. This dictates that for the best overall match to an external resistance, R, the arrangements in Fig. 56 as viewed from the π directions should be used as *end* half sections and that the internal sections of the filter should be T sections.

Such a filter can be constructed as shown in Fig. 57. A low-pass circuit is

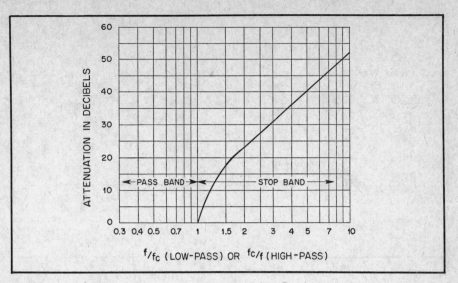

Fig. 54

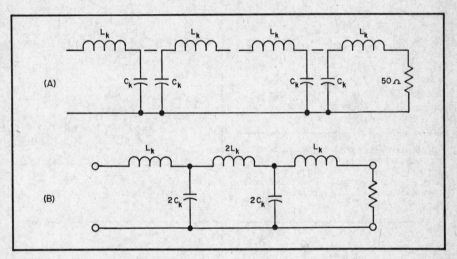

Fig. 55

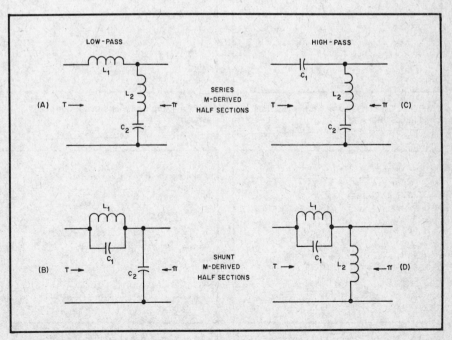

Fig. 56

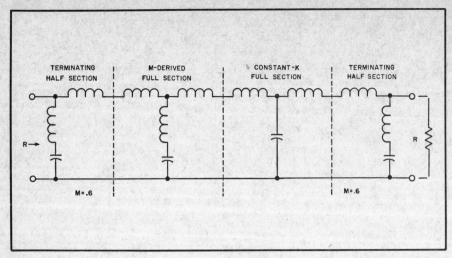

Fig. 57

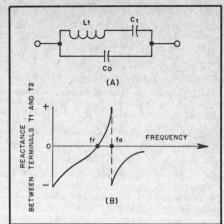

Fig. 64 — The equivalent electrical circuit of a piezoelectric crystal is shown at A. The reactance varies with frequency as in B.

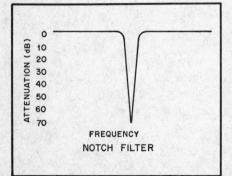

Fig. 58 — Response curve for hypothetical band-pass filter. Those points on the curve representing 6- and 60-dB down are indicated because they are commonly used to calculate the shape factor.

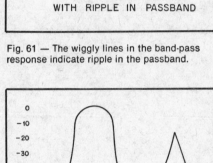

Fig. 61 — The wiggly lines in the band-pass response indicate ripple in the passband.

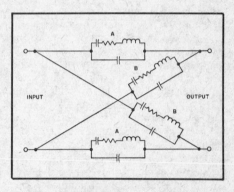

Fig. 65 — Equivalent circuit of a full-lattice crystal filter. Note that the lattice could be redrawn as a bridge circuit.

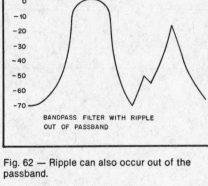

Fig. 59 — Response curve for hypothetical band-reject filter.

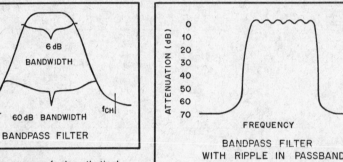

Fig. 62 — Ripple can also occur out of the passband.

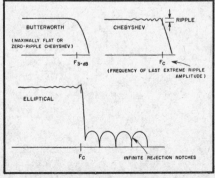

Fig. 60 — Response curve for hypothetical notch filter.

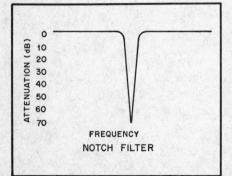

Fig. 63 — Response characteristics of "modern filters."

used as an example. Simply for illustration, one of the two intermediate T sections is a constant-k type and the other is m-derived. Both could be of the same type, and more sections could be used as required for a given overall attenuation. The value of m for the intermediate section or sections can be chosen at will for desired maximum-attenuation frequencies, because these sections and the adjoining Ts will always be matched.

Modern Network Design

The process of filter design described so far in this section is known as the image-parameter method. These filters have limitations with respect to maintaining a constant impedance. Also, the performance of a practical filter will be affected to some extent by the losses in inductances and capacitances (particularly with inductances). However, for the applications in which the requirements with respect to such things as flatness or response in the passband, sharpness of cutoff, etc., are not too strict, the overall performance will be good enough.

However, when an application requires strict specifications with regard to flatness of response and rapidity of attenuation beyond cutoff, it is necessary to use a computer to calculate the optimum value of the filter components. Tables summarizing these computations can be found in the ARRL *Handbook*. There are many kinds of so-called "modern filters": Butterworth, Chebyshev and Elliptical are three kinds that have many applications in Amateur Radio. A Butterworth filter is used when you want a "maximally flat" response and no ripple in the passband. (Ripple is a variation of attenuation, and you could get these "ups and downs" inside the passband and/or outside the passband. The Chebyshev filter has a sharp cutoff, with some ripple in the passband. Higher VSWR increases the ripple. The elliptical filter has sharp cutoff, with ripple in the passband and stop band, but has infinite rejection notches. See Fig. 63.

Crystal Lattice Filters

A quartz crystal acts as an extremely high-Q circuit. The equivalent electrical circuit is depicted in Fig. 64A. Fig. 64B shows a graph of the reactance vs. frequency for the crystal. Even though crystals can be used singly as filtering devices, the normal practice is to wire two or more together in various configurations to provide a desired response curve. Fig. 65 details a configuration known as the full-lattice filter (equivalent electrical circuits are shown instead of the crystals).

Oscillators

To start a circuit *oscillating*, which means generating a frequency of alternating current (usually a radio frequency), we need to feed power from the plate back to the grid of a tube or from the collector to the base of a transistor. This is called *feedback*. We use the term feedback when a person using a public address system gets the microphone too close to the loudspeaker. When he speaks, his voice is amplified in the public address system and leaves the loudspeaker. If he stands too close to the speaker, however, the sound that leaves the speaker enters the microphone and goes through the whole process again. It will continue to go around and around, out the speaker and back into the public address system via the microphone until the "circuit" is broken. Usually, the microphone has to be moved away from the speaker or the volume must be turned down. The "pig squeal" we hear during feedback is a high audio frequency being generated.

The same sort of process occurs in radio circuits when we apply the output of a transistor or tube to its own input. Any small irregularity in the plate current (or collector current) will supply a signal that will start oscillations going at the same frequency the circuit of the tube or transistor happens to be tuned to.

When the output signal we apply to the input reinforces the exciting signal at the input, we call it *positive feedback*. Negative feedback opposes the regular input signal.

Positive feedback can be created in many ways — so many ways, in fact, that we can't possibly cover them all here. There are three major oscillator circuits used in Amateur Radio. They are shown in Figs. 66 and 67. The *Hartley oscillator* belong to the *inductive feedback* class of oscillator circuits. Alternating current flowing through the lower part of the coil induces a voltage in the upper part, which is connected to the input of the circuit.

The second general type is the *Colpitts circuit*. It uses *capacitive feedback*. The plate-circuit energy is fed back by introducing it across the capacitor, which is part of the tuning capacitance of the circuit. This coupling sets up an rf voltage across the whole circuit. The voltage that consequently develops is applied to the grid.

Another general circuit is the *Pierce* circuit. It is a *crystal-controlled* oscillator circuit, while the Hartley and Colpitts are variable-frequency oscillator circuits. The Pierce circuit uses capacitive feedback, with the necessary capacitances supplied by the grid-to-cathode and plate-to-

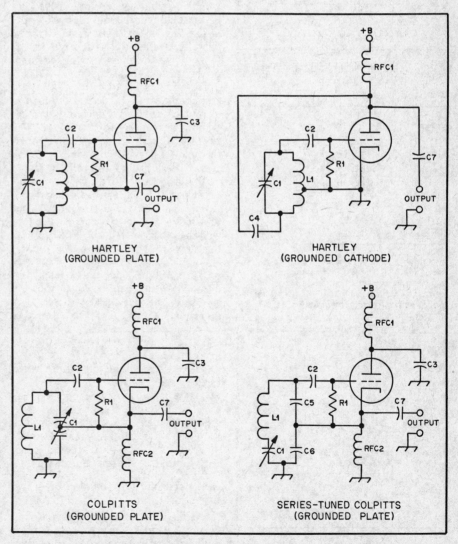

HARTLEY
(GROUNDED PLATE)

HARTLEY
(GROUNDED CATHODE)

COLPITTS
(GROUNDED PLATE)

SERIES-TUNED COLPITTS
(GROUNDED PLATE)

Fig. 66 — Two common types of oscillator circuits using tubes.

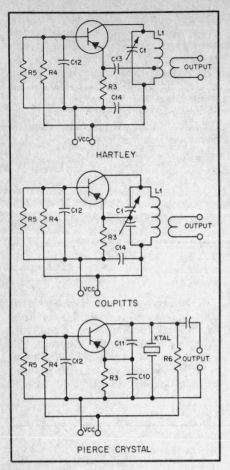

Fig. 67 — Three common types of oscillator circuits using transistors.

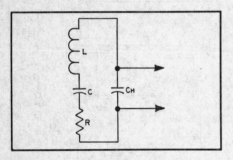

Fig. 68 — Equivalent circuit of a crystal resonator. L, C and R are the electrical equivalents of mechanical properties of the crystal; C$_H$ is the capacitance of the holder plates with the crystal plate between them.

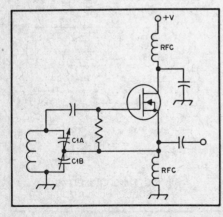

Fig. 69 — A Colpitts VFO.

cathode capacitances of the tube itself. In the transistorized Pierce oscillator circuit shown in Fig. 67, the feedback necessary to maintain oscillation is regulated by the capacitors, C10 and C11.

Crystals

A number of crystallized substances can be found in nature. Of these, some have the ability to change mechanical energy into an electrical potential, and vice versa. This property is known as the *piezoelectric effect*. A small plate or bar properly cut from a quartz crystal and placed between two conducting electrodes will be mechanically strained when the electrodes are connected to a voltage source. The opposite can happen, too. If the crystal is squeezed, a voltage will develop between the electrodes.

Crystals are used in microphones and phonograph pickups, where mechanical vibrations are transformed into alternating voltages of corresponding frequency. They are used in headphones to change electrical energy into mechanical vibration.

Crystalline plates have natural frequencies of vibration ranging from a few thousand hertz to tens of megahertz. The vibration frequency depends on the kind of crystal, and the dimensions of the plate. What makes the *crystal resonator* (vibrator) valuable is that it has an extremely high Q, ranging from a minimum of about 20,000 to as high as 1,000,000.

The mechanical properties of a crystal are very similar to the electrical properties of a tuned circuit. We therefore have an "equivalent circuit" for the crystal. The electrical coupling to the crystal is through the holder plates which "sandwich" the crystal. These plates form, with the crystal as the dielectric, a small capacitor constructed of two plates with a dielectric between them. The crystal itself is equivalent to a series-resonant circuit and, together with the capacitance of the holder, forms the equivalent circuit shown in Fig. 68.

Can we change the crystal in some way so that it will resonate at a different frequency? We sure can. If we lengthen the crystal, or make it thicker, the crystal's resonating frequency will go down. On the other hand, if we want the crystal to vibrate at a higher frequency, we would make it thinner and shorter.

There are to major limitations when using crystals. First, we can't have more than two terminals to the circuit, since there are only two crystal electrodes. In other words, a crystal can't be tapped as we might tap a coil in a circuit. Second, the crystal is an open circuit for direct current, so series feed can't be used with it.

Advantages and Disadvantages of Crystals

The major advantage of a crystal used in an oscillator circuit is its frequency stability. A crystal can hold its frequency

much steadier when mechanically "shook-up" than coils or capacitors: The turns of a coil can change with vibration or temperature change, and the plates of a variable capacitor can move. On the other hand, the frequency of a crystal is much less apt to change when the equipment is moved.

But a crystal used in an oscillator circuit is easily affected by temperature, although much less than a variable-frequency oscillator. Some crystals are X-cut crystals. This gives them a *negative temperature coefficient*, which means that when the temperature of the crystal rises, the frequency of the crystal decreases. Other crystals are cut so that they have *positive temperature coefficients*. When their temperatures rise, their frequencies also rise.

Variable Frequency Oscillators

The major advantage of variable-frequency oscillators (VFO) is that a single oscillator can be tuned over a wide range of frequencies. However, since the frequency is determined by the coil and capacitors in the tuned circuit, the frequency is often not as stable as in the crystal-controlled configuration. The Colpitts oscillator (Fig. 69) is one of the more common types of VFO. The FET in the diagram is connected like an emitter follower (actually, here it's a source follower) with the input (gate) connected to the top of the tuned circuit and the output (source) tapped down on the tuned circuit with a capacitive divider. Although the voltage gain of a source follower can never be greater than one, the voltage step-up that results from tapping down on the tuned circuit ensures that the signal at the gate will be large enough to sustain oscillation. Even though the FET voltage gain is less than one, the power gain must be great enough to overcome losses in the tank circuit and the load.

The amplitude and frequency stability

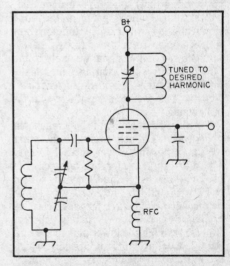

Fig. 70 — A Colpitts harmonic oscillator, also known as an electron-coupled Colpitts.

of a variable-frequency Colpitts oscillator is quite good, although it doesn't approach that of a crystal controlled oscillator. The large capacitances used in the tank circuit minimize frequency shifts that are caused by small variations in capacitance due to vibration or variations in tube or transistor characteristics.

Most oscillator circuits are characterized by the use of *grid-leak bias*. During some point in the oscillation cycle, the grid is driven positive with respect to the cathode so that a small amount of grid current is drawn — a situation that would not normally occur in an amplifier circuit using the same device. This small current is made to flow through a very high resistance. The resulting voltage is averaged out by the input coupling capacitor so that during the portion of the oscillation cycle when no grid current flows, the capacitor discharges slowly through the resistor to maintain bias voltage.

Most oscillators provide an output rich in harmonic content. The relative amplitude of any given harmonic can be enhanced by choosing the optimum bias voltage. A Colpitts oscillator that has a second tank circuit tuned to the desired harmonic and connected to the output (plate or collector) makes an excellent harmonic generator. A diagram of a VFO-type Colpitts harmonic oscillator is given in Fig. 70. The equivalent crystal-controlled circuit would have the coil in the grid-tuned circuit replaced with a crystal, and the double-section variable capacitor would probably be replaced by two fixed capacitors.

Amplification

The energy that produces the sound coming out of the headphones of a crystal set is furnished by the radio signal itself. No power source is necessary. The energy, in other words, is the energy that travels from the transmitting station to the receiving antenna. But if we had to depend solely on the transmitted energy for producing the sound waves that eventually come from the receiver, the distances over which we could communicate would be very limited.

How do we strengthen the received signals? What's needed is another process, another step in the reception of a radio signal. We call this next step *amplification*. In broad terms, an amplifier is a device that uses locally supplied energy to magnify the signal fed into it into a bigger reproduction of itself. If we choose to amplify the radio signal before it reaches the detector, we are amplifying a radio frequency. If, however, we put the amplifier after the detector, the amplifier will be strengthening *audio frequencies*. Because each method has its advantages, a combination of both is generally used.

The Limit of Amplification

The energy extracted by the receiving antenna is extremely small. Therefore, the amount of amplification used in receivers is very large — often a factor of millions. You might think that this amplification process could be carried on indefinitely, so that even the weakest radio signals could be brought up to usable strength. Unfortunately, it can't.

What limits this usable amplification is the *noise* across the radio spectrum. Unlimited amplification of a particular frequency cannot reduce the noise mask covering a desired signal since they are both rf emissions. Where does this noise come from? It's from electrical currents generated in nature (static) and in electrical circuits and devices. Noise which occurs at all frequencies, both radio and audio, is inescapable.

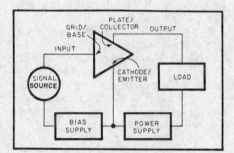

Fig. 71 — Typical amplifier configuration.

Amateurs don't give up in their battle against noise, though, because there are means to make it less bothersome. One of the big objectives in designing good receivers is to improve the *signal-to-noise ratio*. This is amplifying the signal as much as possible while amplifying the noise as little as possible.

Bias

The basic operation of an amplifier is selected by choosing a bias or dc input when there is no signal applied to the amplifier. In the most common amplifier configuration tubes are operated with a slightly negative bias voltage applied to the grid, and npn transistors with a slightly positive bias voltage applied to the base. The bias depends upon the amplifying device used and the type of amplification desired.

Transfer Function

The transfer function is a graph of the output versus the input of an amplifying device. The actual shape of the curve depends upon the device. Values for input and output and whether they are in units of volts, amperes, or power also depend upon the amplifying device.

The transfer functions for all amplifiers have some characteristics in common. There is usually a point where more input will not result in more output, called the *saturation region*. The opposite case of where less input does not decrease output is called the *cutoff region*. These are determined by physical limitations of the amplifying devices. Then there is a third region between cutoff and saturation where the curve is almost straight. This is called the *linear region*. The slope of this line is called the *gain*.

Two factors of the input are extremely important. The first, called the *bias,* is the average input level of the signal or the dc input level. The second is the size of the input signal. These levels must be managed to produce the desired type of amplification.

Class C amplification requires that the bias be well below cutoff and that the signal be very large so that the half of it above the bias level will bring the input up into the saturation region. Class B operation sets the bias right at the level where cutoff begins to occur. Class A amplification sets the bias and size of input so that all of the input signals appear between the saturation and cutoff regions.

Distortion

The class of amplifier chosen depends on many factors. This is a fairly complex, technical matter. Just remember that operating an amplifier with bias near or beyond cutoff helps increase the efficiency of the amplifier.

You're probably thinking we can't get something for nothing; what does all this cost? If you are thinking this, you're right, because we do lose something when we increase efficiency. The output signal can't be exactly like the input signal in its shape if the input goes into saturation or cutoff regions on the transfer function graph. In other words, there is *distortion*. Distortion occurs when the signal we get out of a circuit is different than the signal we put into it.

Sometimes there is a lot of distortion. In many kinds of amplifiers, though, distortion doesn't matter. Audio amplifiers, such as the last stage in a receiver, may have a lot of distortion.

Amplifiers for cw and fm signals may also have a lot of distortion because the shape of the wave is not important. Amplifiers for ssb transmitters and hi-fi audio systems are examples of where a low amount of distortion is necessary.

Voltage and Power Amplification

As mentioned previously, the transfer function may be a graph of volts, amperes or watts. Amateurs are mainly concerned only with two kinds of amplification, though. In one type, we try to get the largest possible voltage from the amplifier, which is worthwhile when that voltage will be amplified later by a following amplifier stage. *Stage,* by the way, is the name we give to one of a number of amplifiers used one after another.

The second kind of amplifiers amateurs use is the power amplifier. We use it when we want as much power as possible from the amplifier, this often requires driving the grid positive, which is never done with voltage tube amplifiers.

Amplifier Gain

The gain of an amplifier in dB is the ratio of the input signal to the output signal. Voltage-amplifier gain is based on the ratio of voltages and power-amplifier is the ratio to output power levels.

This ratio can become unwieldy when several stages are combined or when the gain is very large. This is why the decibel is often used. Usually you'll have no trouble seeing what is meant, because it is customary to speak of voltage gain of 1000 or a power gain of 250, or a gain of 30 dB — using the appropriate number, or course.

Amplifier characteristics

Because we've mentioned that there are Class A, B and C types of amplification, it's now time to sort them out. First, there is the kind which has as its distinguishing feature the presence of output throughout the signal cycle — the input never goes into the cutoff region, even for a split second. This type of amplifier is called a *Class A* amplifier. Because its output is

driven down just as much as it's driven up by the signal, the average output stays just about the same whether or not an input signal exists.

Now suppose that the bias is set at cutoff or slightly to the right of the cutoff on the transfer function shown in Fig. 72 so that just a little output flows when there is no input. During the negative half of the signal the output stays off. During the positive half, the output will be approximately in proportion to the amplitude of the input. That is, the average output changes when an input signal is applied, and the bigger the signal, the greater the output. This means that there is distortion of the signal. This is called *Class B* amplification.

When the bias is adjusted so that it lies somewhere between normal Class A and normal Class B operation, we call this *Class AB* amplification.

By now you've figured out that the next type of amplification is *Class C.* Here, the bias is well beyond the cutoff point — up to twice the bias required for cutoff, usually large input is used — so large that making it larger wouldn't cause any further increase in output. This is called driving the amplifier to *saturation.*

Class C operation gives the highest obtainable efficiency and is commonly used in rf power amplifiers for code work (cw) or fm phone. It's used everywhere in transmitters except where an *amplitude-modulated* signal must be amplified. Class C output distorts such a signal applied to the amplifier input. For amplifying an a-m signal, we use a Class A or Class B amplifier.

Biasing in Transistor Amplifiers

Transistors must be forward biased in order to conduct significant current. If your circuit includes an npn transistor, the collector and base must be positive with respect to the emitter, the collector more positive with the base. The same is true when working with a pnp transistor, but the base and collector must be negative with respect to the emitter. The required bias is provided by the collector-to-emitter voltage, and by the emitter-to-base voltage. These bias voltages cause two currents to flow: emitter-to-collector current and emitter-to-base current. Either type of transistor, pnp or npn, can be used with a negative- or positive-ground power source. Forward bias must still be maintained, however.

The lower the forward bias, the lower the collector current. As you increase the forward bias, the collector current rises and the junction temperature rises. If the bias is continuously increased, the transistor eventually overloads and burns out. This condition is called thermal runaway. To prevent damage to the transistor, some form of bias stabilization should be included in a transistor amplifier design. However, if the bias is *not* increased, ther-

mal runaway can occur. As the transistor heats up, its beta increases, causing more collector current to flow. This causes more heating, even higher beta, and even more current, until eventually the transistor burns out.

Transistor Amplifiers

Amplifier circuits used with transistors fall into one of three types, known as the common-base, common-emitter and common-collector circuits. These are shown in Fig. 74 in elementary form. The three circuits correspond approximately to the grounded-grid, grounded-cathode and cathode-follower circuits, respectively, when vacuum tubes are used.

Common-Base Circuit

The input circuit of a common-base amplifier must be designed for low impedance, since the emitter-to-base resistance is of the order of $25/I_e$ ohms, where I_e is the emitter current in milliamperes. The optimum output load impedance, R_L, may range from a few thousand ohms to 100,000, depending upon the requirements.

In this circuit the phase of the output (collector) current is the same as that of the input (emitter) current. The parts of these currents that flow through the base resistance are likewise in phase, so the circuit tends to be regenerative and will oscillate if the current amplification factor is greater than one.

Common-Emitter Circuit

The common-emitter circuit is shown in Fig. 74. The base current is small and the input impedance is therefore fairly high — several thousand ohms in the average case. The collector resistance is some tens of thousands of ohms, depending on the signal source impedance. The common-emitter circuit has a lower cutoff frequency than does the common-base circuit, but it gives the highest power gain of the three configurations.

In this circuit the phase of the output (collector) current is opposite to that of the input (base) current so such feedback as occurs through the small emitter

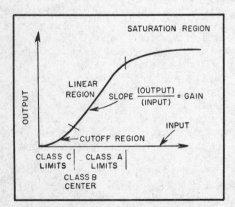

Fig. 72 — Transfer function displaying output versus input of different classes of amplifiers.

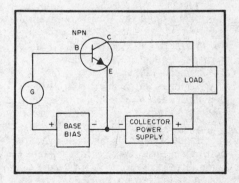

Fig. 73 — The transistor amplifier in bare essentials. If a pnp transistor is used, the bias and collector supply voltages must be negative with respect to the emitter.

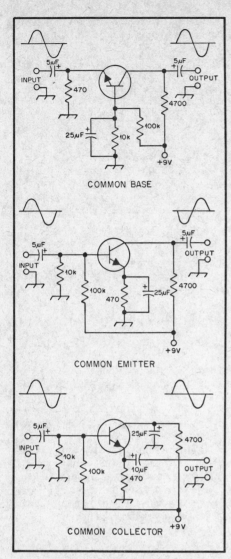

Fig. 74 — Basic transistor amplifier circuits. Typical component values are given for use at audio frequencies, where these circuits are used most often. The input and output phase relationships are shown.

resistance is negative and the amplifier is stable.

Common-Collector Circuit

The common-collector transistor amplifier has high input impedance and low output impedance. The latter is approximately equal to the impedance of the signal input source multiplied by $(1 - \alpha)$. The input resistance depends on the load resistance, being approximately equal to the load resistance divided by $(1 - \alpha)$. The fact that input resistance is directly related to the load resistance is a disadvantage of this type of amplifier if the load is one whose resistance or impedance varies with frequency.

The current transfer ratio with this circuit is

$$\frac{1}{1 - \alpha}$$

and the cut-off frequency is the same as in the grounded-emitter circuit. The output and input currents are in phase.

Calculating Values in Common Emitter Class A Amplifier

A typical common emitter class A audio amplifier is shown in Fig. 75. Resistors R1, R2 and R3 form the dc bias network that sets the operating point of the transistor. R1 and R2 form a voltage divider between V_{cc} and ground that sets the dc base voltage. Ohm's Law gives the base voltage as

$$V_b = \frac{R2}{R1 + R2} \times V_{cc} \text{ volts} \qquad \text{(Eq. 30)}$$

Using the values shown in Fig. 75

$$V_b = \frac{5k}{10k + 5k} \times 12 = 4.0 \text{ V.}$$

This assumes that the current flowing into the base is small compared to the current flowing through R2. This assumption will be tested later in the analysis. If we know the base voltage, the emitter voltage and current can be determined. For the transistor to conduct, the base-emitter junction must be forward biased; thus, with an npn transistor, the base will be approximately 0.6 volt more positive than the emitter

$$V_e = V_b - 0.6 \text{ V} \qquad \text{(Eq. 31)}$$

In Fig. 75 this yields

$$V_e = 4.0 - 0.6 = 3.4 \text{ V}$$

The emitter current is simply

$$I_e = \frac{V_e}{R3} \text{ A} \qquad \text{(Eq. 32)}$$

For Fig. 75 this is

$$I_e = \frac{3.4}{2k} = 0.0017 \text{ A or } 1.7 \text{ mA}$$

To test the assumption made earlier (that the base current is much smaller than the divider current), the value of each must be calculated. The base current, I_b, is related to the emitter current, I_e, by beta, β

$$I_b = \frac{I_e}{\beta} \text{ A} \qquad \text{(Eq. 33)}$$

Given a beta of 100 the base current is approximately

$$I_b = \frac{1.7 \text{ mA}}{100} = 0.017 \text{ mA}$$

The divider current is

$$I_d = \frac{V_{cc}}{R1 + R2} \text{ A} \qquad \text{(Eq. 34)}$$

In Fig. 75

$$I_d = \frac{12 \text{ V}}{10k + 5k} = 0.0008 \text{ A or } 0.8 \text{ mA}$$

In as much as 0.8 mA is much larger than 0.017 mA the assumption is justified and the dc bias network analysis is complete. To determine the ac signal gain it must be

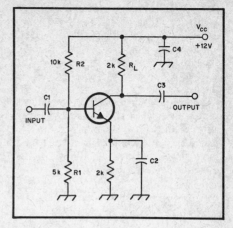

Fig. 75

remembered that bypass capacitors C2 and C4 effectively ground the emitter and V_{cc} for ac. If an ac voltage is applied to the base it will cause a current to flow into the base terminal of the transistor. This current is given by

$$I_B = \frac{V_B}{R_B} \text{ A} \qquad \text{(Eq. 35)}$$

where R_B is the resistance looking into the base terminal of the transistor. Its value is approximately

$$R_B = \frac{V_B}{R_B} \text{ A.} \qquad \text{(Eq. 36)}$$

Note that I_e in Eq. 36 is the dc emitter current found in the earlier analysis of the bias network and it is in mA. Assume that a 0.001-V rms signal is applied to the input of the amplifier shown in Fig. 75. The value of R_B will be

$$R_B = \frac{26 \times 100}{1.7} = 1300 \text{ ohms}$$

and the ac base current will be

$$I_B = \frac{0.001}{1300} = 0.77 \text{ uA.}$$

The ac collector current is then

$$I_C = I_B \times \beta = 0.77 \text{ uA} \times 100$$
$$= 77 \text{ uA or } 0.077 \text{ mA}$$

This is the current flowing into the collector through R_L, the load resistance. The output voltage developed across R_L is simply

$$V_L = I_C \times R_L = 0.077 \text{ mA} \times 2k$$
$$= 0.154 \text{ V}$$

The voltage gain is defined as

$$A_V = \frac{V_L}{V_B} = \frac{0.154 \text{ V}}{0.001 \text{ V}} = 154 \qquad \text{(Eq. 37)}$$

Because the current is flowing through R_L

into the collector and the V_{cc} end of R_L is at ground potential (because of the bypass capacitor C4), V_L is actually -0.154 V and the voltage gain is -154. This minus sign merely indicates that the output voltage is 180 degrees out of phase with the input voltage.

The input impedance of the circuit is the transistor base resistance, R_B, in parallel with the base bias resistors, R1 and R2. Remembering that the V_{cc} terminal is at ground potential for ac signals the input impedance is

$$R_{in} = \frac{1}{\frac{1}{R1} + \frac{1}{R2} + \frac{1}{R_B}} = 935 \text{ ohms} \quad \text{(Eq. 38)}$$

The output impedance of the circuit is simply the value of the load resistance, R_L, or 2k ohms in Fig. 75. The above analysis is based on a simple transistor

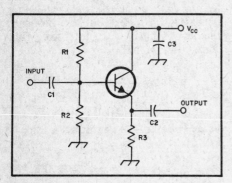

Fig. 76

model, but the results obtained using this model are very good at low frequency.

Calculating Values in a Common Collector Class A Amplifier

A common-collector, class A amplifier is shown in Fig. 76. This circuit is also known as the emitter follower. The analysis of the dc bias network, R1, R2 and R3, is the same as that for the common emitter circuit.

The voltage gain of the emitter follower is approximately 1. This is the result of not bypassing the emitter resistor, R3, to ground as it was in the common emitter circuit. Without bypassing R3, any change in base voltage will produce an equal voltage change across R3. As the output is taken between the emitter and ground, the voltage gain will be

$$A_V = \frac{V_E}{V_L} = 1 \quad \text{(Eq. 39)}$$

If we know the voltage gain, the input and output impedances can be determined. If a voltage is applied to the base of the transistor, it will cause a current to flow into the base and this produces a current through R3. Remembering that the change in emitter voltage is equal to the change in base voltage (Eq. 39) the emitter current will be

$$I_E = \frac{V_E}{R3} = \frac{V_B}{R3} \quad \text{(Eq. 40)}$$

This can be solved for V_B

$$V_B = I_E \times R3 \quad \text{(Eq. 41)}$$

The base current needed to produce this emitter current is

$$I_B = \frac{I_E}{\beta} \quad \text{(Eq. 42)}$$

The input impedance is given by Ohm's Law as

$$Z_{in} = \frac{V_B}{I_B} \quad \text{(Eq. 43)}$$

Combining Eqs. 41, 42 and 43

$$Z_{in} = \frac{I_E \times R3}{(I_E/\beta)} = R3 \times \beta \quad \text{(Eq. 44)}$$

The output impedance is given by

$$Z_{out} = \frac{V_E}{I_E} = \frac{V_B}{I_E} \quad \text{(Eq. 45)}$$

The emitter current is

$$I_E = I_B \times \beta \quad \text{(Eq. 46)}$$

The base current, I_B, is given by

$$I_B = \frac{V_B}{R_S} \quad \text{(Eq. 47)}$$

where R_S is the impedance of the signal source. Combining Eqs. 46 and 47 with Eq. 45 yields

$$Z_{in} = \frac{I_B \times \beta}{I_B \times R_S} = \frac{\beta}{R_S} \quad \text{(Eq. 48)}$$

While the common collector, or emitter follower circuit has only unity voltage gain, the output impedance is normal low. Thus, the power gain of the circuit is high. This and a relatively high input impedance make it a very useful circuit.

Signals and Emissions

Electromagnetic Energy

All electromagnetic waves are moving fields of electric and magnetic force. Their lines of force are at right angles, and are mutually perpendicular to the direction of travel. They can have any position with respect to the earth. The plane containing the continuous lines of electric and magnetic force is called the *wave front.*

The medium in which electromagnetic waves travel has a marked influence on their speed of movement. In empty space the speed, as for light, is just under 300,000,000 meters per second. It is slightly less in air, and it varies with temperature and humidity to a degree, depending on the frequency. It is much less in dielectrics, where the speed is in-

versely proportional to the square root of the dielectric constant of the material.

Waves cannot penetrate a good conductor to any extent because the electric lines of force are practically short-circuited. Radio waves travel through dielectric materials with ease.

Polarization

If the lines of force in the electric field are perpendicular to the surface of the earth, the wave is said to be *vertically polarized.* If parallel with the earth, the polarization is said to be *horizontal.* It is possible to generate waves with rotating field lines. Known as *circular polarization,* this is useful in satellite communication, where polarization tends to be random. When the earth's surface is not

available as a reference, polarization not of a rotating nature is described as linear or plane polarization, rather than vertical or horizontal, which become meaningless. Circular polarization is usable with plane-polarized antennas at the other end of the circuit, though with some small loss on most paths.

Emission Types

Since most of the increase in operating privileges carried by the Advanced class license involves expanded radio-telephone bands, you will be expected to have a good knowledge of the various kinds of modulation amateurs use. Modulation is the process by which information is superimposed on a steady rf signal, or carrier. Some forms of modulation vary the

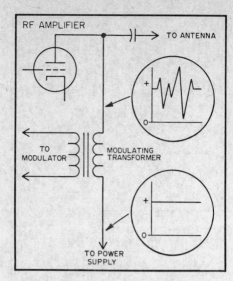

Fig. 77 — A-m plate modulation is accomplished by superimposing the modulation on the dc supply voltage.

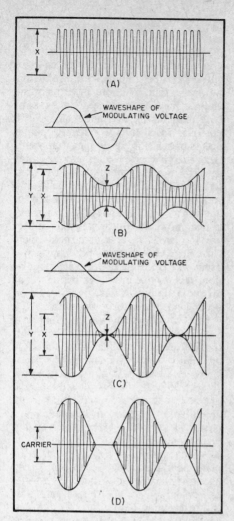

Fig. 78 — At A is depicted an unmodulated (cw) carrier of amplitude X. When sine-wave modulation is applied, a modulated waveform similar to that at B results. Modulation percentage is equal to 100 × (Y − X)/X. The signal at C is 100-percent modulated. When the peak modulation voltage is greater than the dc supply voltage, the negative peaks become clipped as at D. This results in unwanted sideband frequencies called *splatter*.

instantaneous amplitude of the signal. For this reason, they are called *amplitude modulation* or a-m for short. Other forms of modulation do not vary the amplitude; rather, they vary the frequency above and below the carrier frequency. This, of course, is known as *frequency modulation*, or fm for short. The FCC identifies the specific modulation form by a combination of letter and number, A1, F2, A5 and so forth. The first letter refers to the basic form: A represents a-m, and F stands for fm. A complete listing of modulation types and symbols is given in Appendix 3 in Chapter 9.

Note particularly the differences between F1 and F2 and between A5 and F5. F1 refers to frequency-shift keying (fsk); that is, telegraphy by shifting a carrier back and forth between two frequencies rather than by turning it on and off. Radio teleprinter emissions are commonly sent by fsk. F2 is a keyed audio tone (as from a code-practice oscillator) modulating an fm transmitter. A5 is amplitude-modulated television such as is used in commercial and amateur fast-scan TV transmission in this country. F5, on the other hand, is *frequency*-modulated television such as is used in some foreign countries.

Amateur slow-scan television on the hf bands consists of a variable-frequency audio tone fed into the microphone jack of a single-sideband transmitter. Since an ssb rig is a type of A3 transmitter, FCC considers SSTV to be A5. Actually, since the output signal is of constant amplitude, its characteristics more closely resemble F5 or even F4 than they do A5. The point is rather moot, however, since A5 and F5 emissions are permitted on exactly the same frequencies.

Amplitude Modulation

Double-sideband amplitude modulation used to be the most commonly used

voice mode in the high-frequency region. It is still sometimes used for local communications on vhf. Although you should be acquainted with screen and cathode or emitter modulation, the FCC is most concerned with *plate-modulation* and *grid-modulation* techniques.

Plate modulation, or collector modulation in the case of a transistor circuit, is produced by varying the instantaneous plate or collector voltage by superimposing the modulating voltage on the dc-supply voltage. This is usually accomplished by passing the plate (or collector) current through the secondary winding of a modulation transformer. Since the modulator-output amplifier is connected to the primary winding, the variance of the plate-supply voltage depends on how much power the modulator can deliver. The *modulation percentage* is a measure of the ratio between the modulating voltage and the peak rf-carrier voltage. For example, if the peak-modulating voltage equals the power-supply voltage, the ratio between the two is 1:1 or 100 percent. If it equals just one-half the supply voltage, the ratio is 1:2 or 50 percent. The *modulation capability* is a measure of the maximum percentage of undistorted modulation a transmitter can achieve. In order to achieve 100-percent modulation, the modulator must be capable of delivering one-half the dc-input power of the modulated stage. A 100-watt, plate-modulated transmitter requires 50 watts of undistorted modulator power to achieve 100-percent modulation. Modulation capability may also be limited by improper operating conditions on the final amplifier tube or transistor.

Overmodulation and Splatter

It is important to know the modulating capability of the modulator being used with a given transmitter, because too high a capability may result in *overmodulation* if the operator turns up the microphone gain control too high. Overmodulation is a condition that exists when modulation exceeds 100 percent. The major problem occurs during the negative half cycle of the modulating signal. At the instant that the modulating voltage is equal and opposite to the supply voltage, final amplifier current is zero. If the modulation amplitude increases, the plate or collector current remains zero and the waveform becomes clipped. Such clipping causes the generation of considerable audio harmonics in the signal's modulation. This is heard on the air outside the normal a-m bandwidth as a garbled sound called *splatter*.

To guard against splatter, it is desirable to include *modulation limiting* to ensure that peak modulation never exceeds 100 percent. Frequently, an audio *clipper* is used to automatically clip off the peaks of the audio waveform so that they will not

drive the modulator output beyond the 100-percent modulation level. Unfortunately, any audio clipping creates audio harmonics in a manner very similar to the clipping that is caused by overmodulation. For this reason, the modulation limiter must be followed by a low-pass audio filter to prevent these frequencies from reaching the modulated stage.

Audio clipping is most effective with a-m and fm transmitters. For ssb, rf clipping is more effective. Since most modern ssb transmitters first generate the ssb signal at a fixed intermediate frequency, it is possible to clip this waveform and then pass it through a sharply tuned i-f filter to eliminate the splatter.

Grid or Base Modulation

Plate or collector modulation is sometimes called *high-level modulation* because it is accomplished at a high-power stage of the transmitter. It is possible, however, to obtain amplitude modulation at low level. By superimposing the modulating signal on the final amplifier grid or base bias, the plate or collector current can be modulated, and thus the power output. Although virtually no audio driving power is needed for grid or base modulation, overmodulation is still possible. In high-level systems, splatter occurs because of the clipping that results from the plate or collector current falling to zero. In a vacuum tube type transmitter, this plate-current cut off is caused in turn by the plate voltage falling to zero or going negative. The same effect can be obtained, however, by driving the control grid too far negative. At some point, plate current will fall to zero and clipping will occur. As is the case with plate modulation, this may be prevented by the use of an audio clipper. An analogous situation occurs with transistorized circuits.

One disadvantage of grid or base modulation is that it has only about half the efficiency of a plate- or collector-modulated stage of similar characteristics. Consider a transmitting tube or transmitter with 30-watts dissipation which can be operated as a 70-percent-efficient class C amplifier. It can thus run 100-watts input power with 70-watts average output as a plate-modulated class C stage. The same tube or transistor operated as a grid- or plate-modulated stage could run only about 45-watts input with about 15-watts carrier output power. The advantage of the latter method, of course, is that you could dispense with the 50-watt plate or collector modulator.

A-M Sidebands

Regardless of the method used, the modulation process is, in effect, nothing more than the mixing together of two signals — one at the rf-carrier frequency and the other at the audio-modulating frequency. Whenever two signals are mixed, four frequencies result in the mixer output — the two original signals and two others at their sum and difference frequencies.[1] Because it is so far removed from the carrier frequency, the audio-frequency modulating signal is completely eliminated by the transmitter output circuits. What remains then is the carrier, the carrier plus the modulating frequency, and the carrier minus the modulating frequency. For example, if a 10-MHz rf carrier is modulated by a 3-kHz audio signal, the transmitter output consists of a signal at 9.997 MHz, 10.0 MHz and 10.003 MHz. The signal at 9.997 MHz is part of the *lower sideband* and the signal at 10.003 is part of the *upper sideband*. Actually, the modulating signal would not usually consist of only a single frequency because the important components of the

[1]A *balanced* mixer will automatically eliminate one or both of the inputs so that only the sum and difference frequencies remain at the output.

human voice are between about 200 and 3000 Hz. Thus the upper and lower sidebands extend to about 3000 Hz above and below the carrier frequency. A signal consisting of both sidebands plus the carrier is commonly referred to as double sideband a-m and is designated A3. For more detailed information about amplitude modulation refer to Chapter 12 of the ARRL *Handbook,* 58th edition, 1981.

Frequency Modulation

Frequency modulation operates on an entirely different principle than a-m. Although not very common in the high-frequency spectrum, fm enjoys considerable popularity on the vhf bands. In fm, the signal is shifted above and below the carrier frequency at a rate equal to the modulating-signal frequency. For example, if a transmitter is frequency modulated by a 1000-Hz audio tone, the carrier will vary above and below the center frequency 1000 times per second. However, the amount of frequency shift, or *deviation* as it's called, depends on the instantaneous amplitude of the modulating signal. In the example above, the 1000-Hz tone might produce, say, a 5-kHz deviation. If the amplitude of the tone were doubled, it would produce a 10-kHz deviation.

The ratio betwen the frequency deviation, in hertz, and the modulating frequency, also in hertz, is called the *modulation index.* That is

Modulation index =

$$\frac{\text{carrier frequency deviation}}{\text{modulating frequency}} \qquad \text{(Eq. 49)}$$

For example, the maximum frequency deviation in an fm transmitter is 3000 Hz either side of the carrier frequency. The modulation index when the modulation frequency is 1000 Hz is

$$\text{Modulation index} = \frac{3000}{1000} = 3 \qquad \text{(Eq. 50)}$$

In an fm system, the frequency deviation is independent of the modulating frequency — all audio frequencies swing the carrier an equal amount. Thus the *ratio* between the frequency deviation and the modulating audio frequency (the *modulation index*) is different for equal-amplitude signals of different frequencies. For example, if the deviation is 3 kHz, then the modulation index is 3 for a 1-kHz modulating tone but only 1-1/2 for 2-kHz modulation. The *deviation ratio* is defined as the ratio of the *maximum* deviation to the *highest* audio modulating frequency used and is thus independent of the specific modulating frequency applied at any moment.

FM Sidebands

In amplitude modulation, there are just

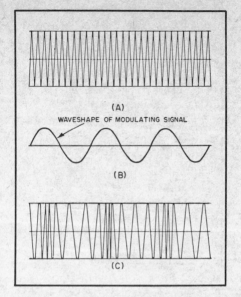

Fig. 79 — Graphical representation of frequency modulation. In the unmodulated carrier at A, each rf cycle occupies the same amount of time. When the modulating signal, B, is applied, the radio frequency is increased and decreased according to the amplitude and polarity of the modulating signal.

two sidebands, an upper and a lower. A frequency-modulated signal, on the other hand, has many pairs of sidebands at multiples of the modulating frequency from the carrier. The amplitude of these sidebands depends on both the amplitude and frequency of the modulating audio. For example, if you modulate an fm transmitter with a 2-kHz tone so that it has a 6-kHz deviation, there will be sidebands at 2, 4 and 6 kHz either side of the carrier. The fourth and higher order sidebands will be present, but will have a relatively small amplitude. Actually, one or more of the lower-order sidebands may also have a small amplitude — the sidebands do not necessarily get smaller the farther they are from the carrier. Also, unlike a-m the *carrier* varies in amplitude with modulation. Under the proper modulating conditions, the carrier or one or more of the sidebands may disappear entirely. Prediction of the exact amplitude of any sideband depends on a complicated mathematical technique using Bessel functions. Fortunately, this information can be reduced to tabular form for easy use. One source for this information is chapter 11 of the ARRL's *FM and Repeaters for the Radio Amateur.* Using these tables, you can determine your frequency deviation by listening for the disappearance of the carrier with a highly selective cw-type receiver. For example if the modulating frequency is 2079 Hz, the table says that the carrier will disappear when the deviation just reaches 5-kHz maximum.

With some fm modulators it is possible to measure deviation directly. If a true frequency modulator is used, and it is possible to feed a dc voltage directly into its "audio" input, then you can plot the output frequency versus input voltage. Since you know the input audio voltage, the output frequency (and thus the deviation) is easy to compute.

Perhaps the easiest way to measure fm deviation is with a wide band fm receiver. The audio voltage at the fm detector output is directly proportional to the deviation. If this voltage is calibrated against a signal of known characteristics, then the deviation can be determined for any signal. If, for example, 5-kHz maximum deviation causes 10-volts peak-audio output from the de ector, then you know that a signal with 20-volts output has a deviation of 10 kHz.

FM Bandwidth

FCC amateur regulations (§97.61) limit the bandwidth of F3 emissions to that of an a-m transmission having the same audio characteristics for operating frequencies below 29.0 MHz. Greater bandwidths are allowed above 29.0 MHz.

If the modulation index (with single-tone modulation) does not exceed 0.6 or 0.7, the most important extra sideband, the second, will be at least 20 dB below the unmodulated carrier level. This should represent an effective channel width about equivalent to that of an a-m signal. In the case of speech, a somewhat higher modulation index can be used. This is because the energy distribution in a complex wave is such that the modulation index for any one frequency component is reduced compared to the index with a sine wave having the same peak amplitude as the voice wave.

The chief advantage of fm for frequencies below 30 MHz is that it eliminates or reduces certain types of interference to broadcast reception. Also, the modulating equipment is relatively simple and inexpensive. However, assuming the same unmodulated carrier power in all cases, narrow-band fm is not as effective as a-m *with the methods of reception used by many amateurs*. To obtain the benefits of the fm mode, a good fm receiver is required. When copied on an a-m receiver, a narrow-band fm transmitter is about equivalent to a 100-percent modulated a-m transmitter operating at one-fourth the carrier power. On a suitable (fm) receiver, fm is as good or better than a-m, watt for watt.

The deviation standard now is ± 5 kHz, popularly know as *narrow band*. For a while after WW II, 2.5- to 3-kHz deviation ("sliver band") was used on 10 meters and the vhf bands. During the '60s and early '70s 15 kHz was extensively used since many amateur rigs were commercial surplus. Narrow-band deviation developed as a middle ground between audio quality and spectrum conservation. The rule-of-thumb for determination of bandwidth requirements for an fm system is

$$2(M + DK) \qquad \text{(Eq. 51)}$$

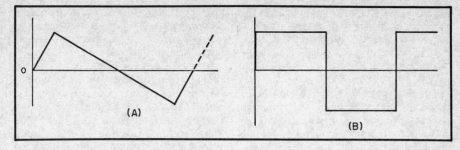

Fig. 80 — Any waveform that is not a pure sine wave contains harmonics. Sawtooth waves (A) consist of both odd and even harmonics as well as the fundamental. Square waves consist of only fundamental and odd-harmonic frequencies.

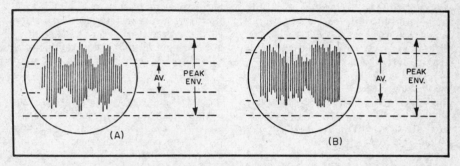

Fig. 81 — Two envelope patterns which show the difference between average power and peak envelope power. In each case, the rf amplitude (current or voltage) is plotted as a function of time. In B, the average level or the power output has been increased.

where
M = maximum modulation frequency of 3000 Hz
D = deviation frequency of 5000 Hz
K = 1

Thus for narrow-band fm, the bandwidth equals 2 (3 + 5) or 16 kHz. Wide-band systems need a 33-kHz receiver bandwidth.

Sinusoidal Waveforms

We went into detail about sinusoidal waveforms in the Technician/General class chapter. It would be a good idea to review that section at this time. Most ac circuit theory is based on the use of a pure sinusoidal waveform. Voltages, for example, are given as root-mean-square (rms) values unless otherwise specified. While the peak voltage of a sine wave is equal to 1.41 times the rms value (the exact number is $\sqrt{2}$ times the rms value), this is not usually true for nonsinusoidal waves. In addition, while nonsinusoidal waves contain a variety of frequency components, an unmodulated sine wave contains energy at only a single frequency.

Nonsinusoidal Waveforms

A *sawtooth wave*, as shown in Fig. 80A, is so named because it closely resembles the teeth on a saw blade. It is characterized by a rise time significantly faster than the fall time (or vice versa). A sawtooth wave is made up of a sine wave at the fundamental frequency and sine waves at all the harmonic frequencies as

well. When a sawtooth voltage is applied to the horizontal deflection plates of an oscilloscope, the electron beam sweeps slowly across the screen during the slowly changing portion of the waveform and then flies quickly back during the rapidly changing portion of the signal. This is what is desired to obtain a linear sweep in an oscilloscope.

A *square wave* is one which abruptly changes back and forth between two voltage levels and which remains an equal time at each level (Fig. 80B). (If it spends an unequal time at each level, it is known as a *rectangular wave*.) A square wave is made up of sine waves of the fundamental and all the *odd* harmonic frequencies.

Peak Envelope Power (PEP)

Fig. 81 is more or less typical of a few voice-frequency cycles of the modulation envelope of a single-sideband signal. Two amplitude values associated with it are of particular interest. One is the *peak amplitude,* the greatest amplitude reached by the envelope at any time. The other is the *average amplitude,* which is the average of all amplitude values contained in the envelope over some significant period of time, such as the time it takes for one syllable of a word to be spoken.

The power contained in the signal at the peak amplitude is the basic transmitter rating. It is called the *peak-envelope power,* abbreviated PEP.

Peak vs. Average Power

Envelope peaks occur only sporadically

during voice transmission and have no direct relationship with meter readings. The meters respond to the amplitude (current or voltage) of the signal averaged over several cycles of the modulation envelope.

The ratio of peak-to-average amplitude varies widely with voices of different characteristics. In the case shown in Fig. 81A, the average amplitude (found graphically) is such that the peak-to-average ratio of amplitudes is almost 3:1.

DC Input

FCC regulations require that the transmitter power be rated in terms of the dc input to the final stage. Most ssb final amplifiers are operated class AB1 or AB2, so that the plate current during modulation varies upward from a "resting" or no-signal value that is generally selected to minimize distortion. There will be a peak-envelope value of plate current that, when multiplied by the dc plate voltage, represents the instantaneous tube power input required to produce the peak-envelope output. This is the "peak-envelope dc input" or "PEP input." It does not register on any meter in the transmitter. Meters cannot move fast enough to show it — and even if they did, the eye couldn't follow. What the plate meter *does* read is the plate current averaged over several modulation-

envelope cycles. This, multiplied by the dc plate voltage, is the number of watts input required to produce the *average* power output described earlier.

In voice transmission the power input and power output are both continually varying. The power input peak-to-average ratio, like the power output peak-to-average ratio, depends on the voice characteristics. Determining this input ratio is made even more difficult because there's a resting value of dc plate input even when there is no rf power. *No exact figures are possible.* However, experience has shown that for many types of voices and for ordinary tube operating conditions where a moderate value of resting current is used, the ratio of PEP input to average input (during a modulation peak) will be no less than 2:1.

When speaking of rf amplifiers, the peak power is rarely mentioned. When we speak of a 100-watt transmitter, we mean it runs 100 watts rms. However, linear amplifiers designed for single sideband use do not operate at their maximum power level continuously. The rms power of the ssb-output signal varies at an audio rate, reaching its maximum only on peaks. For this reason, we speak of the *peak-envelope power* (PEP), which is the maximum rms power of a single-sideband signal. The same term may be used for amplitude modulation (a-m). The peak-envelope power of a 100-percent

modulated a-m transmission is four times the average carrier power. Unfortunately, you will sometimes hear people use the term "peak power" to refer to PEP, but you should remember that they are talking about the maximum rms power of the signal, not the peak power of the rf wave.

Signal-to-Noise Ratio

Noise is directly proportional to the effective bandwidth used in a system. The noise we are considering now is "thermal noise," frequently called "receiver hiss." This is not to be confused with man-made noises of the impulse type such as automobile ignition noise, commutation noise, or even an interfering radio transmission.

A single-sideband signal requires only half as much i-f bandwidth as required by an a-m signal to provide a given audio bandwidth. Therefore, we should not use more receiver bandwidth than the type of transmission requires us to use. Reducing the effective receiver bandwidth by a factor of two cuts down the noise power output of the receiver by the same factor, when *only* thermal noise is considered.

Wave Polarization

To wrap up this section on signals and emissions, review the material in the Technician/General class chapter on wave polarization.

Radio Wave Propagation

The FCC study outline for the Advanced class exam mentions four subjects under the title "Radio Wave Propagation." This section discusses each subject. If you need background information in order to understand these concepts, review the appropriate sections in the Technician/-General class chapter in this manual. We also recommend reading chapter 18, "Wave Propagation," in the 1981 *Radio Amateur's Handbook*.

Radio Path Horizon

The structure of the atmosphere near the earth is such that under "normal" conditions (a theoretical normal, rather than an actual one; in many parts of the world, at least, the "normal" is an average which is statistically useful but seldom represents the actual condition of the atmosphere) the waves are bent into a curved path that keeps them nearer to the earth than true straight-line travel would. This effect can be approximated by assuming that the waves travel in straight lines but that the earth's radius is increased in dimension by one third. On this

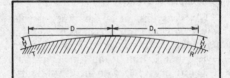

Fig. 82 — The distance, D, to the horizon from an antenna of height H is given by the formulas in the text. The maximum line-of-sight distance between two elevated antennas is equal to the sum of their distances to the horizon, as indicated in the drawing.

assumption, the distance from the transmitting antenna to the horizon is given by the following formula:

$$D(mi) = 1.415 \sqrt{H(ft)} \qquad (Eq.\ 52)$$

or

$$D(km) = 4.124 \sqrt{H(m)} \qquad (Eq.\ 53)$$

where H is the height of the transmitting antenna, as shown in Fig. 82. The formula assumes that the earth is perfectly smooth

out to the horizon; of course, any obstructions that rise along any given path must be taken into consideration. The point at the horizon is assumed to be on the ground. If the receiving antenna also is elevated, the maximum line-of-sight distance between the two antennas is equal to $D + D_1$; that is, the sum of the distance to the horizon from the transmitting antenna and the distance to the horizon from the receiving antenna. The distances are given in graph form in Fig. 83. Two stations on a flat plain, one having an antenna on a tower 60 feet high and the other having an antenna supported 40 feet in the air, could be separated approximately 20 miles for line-of-sight communication.

In addition to the "normal" refraction or bending, the waves also are diffracted around the curvature of the earth, so that the actual distance that can be covered does exceed the line-of-sight distance. However, under ordinary conditions the amount of diffraction at vhf and uhf where the space wave is of chief importance is rather small, and the signal

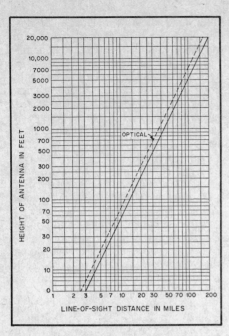

Fig. 83 — Distance to the horizon from an antenna of given height. The solid curve includes the effect of atmospheric refraction. The optical line-of-sight distance is given by the broken curve.

strength drops off very rapidly in a short distance beyond the earth's "shadow."

To make maximum use of the ordinary space wave discussed here it is necessary that the antenna be as high as possible above the surrounding country. A hill that juts above the adjacent terrain is usually an excellent location. However, the peak of a hill is not necessarily the best spot, particularly if it is of the nature of a plateau. Arriving waves may have to be diffracted over the brow of the hill to reach the antenna unless it is placed on a high pole or tower; in other words, the brow of the hill may shield the antenna from waves arriving from a desired direction. Also, it is advantageous to have the ground drop off fairly sharply in front of the antenna, as this frequently prevents the ground-reflected ray from approaching at such a flat angle as it would over level ground. Generally speaking, a location just below the peak of a hill is the optimum one for transmitting and receiving in a desired direction, as indicated in Fig. 84.

Since the space wave goes essentially in a straight line from the transmitter to the receiver, the antenna used for radiating it should concentrate the energy toward the horizon. That is, the antenna should be a "low-angle" radiator, because energy radiated at angles *above* the horizon obviously will pass over the receiving antenna. Similarly, the receiving antenna should be most responsive to waves that arrive horizontally.

In general, the polarization of a space wave remains constant during its travels. Therefore, the receiving antenna should be designed to give maximum response to the polarization set up at the transmitting antenna. For vhf work both horizontal and vertical polarization are used, the former being more generally preferred. The principal reason for this preference is that the chief source of radio noise at vhf —that generated by the spark in the ignition systems of automobiles — is predominantly vertically polarized. Thus horizontally polarized antennas tend to discriminate against such noise and thereby improve the signal-to-noise ratio.

Sporadic-E

At about the height of the E layer, highly ionized clouds are randomly and sporadically formed. They are small and last for only a few hours at a time. Because of their transient nature and their altitude, they are called *sporadic-E* clouds. To differentiate them from other E-layer phenomena these sporadic E clouds are designated E_s.

E_s clouds vary in intensity and move rapidly from southeast to northwest, at midlatitudes in the northern hemisphere. In the northern hemisphere they occur predominantly from May through August, with a minor peak in midwinter. The seasonal months are reversed in the southern hemisphere.

The mechanism for the formation of E_s is believed to be wind shear. This explains ambient ionization being redistributed and compressed into a ledge of high density without the need for production of extra ionization. Neutral winds of high velocity, flowing in opposite directions at slightly different altitudes, produce shears and, in the presence of the geomagnetic field, the ions are collected at a particular altitude, forming a thin over-dense layer. Data from rockets penetrating E_s layers confirm the electron density, wind velocities and height parameters.

Since midlatitude E_s is directly associated with terrestrial or meterological rather than solar phenomena, it is not surprising that the occurrence of intense E_s does *not* show direct correlation with sunspot activity.

The occurrence of intense E_s is markedly reduced at middle latitudes when the earth's magnetic field is disturbed.

The muf of intense E_s clouds is a function of their ionization density. The highest frequency which can be propagated obliquely is not known, but propagation to approximately 200 MHz has been reported a number of times. The probability of a 144-MHz opening is about 3 to 4 percent of the occurrence of 50-MHz openings. However, signal strength observed over the vhf range does not appear to be frequency dependent.

Normal one-hop, single-cloud E_s DX is limited to about 1250 miles, but during the summer season multiple clouds are common, and most propagation is via more than one cloud. With the right

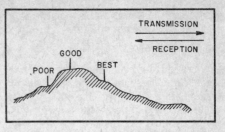

Fig. 84 — Propagation conditions are generally best when the antenna is located slightly below the top of the hill on the side that faces the distant station. Communication is poor when there is a sharp rise immediately in front of the antenna in the direction of communication.

distribution, distances up to 2500 miles or more are possible over land.

Auroral Propagation

During magnetic storms auroral activity becomes more pronounced and extends farther from the polar regions than is normally the case. During abnormal auroral activity a peculiar form of wave propagation is frequently observed, in which the auroral curtain acts as a reflector. Waves directed toward the polar regions will be reflected back and can be used for communication on frequencies and over distances that normally would be skipped over. When this condition prevails, it is necessary, when directive antennas are used, that both transmitting and receiving antennas be directed toward the polar regions rather than along the great-circle path between the two stations. While most of the hf bands are rendered useless for long-distance communication because of the increased absorption and instability of the ionosphere, the higher frequencies, beginning with about 28 MHz, are enhanced for beyond-local communications. East-west paths of up to about 1300 miles are possible using this form of propagation. In the southern hemisphere one would beam southward, since the aurora is a geomagnetic polar phenomenon.

Characteristically, aurora imparts a rapid flutter to signals. This flutter, which is not constant, may be anywhere from 100 to 2000 Hz and makes cw the preferred mode for communications, as most phone signals (even ssb) are difficult to read unless signal levels are extremely high. The higher one goes in frequency to work via an auroral opening, the stronger phone signals must be to be readable.

Propagation via auroral-curtain reflection occurs more often near the poles than at midlatitudes. It is nonexistent in the tropics. The auroral display need not be visible at a given location in order to take advantage of its properties; auroral propagation may continue night and day for several days but the display would not be visible during the daylight hours in most latitudes. In December and January, auroral propagation is least likely. Its peaks occur in March and September, but it is apt to happen at any time.

Fading

Variations in the strength of a received signal are classified under the general term, *fading*. Long-period variations are to be expected through the day, on any given frequency, because the absorption changes with the height of the sun. There is also the daily variation of the muf; when the muf drops below the frequency in use, the signal will "fade out."

In addition, the ionization at any part of the layer is in a continual state of change; there is turbulence in the ionosphere, just as there is some turbulence in the atmosphere even on quiet days when the weather seems stable. The amount of absorption is continually varying; waves entering the ionosphere at slightly dif-

ferent angles will be refracted differently; the polarization is continually changing with refraction. The wave reaching the receiving antenna is usually made up of a group of rays each of which has been acted on a little differently by the ionosphere. Sometimes the rays are more or less in phase when they strike the receiving antenna; at other times some of the rays may be out of phase with others. The result is a continual variation in signal strength that may occur at rates varying from several times a second to once every few minutes.

When transmission conditions are not alike for waves of slightly different frequency, the sidebands in voice transmission may have a different fading pattern than the carrier or than each other. This is known as selective fading. It causes severe distortion of the modulation, especially when the carrier of an a-m or fm signal

fades down while the sidebands do not. The distortion is, in general, worse with frequency modulation than with amplitude modulation, and is least with single-sideband transmission. Selective fading is more serious at the lower frequencies, such as 4 MHz, where the sideband frequencies represent a larger percentage of the carrier frequency than they do at a frequency such as 28 MHz.

Fading may be entirely different at two receiving points only a short distance apart. By the use of antennas separated by a wavelength or two, feeding separate receivers, it is possible to overcome the effects of amplitude fading, but not of selective fading. Similar use of inputs from antennas of differing polarization will often serve the same purpose. Such receiving arrangements are known as "diversity" systems.

Antennas and Transmission Lines

As an Advanced class amateur, you will be expected to know about multi-band, directional and mobile antennas. Before you tackle this section, make sure you understand the concepts in the Technician/General class chapter on antennas and transmission lines.

Transmission Lines

In the area of transmission lines, the FCC will expect you to know the characteristics of resonant versus non-resonant lines, line discontinuities, power capability and electrical length.

When the characteristic impedance of the transmission line closely approximates that of the antenna, there is a low standing-wave ratio. Under these circumstances, the transmission line can be of any length and is called flat or *nonresonant*. If the standing-wave ratio is high, the input impedance will be a pure resistance only when the line is cut to some specific length. Such a line is said to be tuned or *resonant*.

To conduct the signal from one end to the other without introducing any standing waves of its own, the transmission line must have uniform characteristics throughout its length. When the gauge or spacing of the wire changes, or the properties of the insulating material change, or a feed-line connector is used that does not have constant-impedance characteristics, there is a *discontinuity* in the line impedance at that point. Since any such discontinuities cause reflection of part of the signal, they can increase the SWR.

An important consideration in choosing a transmission line is the *power-handling capability*. The amount of power that a

transmission line can handle depends on the wire gauge and spacing, and the dielectric properties of the insulator. Use of large wire diameter, large spacing between conductors, and an insulator with high voltage-breakdown and low-loss characteristics improves the power-handling capability of the line.

Electrical Length and Velocity Factor

The *electrical length* of a transmission line is a function of the frequency at which it is used and is measured in terms of wavelength. For example, a given length of line might have an electrical length of just one wavelength at 3.5 MHz but would be 100 wavelengths long at 350 MHz. The electrical length of a transmission line will always be longer than its physical length. The reason for this is that one electrical wavelength is the distance the signal travels down the line during one complete rf cycle. The length of time of one cycle is dependent only on the frequency, but the distance traveled depends on the speed of propagation of the wave in the transmission line. In a practical feed line, the speed of a radio signal is somewhat slower than the speed of light in a vacuum. The ratio of the actual velocity at which a signal travels through a line to the speed of light in a vacuum is called the *velocity factor*. For a typical coaxial cable, for example, the velocity factor might be 0.66. To calculate the physical length of a transmission line that will have an electrical length of one wavelength, use the formulas:

$$\text{Length (m)} = \frac{300V}{f} \qquad \text{(Eq. 54)}$$

$$\text{Length (ft)} = \frac{984V}{f} \qquad \text{(Eq. 55)}$$

where
V = velocity factor
f = operating frequency in MHz

Current and Voltage Distribution

When power is fed to an antenna, the current and voltage vary along its length. The current is maximum (*loop*) at the center and nearly zero (*node*) at the ends, while the opposite is true of the rf voltage. The current does not actually reach zero at the current nodes, because of the end effect; similarly, the voltage is not zero at its node because of the resistance of the antenna, which consists of both the rf resistance of the wire (*ohmic resistance*) and the *radiation resistance*. The radiation resistance is an *equivalent* resistance, a convenient conception to indicate the radiation properties of an antenna. The radiation resistance is the equivalent resistance that would dissipate the power the antenna radiates, with a current flowing in it equal to the antenna current at a current loop (maximum). The ohmic resistance of a half-wavelength antenna is ordinarily small enough, compared with the radiation resistance, to be neglected for all practical purposes.

ANTENNAS

Multiple-Dipole Antennas

The antenna system shown in Fig. 85 consists of a group of center-fed dipoles all connected in parallel at the point where the transmission line joins them. One such dipole is used for each band; as many as four have been used, as indicated in Fig. 85. It is not generally necessary to provide a separate dipole for the 21-MHz band since a 7-MHz dipole works satisfactorily as a third-harmonic antenna on this band.

Although there is some interaction between the dipoles it has been found in practice that the ones that are not resonant at the frequency actually applied to the antenna have only a small effect on the feed-point impedance of the "active" dipole. This impedance is therefore approximately that of a single dipole, or in the neighborhood of 60 to 70 ohms, and the system can be fed through a 50- or 75-ohm line with a satisfactorily low standing-wave ratio on the line.

Since the antenna system is balanced, it is desirable to use a balanced transmission line to feed it. The most desirable type of line is 75-ohm solid-dielectric twin-lead. The transmitting variety of line should be used, since the 75-ohm receiving-type line has rather high loss, even when matched. However, either 52-ohm or 75-ohm coaxial line can be used; coax line introduces some unbalance, but this is not intolerable on the lower frequencies.

The separation between the dipoles for the various frequencies does not seem to be especially critical, so far as experience indicates. One set of wires can be suspended from the next larger set, using insulating spreaders (of the type used for feeder spreaders) to give a separation of a few inches.

Trap Dipoles

By using tuned circuits of appropriate design strategically placed in a dipole, the antenna can be made to show what is essentially fundamental resonance at a number of different frequencies. The general principle is illustrated by Fig. 86. The two inner lengths of wire, X, together form a simple dipole resonant at the highest band desired, say 14 MHz. The tuned circuits L1-C1 are also resonant at this frequency, and when connected as shown offer a very high impedance to rf current of that frequency which may be flowing in the section X-X. Effectively, therefore, these two tuned circuits act as insulators for the inner dipole, and the outer sections beyond L1-C1 are inactive.

However, on the next lower frequency band, say 7 MHz, L1-C1 shows an inductive reactance and is the electrical equivalent of a coil. If the two sections marked Y are now added and their length adjusted so that, together with the loading coils represented by the inductive reactance of L1-C1, the system out to the ends of the Y sections is resonant at 7 MHz. This part of the antenna is equivalent to a loaded dipole on 7 MHz and will exhibit about the same impedance at the feed point as a simple dipole for that band. The tuned circuit L2-C2 is resonant at 7 MHz and acts as a high impedance for this frequency, so the 7-MHz dipole is in turn insulated, for all practical purposes, from the remaining outer parts of the antenna. Carrying the same reasoning one step farther, L2-C2 shows inductive reactance

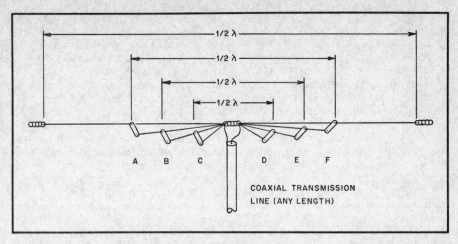

Fig. 85 — Multiband antenna using paralleled dipoles all connected to a common low-impedance transmission line. The half-wave dimensions may be either for the centers of the various bands or selected to fit favorite frequencies in each band. Length of half wave in feet is 468/frequency in MHz.

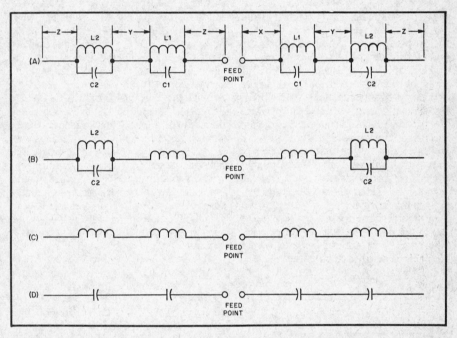

Fig. 86 — Development of the trap dipole for operation on fundamental-type resonance in several bands.

on the next lower frequency band, 3.5 MHz, and is equivalent to a coil on that band. The length of the added sections, Z-Z, is adjusted so that, together with the two sets of equivalent loading coils now indicated in C, the whole system is resonant as a loaded dipole on 3.5 MHz. A single transmission line having a characteristic impedance of the same order as the feed-point impedance of a simple dipole can be connected at the center of the antenna and will be satisfactorily matched on all three bands, and so will operate at a low SWR on all three. A line of 75-ohm impedance is satisfactory; coax may be used, but twin-lead will maintain better balance in the system since the antenna itself is symmetrical.

Since the tuned circuits have some inherent losses the efficiency of this system depends on the Qs of the tuned circuits. Low-loss (high-Q) coils should be used, and the capacitor losses likewise should be kept as low as possible. With tuned circuits that are good in this respect — comparable with the low-loss components used in transmitter tank circuits, for example — the reduction in efficiency as compared with the efficiency of a simple dipole is small, but tuned circuits of low Q can lose an appreciable portion of the power supplied to the antenna.

The lengths of the added antenna sections, Y and Z in the example, must in general be determined experimentally. The length required for resonance in a given band depends on the length/diameter ratio of the antenna conductor and on the L/C ratio of the trap acting as a loading coil. The effective reactance of an LC circuit on half the frequency to which it is resonant is equal to 2/3 the reactance of the inductance at the resonant frequency. For example, if L1-C1 resonates at 14 MHz and L1 has a reactance of 300 ohms at 14 MHz, the inductive reactance of the circuit at 7 MHz will be equal to $2/3 \times 300 = 200$ ohms. The added antenna section, Y, would have to be cut to the proper length to resonate at 7 MHz with this amount of loading. Since any reasonable L/C ratio can be used in the trap without affecting its performance materially at its resonant frequency, the L/C ratio can be varied to control the added antenna length required. The added section will be shorter with high-L trap circuits and longer with high-C traps.

Folded Dipoles

In Fig. 87, suppose for the moment that the upper conductor between points B and C is disconnected and removed. The system is then a simple center-fed dipole, and the direction of current flow along the antenna and line at a given instant is as given by the arrows. Then if the upper conductor between B and C is restored, the current in it will flow away from B and toward C, in accordance with the rule for reversal of direction in alternate half-wave sections along a wire. However, the fact that the second wire is "folded" makes the currents in the two conductors of the antenna flow in the same direction. Although the antenna physically resembles a transmission line, it is not actually a line but is merely two conductors in parallel. The connections at the ends of the two are assumed to be of negligible length.

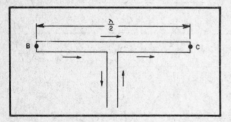

Fig. 87 — Direction of current flow in a folded dipole and associated transmission line.

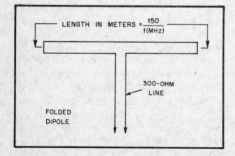

Fig. 88 — The folded dipole.

A half-wave dipole formed in this way will have the same directional properties and total radiation resistance as an ordinary dipole. However, the transmission line is connected to only *one* of the conductors. It is therefore to be expected that the antenna will "look" different, in respect to its input impedance, as viewed by the line.

The effect on the impedance at the antenna input terminals can be visualized quite readily. The center impedance of the dipole *as a whole* is the same as the impedance of a single-conductor dipole — that is, approximately 70 ohms. A given amount of power will therefore cause a definite value of current, I. In the ordinary half-wave dipole this current flows at the junction of the line and antenna. In the folded dipole the same total current also flows, but is equally divided between two conductors in parallel. The current in each conductor is therefore I/2. Consequently, the line "sees" a higher impedance because it is delivering the same power at only half the current. It is easy to show that the new value of impedance is equal to four times the impedance of a simple dipole. If more wires are added in parallel the current continues to divide between them and the terminal impedance is raised still more. This explanation is a simplified one based on the assumption that the conductors are close together and have the same diameter.

The two-wire system in Fig. 88 is an especially useful one because the input impedance is so close to 300 ohms that it can be fed directly with 300-ohm twin-lead or open line without any other matching arrangement.

The folded dipole has a somewhat "flatter" impedance-vs.-frequency characteristic than a simple dipole. That is, the reactance varies less rapidly, as the frequency is varied on either side of resonance, than with a single-wire antenna.

A folded dipole will not accept power at twice the fundamental frequency, or any even multiples of the fundamental. At such multiples the folded section simply acts like a continuation of the transmission line. No other current distribution is possible if the currents in the two conductors of the actual transmission lines are to flow in opposite directions.

On the third and other odd multiples of the fundamental the current distribution is correct for operation of the system as a folded antenna. Since the radiation resistance of a 3/2-wave antenna is not greatly different from that of a half-wave antenna, a folded dipole can be operated on its third harmonic.

Radiation Resistance and Ohmic Resistance

The energy supplied to an antenna is dissipated in the form of radio waves and in heat losses in the wire and nearby dielectrics. The radiated energy is the useful part, and so far as the antenna is concerned it represents a loss just as much as the energy used in heating the wire is a loss. In either case the dissipated power is equal to I^2R. In the case of heat losses, R is a real resistance, but in the case of radiation, R is an assumed resistance, which, if present, would dissipate the power that is actually radiated from the antenna. This fictitious resistance is called the radiation resistance. The total power loss in the antenna is therefore equal to $I^2(R_0 + R)$, where R_0 is the radiation resistance and R the real, or ohmic, resistance.

In the ordinary half-wave antenna operated at amateur frequencies the power lost as heat in the conductor does not exceed a few percent of the total power supplied to the antenna. This is because the rf resistance of copper wire even as small as No. 14 is very low compared with the radiation resistance of an antenna that is reasonably clear of surrounding objects and is not too close to the ground. Therefore it can be assumed that the ohmic loss in a reasonably well-located antenna is negligible, and that all of the resistance shown by the antenna is radiation resistance. As a radiator of electromagnetic waves such an antenna is a highly efficient device.

The value of radiation resistance, as measured at the center of a half-wave antenna, depends on a number of factors. One is the location of the antenna with respect to other objects, particularly the earth. Another is the length/diameter ratio of the conductor used. In "free space" — with the antenna remote from everything else — the radiation resistance of a resonant antenna made of an infinitely thin conductor is approximately 73 ohms. The concept of a free-space antenna forms a convenient basis for calculation because the modifying effect of the ground can be taken into account separately. If the antenna is at least several wavelengths away from ground and other objects, it can be considered to be in free space insofar as its own electrical properties are concerned. This condition can be met with antennas in the vhf and uhf range.

As the antenna is made thicker the radiation resistance decreases. For most wire antennas it is close to 65 ohms. It will usually lie between 55 and 60 ohms for antennas constructed of rod or tubing.

The actual value of the radiation resistance — at least as long as it is 50 ohms or more — has no appreciable effect on the radiation efficiency of the antenna. This is because the ohmic resistance is only of the order of 1 ohm with the conductors used for thick antennas. The ohmic resistance does not become important until the radiation resistance drops to very low values — say less than 10 ohms — as may be the case when several antennas are coupled to form an array of elements.

The radiation resistance of a resonant antenna is the "load" for the transmitter or for the rf transmission line connecting the transmitter and antenna. Its value is important, therefore, in determining the way in which the antenna and transmitter or line are coupled.

Antenna Efficiency

The *efficiency* of the antenna is the ratio of the radiation resistance to the total resistance of the system. The total resistance includes radiation resistance, resistance in conductors and dielectrics, including the resistance of loading coils if used, and the resistance of the grounding system, usually referred to as "ground resistance."

It was stated earlier in this chapter that a half-wave antenna operates at very high efficiency because the conductor resistance is negligible compared with the radiation resistance. In the case of the grounded antenna the ground resistance usually is not negligible, and if the antenna is short (compared with a quarter wavelength) the resistance of the necessary loading coil may become appreciable. To attain an efficiency comparable with that of a half-wave antenna, in a grounded antenna having a height of 1/4 wavelength or less, great care must be used to reduce both ground resistance and the resistance of any required loading inductors. Without a fairly elaborate grounding system, the efficency is not likely to exceed 50 percent and may be much less, particularly at heights below 1/4 wavelength.

Directional Antennas

At high frequencies, the most common directional antenna is the *Yagi* beam. It consists of a *driven element* equal to an electrical half wavelength at the operating frequency. A two-element beam may also have a director element which is slightly shorter and is placed forward of the driven element. A three-element beam will have in addition a reflector which is slightly longer and is placed behind the driven element. Larger beams have additional directors. Reflectors and directors are known as *parasitic elements* because they are not fed directly from the feed line. Instead, the field generated by the driven element generates currents in them which in turn generate new fields. Since these fields add together in the forward direction but cancel in the back and side directions, the transmitted energy is concentrated into a beam going out in the forward direction. In a perfect directional antenna, the radio wave would be concentrated in the forward direction only. This is known as the *major lobe* of radiation. (Most beams also have non-negligible *minor lobes* in the back and side directions.) The greater the number of elements and the longer the distance between

elements (up to an optimum spacing), the narrower the radiated beam. By reducing radiation in the side and back directions and concentrating it instead into a narrow beam in the forward direction, a beam antenna can have more effective radiated power than a dipole. The ratio expressed in dB between the signal received from a beam and the signal received from a dipole at the same transmitting location is called the *gain* of the beam. A typical beam might have "6-dB gain" which means that it makes your signal sound four times (6-dB) louder than if you were using a dipole with the same transmitter.

The gain of directional antennas is, as we said, the result of concentrating the radio wave in one direction at the expense of radiation in the other directions. Since practical antennas are not perfect, there is always some radiation in undesired directions as well. A plot of the relative field strength in all horizontal directions is called the *horizontal-radiation pattern*. The *vertical-radiation pattern* is a similar plot of the field strength in the vertical plane.

The *beamwidth* is the distance between the angles at which the gain is 3 dB below the maximum. A three-element beam, for example, might be found to have a beamwidth of 74 degrees. This means if you turn your beam plus or minus 37 degrees from the optimum heading, the received signal (and the signal received from your transmission) will drop 3 dB.

Most beams exhibit low vertical radiation angles. However, this angle can be further reduced, with a resulting increase in gain, by stacking one beam the proper distance above another. This combination of two or more antennas is called an *array*.

In addition to the Yagi, many amateurs make use of the *quad* antenna. The quad consists of two or more one-wavelength-long loops of wire in the shape of a square. As is the case with the Yagi, the director element(s) are slightly smaller than the driven element and the reflector is slightly longer.

The Yagi beam and the quad are designed to be mounted on a tower or other support so they can be rotated. This normally restricts their use, because of mechanical considerations, to the bands above 14 MHz. However, rotary beams do exist for 40 meters and even lower frequencies for those with the means to put them up. In addition, quads and Yagis can be constructed of wire and permanently mounted between masts or convenient trees. Such construction makes these antennas more practical for use on the lower frequencies.

Mobile Antennas for HF

Fig. 90 shows a typical bumper-mounted, center-loaded whip suitable for operation in the hf range. The antenna could also be mounted on the car body

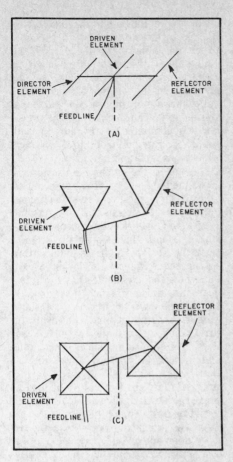

Fig. 89 — Three rotatable directional antennas. All make use of parasitic elements that reradiate energy that is electromagnetically coupled from the driven element. The Yagi (A) is most popular among radio amateurs. The delta loop (B) is nearly identical to the quad (C) except that the delta loop uses triangular rather than square elements.

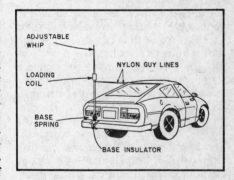

Fig. 90 — A typical bumper-mounted hf-mobile antenna. Note the nylon guy lines.

proper (such as a fender). The base spring acts as a shock absorber for the base of the whip since the continual flexing while in motion would otherwise weaken the antenna. A short, heavy mast section is mounted between the base spring and loading coil. Some models have a mechanism which allows the antenna to be tipped over for adjustment or for fastening to the roof of the car when not in use. It is also advisable to extend a couple of guy lines from the base of the loading coil to clips or hooks fastened to the rain trough on the roof of the car. Nylon fishing line of about 40-pound test strength is suitable for this purpose. The guy lines act as safety cords and also reduce the swaying motion of the antenna considerably. The feed line to the transmitter is connected to the bumper and base of the antenna. Good low-resistance connections are important here.

Tune-up of the antenna is usually accomplished by changing the height of the adjustable whip section above the precut loading coil. First, tune the receiver and try to determine where the signals seem to peak up. Once this frequency is found, check the SWR with the transmitter on, seeking the frequency of lowest SWR. Shortening the adjustable section will increase the resonant frequency and making it longer will lower the frequency. It is important that the antenna be away from surrounding objects such as overhead wires, 10 feet or more, since considerable detuning can occur. Once the setting is found where the SWR is lowest at the center of the desired operating frequency range, the length of the adjustable section should be recorded.

As the frequency of operation is lowered, an antenna of fixed length looks at its base feed point like a decreasing resistance in series with an increasing capacitive reactance. The capacitive reactance must be tuned out, which necessitates the use of a series inductive reactance or *loading coil*. The amount of inductance required will be determined by the placement of the coil in the antenna system. *Base loading* requires the lowest value of inductance for a fixed-length antenna, and as the coil is placed farther up the whip, the necessary value increases. This is because the capacitance of the shorter antenna section (above the coil) to the car body is now lower (higher capacitive reactance), requiring a bigger inductance in order to tune the antenna to resonance. The advantage is that the current distribution in the whip is improved, which increases the radiation resistance. The disadvantage is that requirement of a larger coil also means the coil losses go up. *Center loading* has been generally accepted as a good compromise with minimal construction problems.

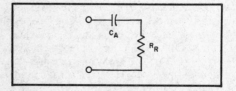

Fig. 91 — At frequencies below the resonant frequency, the whip antenna will show capacitive reactance as well as resistance. R_R is the radiation resistance, and C_A represents the capacitive reactance.

The difficulty in constructing suitable loading coils increases as the frequency of operation is lowered for typical antenna lengths used in mobile work. Since the required resonating inductance gets larger and the radiation resistance decreases at lower frequencies, most of the power may be dissipated in the coil resistance and in other ohmic losses. This is one reason why it is advisable to buy a commercially made loading coil with the highest power rating possible, even though only low-power operation is contemplated. Percentwise, the coil losses in the higher power loading coils are usually less, with subsequent improvement in radiating efficiency, regardless of the power level used. Of course, the above philosophy also applies to homemade loading coils, and design considerations will be considered in a later section.

Once the antenna is tuned to resonance, the input impedance at the antenna terminals will look like a pure resistance. Neglecting losses, this value drops from nearly 15 ohms on 15 meters to 0.1 ohm on 160 meters for an 8-foot whip. When coil and other losses are included, the input resistance increases to approximately 20 ohms on 160 meters and 16 ohms on 15 meters. These values are for relatively high-efficiency systems. From this it can be seen that the radiating efficiency is much poorer on 160 meters than on 15 meters under typical conditions.

Since most modern gear is designed to operate with a 50-ohm transmission line, a matching network may be necessary with the high-efficiency antennas mentioned previously. This can take the form of either a broad-band transformer, tapped coil, or an LC-matching network. With homemade or modified designs, the tapped-coil arrangement is perhaps the easiest one to build, while the broad-band transformer requires no adjustment. As the losses go up, so does the input resistance, and in less efficient systems the matching network may be eliminated.

Effective Radiated Power (erp)

You will notice that there are certain power limitations for repeater operation listed in the Amateur Rules. What this all boils down to is simple: The amount of power one can use with a repeater depends on the height of the repeater antenna above average terrain. The power ratings are based on *effective radiated power* (erp) from the repeater antenna. Before the amateur repeater boom, erp sounded like something from outer space to most hams. Now, though, it is just another word in the amateur's dictionary. Commercial services used erp for many years before amateurs picked it up.

It is not difficult to determine erp for a given installation. First, you need to know the exact power *output* from the transmitter. Next, deduct from this figure any losses caused by duplexers, circulators and

feed lines. Now what do you have? You have the power actually reaching the feed point of the antenna. Combine this figure with the gain of the antenna, and what is left is the effective radiated power.

For instance, let's assume we have 200 watts output from the transmitter. Also assume that our duplexer and circulator have a total of 3-dB loss. This means 100 watts is going into the feed line. Let's also assume that our feed line has an additional 3-dB loss. This means 50 watts of power will reach the feed point of the antenna. Finally, assume our antenna has a gain of 13 dB. With 50 watts reaching the antenna, and 13-dB gain, our effective radiated power is 1000 watts. Have you figured it out yet? All this talk about the effective radiated power is simply the power reaching the antenna multiplied by the gain of the antenna. You will bump into a lot of misnomers in ham radio, but effective radiated power is not one of them.

So far as the FCC rules are concerned, antenna gain is based on a half-wave dipole. This can be important, because many antenna manufacturers use an isotropic source as a reference for listing the gain of their antennas. A half-wave dipole has a *gain* of 2.14 dB over an isotropic source. The gain difference must be taken into account in order to meet FCC regulations. If, for example, an antenna is rated at 9-dB gain over an isotropic radiator, the gain of the antenna by FCC standards is 9 − 2.14, or 6.86 dB.

Antenna Coupling

An antenna coupling circuit has two basic purposes: (1) to provide the proper resistive load for the power-amplifier tube or transistor, and (2) to reduce unwanted emissions (mainly harmonics) to a very low value.

One of the coupling methods used in early transmitters was *variable-link coupling* to the power-amplifier tank circuit (Fig. 92). The coupling between the tank coil L1 and its link L2 is usually varied by rotating the link; maximum coupling occurs when the two coils are parallel. The center tap of the link is grounded for balanced feed lines, and one end is grounded for coaxial feed. Frequently, a variable capacitor is used in series with the output to cancel link inductance. Not only does this facilitate good coupling, but it provides better harmonic rejection as well.

Most modern transmitters use *pi-network coupling* (Fig. 93). Because of the series coil and parallel capacitors, this circuit acts as a low-pass filter to reduce harmonics as well as an impedance-matching device. As with the link-coupled circuit the circuit Q will be equal to the plate load impedance divided by the reactance of the tuning capacitor C1. Coupling is adjusted by varying C2, which generally has a reactance somewhat less than the load resis-

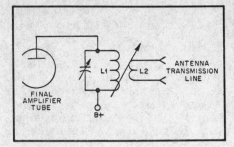

Fig. 92 — A variable-link coupling circuit.

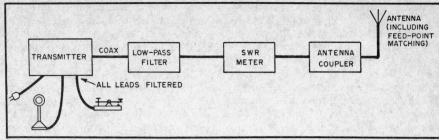

Fig. 94 — Proper connecting arrangement for a low-pass filter and antenna coupler. The SWR meter is included for use as a tuning indicator for the antenna coupler.

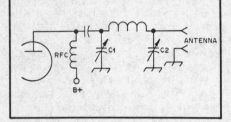

Fig. 93 — A pi-network coupling circuit. Capacitor C2 is the coupling (loading) control, and C1 is for adjusting the tuning.

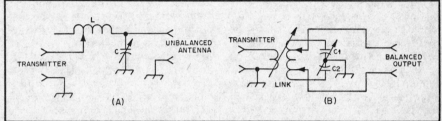

Fig. 95 — At A is an L-network antenna coupler, usable for unbalanced feed. The inductively coupled circuit at B is used with balanced feed line.

tance (usually 50 ohms). Circuit design information for pi- and link-coupled networks appears in chapter 6 of the ARRL *Handbook*.

Harmonic radiation can always be reduced to any desired level by sufficient shielding of the transmitter, filtering of all external power and control leads, and inclusion of a low-pass filter (of the proper cutoff frequency) connected with shielded cable to the transmitter antenna terminals (see Fig. 94). Unfortunately, low-pass filters must be operated into a load of close to their design impedance or their filtering properties will be impaired, and damage may occur to the filter if high power is used. For this reason, if the filter load impedance is not within limits, a device must be used to transform the load impedance of the antenna system (as seen at the transmitter end of the feed line) into

the proper value. We will, hereafter, assume this will be the commonly used value of 50 ohms.

The impedance-matching device is variously referred to as a transmatch, a matchbox or an *antenna coupler*. The *L network* (Fig. 95A) will match any unbalanced load with a series resistance higher than 50 ohms. (This assumes unlimited choice of values for L and C.) Most unbalanced antennas will satisfy this condition. If, however, no combination of L and C will perform the proper impedance transformation, the network may be reversed input-to-output by moving the capacitor to the transmitter side of the coil. To adjust this tuner, the coil tap is moved one turn at a time, each time adjusting C for lowest SWR. Eventually a combination should be found that will give a low value of SWR.

You can convert an L network into a *pi*

network by adding a variable capacitor to the transmitter side of the coil. Using this circuit, any value of load impedance can be matched using some values of coil and capacitors.

Balanced feed lines may be tuned by means of the circuit of Fig. 95B. A capacitor may be added in series with the input to tune out link inductance. As with the L network, the coil taps and tuning capacitor settings are adjusted for lowest SWR, with higher impedance loads being tapped further out from the center of the coil. For very low load impedances, it may be necessary to put C1 and C2 in *series* with the antenna leads (with the coil taps at the extreme ends of the coil). A more complete discussion of antenna couplers appears in chapter 3 of the *ARRL Antenna Book*, and several practical examples are included in the *Handbook*.

Electromagnetic Compatibility

Amateur Radio operators, especially those operating fm repeaters, often face challenges involving electromagnetic compatibility. For example, what would you do if your repeater transmitter's signal were overloading the repeater's receiver? These and other problems and concepts are investigated in this section. For background information, see chapter 15 in the 1981 *Radio Amateur's Handbook*. Also, ARRL publishes an entire book devoted entirely to the repeater and fm-oriented amateur — *FM and Repeaters*. Another League book, *Radio Frequency*

Interference, treats the subject in detail as it relates to consumer electronic devices. This section is limited to the subjects appearing on the FCC Advanced class outline.

Intermodulation Interference

Intermodulation distortion products — commonly called "intermod" or "IMD" — often create serious problems for fm-repeater operators. Intermod can affect a receiver which has poor front-end selectivity, especially if the rf amplifier and mixer stages easily overload.

Bipolar-transistor front ends are quite prone to IMD problems, and some poorly designed tube and FET front ends have no immunity either. What really goes wrong? Nonlinear operation of the rf and/or mixer stages leads to intermod problems when strong signals enter the receiver (more than one incoming signal that can be passed by the tuned circuits). These signals mix in the rf or mixer stages and produce sum-and-difference frequencies, giving rise to reception of unwanted signals and spurious responses across the band.

Even more important to a repeater operator is IMD making its debut in the last stage of the *transmitter*. If this happens to your repeater, you are not alone; most repeater groups have been plagued with transmitter IMD. Here the mixing occurs in the transmitter-output stage, and the spurious or IMD products travel through the feed line and are eventually radiated by the antenna. Single-ended Class C amplifiers are the ones most apt to have IMD, although all amplifiers can produce intermod products.

Often, a repeater owner does not have to wander too far from his repeater until he finds another amateur, or even a commercial, repeater. Sometimes, two or more repeaters operate on the same hill or skyscraper. There, nearby amateur or commercial transmitters frequently get into the "IMD act." What happens is that a strong signal from a nearby transmitter travels down the feed line from the repeater antenna, enters the PA stage, and mixes with the output frequency of the repeater, or with its second or third harmonics. For a moment, the PA tube changes roles and acts as a high-level mixer, producing a relatively strong IMD product.

For example, the offending repeater transmitter produces normal output at 146.88 MHz. On a nearby hill, a second repeater has on output frequency of 146.79 MHz. A third nearby amateur repeater transmits on 146.97 MHz. When the first two repeaters are operating at the same time, interference is heard up to several miles away on the output frequency of the 146.97-MHz system. Why? Here is how. The 146.88-MHz offender has second-harmonic energy within the PA tube (293.76 MHz). The energy from the 146.79-MHz repeater comes down the feed line of the 146.88 machine and mixes within the PA. This 146.79-MHz signal beats against the 293.76-MHz harmonic energy to produce a difference frequency of 146.97 MHz, as follows

$$f_1 \,(146.88 \text{ MHz}) \times 2 - f_2 \,(146.79 \text{ MHz})$$
$$= f_3 \text{ or } 146.97 \text{ MHz} \qquad \text{(Eq. 56)}$$

This IMD product is sent back up the feed line and radiated by the antenna.

Other products can also be produced at the same time. For instance, the 146.88-MHz signal can mix with the 146.79-MHz signal to produce the sum frequency of 293.67 MHz. This type of IMD is seldom serious because the PA tank, duplexer and antenna will attenuate the IMD product. How? They are resonant only in the 2-meter band. Of course, the first example is much more serious, with its 146.97-MHz product effectively transmitted by the 2-meter repeater.

Corrective Measures

It is the legal and moral obligation of each repeater licensee to transmit a clean signal, and to ensure that minimum spurious energy is present at the transmitter output. Therefore, certain precautions should be observed when installing a repeater system.

Using a push-pull amplifier helps reduce the possibility of in-band products (as the one in the example just mentioned). This type of amplifier tends to cancel even-order harmonics. So we reduce the most common product in the IMD dilemma — the second-harmonic current. If the amplifier is operating class C, use the smallest amount of grid current that still provides efficient operation. Excessive grid drive contributes to envelope distortion, and in turn increases the harmonic current in the stage.

Linear amplifiers have fewer IMD problems, so it is a good idea to operate the power amplifier in class AB1. To make certain the various stages of the transmitter do not have parasitic oscillation, neutralize the appropriate stages.

What about low-pass and band-pass filters? Actually, neither does much to reduce in-band IMD products. That's simply because the band-pass characteristics of such filters are never sharp enough at vhf and uhf to weaken the offending signal without also affecting the wanted signal.

Using Circulators

Some commercial firms manufacture and sell what is known as a ferrite isolator, or terminated circulator. This device is a very precisely engineered ferrite component which functions like a lossless transmission pad. Think of it as a one-way valve. Very little transmitter energy is lost through the circulator as rf travels to the antenna, but a considerable loss is imposed on any energy coming down the feed line to the transmitter. By now, a light bulb in your head should light up. That's right, the circulator can be used effectively in reducing IMD products. Another advantage in using a circulator is that it provides a matched load at the transmitter output regardless of what the antenna system SWR might be.

In addition to the circulator, a device called an isolator also helps reduce intermod. A two-port device for reducing IMD products, an isolator has a built-in termination, or load. Circulators are three-port units which can combine two or more transmitters for operation on one antenna.

Circulators and isolators are available for 144- and 450-MHz use. They come in power levels up to a few hundred watts. Typical bandwidth for a 150-MHz unit is 3 MHz. Insertion loss is roughly 0.5 dB, and rejection of the unwanted energy coming down the feeder is usually 20 to 28 dB. The 450-MHz types have greater bandwidth — about 20 MHz — but otherwise perform a lot like the 150-MHz versions. Isolators and circulators are fairly expensive, but they are worth their weight in gold as effective IMD problem solvers.

Receiver Desensitizing

One of the most frequent and serious problems encountered by repeater operators is desensitization or "desensing." Unwanted energy reaching the repeater receiver input port — usually in the form of broadband "white noise" generated in the repeater transmitter — causes this condition. However, severe line noise or energy from some adjacent-channel service (usually near the repeater site) can cause the problem.

Getting rid of a desensing problem is certainly not impossible. Although the plight actually exists in the repeater receiver, the first battle in the war against desensitization should take place in the repeater transmitter. Clean up the transmitter first. Some commercial two-way radio transmitters are designed for use in duplex systems and are very acceptable for use in repeaters. These transmitters are well shielded, their power supplies and signal leads are carefully filtered and the tuned circuits are designed for narrow-band applications (high Q) to further reduce broadband noise output. A Faraday shield between the driver and PA-stage tuned circuits also reduces white noise.

One of the first steps in checking out and preparing a transmitter for repeater service is to "narrow-band" the tuned circuits by adding capacitance across the various tank circuits, or to increase the C-to-L ratio of the circuits. Most two-way radio transmitters are designed to have a fairly wide power-bandwidth without retuning the transmitter to 500 kHz. To do this, it is necessary to reduce the tuned circuit Q, which contributes to the passage of spectrum space.

Next, filter the power and audio leads leaving and entering the transmitter. An effective method is to install a feedthrough capacitor of 500 pF or 0.001 μF (of suitable voltage rating) in each lead at the transmitter shield. If there is room, connect a vhf rf choke inside the transmitter at each feedthrough capacitor terminal. All these steps will prevent unwanted radiation of energy via the power and audio leads.

Thorough shielding of the transmitter is a must if desensing is to be minimized. The same techniques that aid in TVI reduction are useful here. The more rf-tight the shielding, the better. Incidentally, two shields of poor design often work better than one good one. You are successful if the rf output is confined to its intended path, the output terminal of the final stage of the transmitter.

Some form of band-pass filter is recommended at the transmitter output, especially in systems without a duplexer. A high-Q strip-line filter or resonant cavity is useful in reducing both white noise and energy above and below the carrier frequency.

Whenever possible, install the transmitter and receiver in two different metal cabinets. Numerous repeaters have the transmitting gear and the duplexer (if used) in one metal cabinet, and the remainder of the station equipment in another. The feed lines between the duplexer and transmitter, and between the transmitter and filter, should be doubly shielded coaxial cable (RG-9/U or equivalent) to prevent line-leakage radiation. And the same goes for cable between the duplexer and receiver. Aluminum-jacketed coaxial transmission line, sometimes called "hard line," is recommended for connecting the equipment or duplexer to the antenna. This type of line is a much firmer roadblock to leaking rf than the kind which has a shielded braid as an outer conductor.

Cross-Modulation — TVI

Under some circumstances overloading will result in cross-modulation or mixing of the amateur signal with that from a local fm or TV station. For example, a 14-MHz signal can mix with a 92-MHz fm station to produce a beat at 78 MHz and cause interference in channel 5, or with a TV station on channel 5 to cause interference in channel 3. Neither of the channels interfered with is in harmonic relationship to 14 MHz. Both signals have to be on the air for the interference to occur, and eliminating either at the TV receiver will eliminate the interference.

There are many combinations of this type, depending on the band in use and the local frequency assignments to fm and TV stations. The interfering frequency is equal to the amateur fundamental frequency either added to or subtracted from the frequency of some local station, and when interference occurs in a TV channel that is not harmonically related to the amateur transmitting frequency, the possibilities in such frequency combinations should be investigated.

Cross-Modulation — RFI

With phone transmitters, there are occasionally cases where the voice is heard whenever the broadcast receiver is tuned to a bc station, but there is no interference when tuning between stations. This is *cross-modulation*, a result of rectification in one of the early stages of the receiver. Receivers that are susceptible to this trouble usually also get a similar type of interference from regular broadcasting if there is a strong local bc station and the receiver is tuned to some *other* station.

The remedy for cross modulation in the receiver is the same as for images and oscillator-harmonic response — reduce the strength of the amateur signal at the receiver by means of a line filter.

The trouble is not always in the receiver, since cross modulation can occur in any nearby rectifying circuit — such as a poor contact in water or steam piping, gutter pipes, and other conductors in the strong field of the transmitting antenna —

external to both receiver and transmitter. Locating the cause may be difficult, and is best attempted with a battery-operated portable broadcast receiver used as a "probe" to find the spot where the interference is most intense. When such a spot is located, inspection of the metal structures in the vicinity should indicate the cause. The remedy is to make a good electrical bond between the two conductors having the poor contact.

Capture Effect

One of the most notable differences between an amplitude modulated (a-m) receiver and a frequency-modulated (fm) receiver is how noise and interference affects an incoming signal.

From the time of the first spark transmitters, "rotten QRM" has been a major problem for amateurs. The limiter and discriminator stages in an fm set can eliminate a good deal of impulse noise, except that noise which manages to acquire a frequency-modulation characteristic. For good noise suppression, the receiver i-f system and detector phase tuning must be accurately aligned. Fm receivers perform unusually when QRM is present, exhibiting a characteristic known as the *capture effect*. The loudest signal received, even if it is only two or three times stronger than other stations on the same frequency, will be the only transmission demodulated. On the other hand, an S9 a-m or cw signal can suffer noticeable interference from an S2 carrier.

Amateur Radio Practice

Dip Meter

The *dip meter* supplies rf power by coupling a tunable oscillator to a circuit being tested. The circuit absorbs the rf energy when it and the oscillator in the dip meter are tuned to the same frequency and coupled together. In a vacuum-tube version of a dip meter, the energy absorption causes a decrease or *dip* in the rectified grid current of the oscillator. This is measured by a dc microammeter. The same principle, however, can be applied to solid-state oscillators.

The dip meter will check only resonant circuits, since nonresonant circuits or components will not absorb energy at a specific frequency. The circuit must have enough Q to give sufficient coupling to the dip-meter coil for detecting the absorption of rf energy.

Measurements with the dip meter are essentially frequency measurements, and for best accuracy the coupling between the meter and circuit you're checking

must be as loose as possible and still make the *dip* on the meter.

Marker Generator

The *marker generator* in its simplest form is a high-stability oscillator generating a series of signals which, when detected in the receiver, mark the exact edges of the amateur bands (and subbands in some cases). It does this by oscillating at a low frequency that has harmonics falling on the desired frequencies. Most marker generators put out harmonics at 25-kHz or 100-kHz intervals.

The marker generator is very useful in checking transmitter frequency. How? You first tune in the signal from the transmitter on the receiver. Note the dial setting on the receiver. Then tune in and identify the *nearest* marker frequencies above and below the transmitter signal. The transmitter frequency is obviously between these two known frequencies.

If the marker frequencies are accurate,

this is all that needs to be known except that the transmitter frequency must not be so close to a band (or subband) edge that sideband frequencies, especially in phone transmission, will extend over the edge.

If the transmitter signal is "inside" a marker at the edge of an assignment, to the extent that there is an audible beat note with the receiver BFO turned off (if that's possible), normal cw sidebands are safely inside the edge.

When a transceiver is used rather than a transmitter-receiver combination and the transmitting frequency is automatically the same as the frequency the receiver is tuned to, setting the tuning dial to a spot between two known marker frequencies is all that is required.

Frequency Counters

One of the most accurate means of measuring frequency is the frequency counter. This instrument is capable of displaying numerically the frequency of the signal supplied to its input. For example, if an oscillator operating at 8.244 MHz is connected to the counter input, 8.244 would be displayed. At present, there are counters that are usable well up into the GHz range. Most counters that are to be used at high frequencies make use of a prescaler ahead of a basic low-frequency counter. Basically, the prescaler divides the high-frequency signal by 10, 100, 1000 or some other amount so that the low-frequency counter can display the operating frequency.

The accuracy of the counter depends on an internal crystal reference. The more accurate the crystal reference, the more accurate will be the readings. Crystals for frequency counters are manufactured to close tolerances. Most counters have a trimmer capacitor so that the crystal can be set exactly on frequency. A crystal frequency of 1 MHz has become more or less standard. The 10th harmonic of the crystal can be compared to the 10-MHz signal of WWV or WWVH and adjusted for zero beat.

The Oscilloscope

To observe the rapidly changing levels in a sideband transmitter an oscilloscope is absolutely necessary. No meter can keep up with the dynamic variations encountered with the human voice. Monitor scopes will fill the bill completely, or any shop-type scope that has an internal horizontal sweep generator and external vertical deflection-plate connections may be used with a tuning unit. Several inexpensive scope kits are also available.

An audio generator is the other piece of test equipment required. The standard sort of audio generator will do; one often can be borrowed from local RTTYers or hi-fi buffs, or a simple audio generator may be constructed to give a selection of frequencies. The generator should have good sine-wave output and low distortion. A two-tone generator makes testing even easier.

A typical test setup is shown in Fig. 96. All testing should be done with a dummy load, for two-tone tests can make a horrible noise on the air. The audio or two-tone generator is connected to the microphone jack of the transmitter, except when a mike is used for speech patterns. The generator should be adjusted so that its output is about at the level of the microphone you normally use. Gain adjustments should be done at the transmitter with the mike gain control. The pick-up unit is inserted between the transmitter and dummy load, and the tuning unit should be placed so short connections can be made to the scope. Don't forget to ground the scope to the tuning unit. A length of RG-58/U or RG-59/U is used to connect the tuning unit to the pick-up unit.

The transmitter to be tested should be tuned up in the cw position, or in the sideband position with a single audio tone injected, for normal input. Then adjust the tuning unit to give about half-scale deflection on the scope face, and turn on the horizontal sweep generator in the oscilloscope. Then you are ready to start testing!

Speech Patterns

Speech patterns offer rather a poor way of telling what is going on in the sideband transmitter because they come and go so fast. Yet with a little experience one can learn to recognize signs of transmitted carrier and flattening. These are useful later in monitoring on-the-air operation with a scope.

Connect a microphone to the transmitter, set the oscilloscope sweep for about 30 Hz and say a few words. The number "five" will produce a "Christmas tree" pattern similar to Fig. 97A. Each different word will produce a different pattern, which is one of the reasons that speech patterns are so hard to interpret. The important thing here is to observe the peaks to see if they are sharp, as in Fig. 97A.

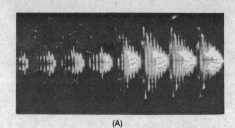

(A)

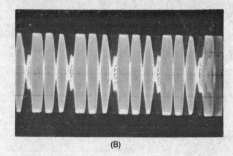

(B)

Fig. 97 — (A) Speech pattern of a correctly adjusted sideband transmitter. (B) The same transmitter with excessive drive causing peak clipping in the final amplifier.

Fig. 97B is the number "five" again but this time the mike gain is set way too high; the final stage is being overdriven resulting in clipping of the voice peaks as the final tube reaches plate-current saturation. Underloading the final stage will produce the same results. Operating a transmitter this way will produce a lot of splatter, making you unpopular with your neighbors on the band. Usually, reducing the gain control a little will remove all signs of flattening. Try different settings of the gain control until you can tell a correct pattern from one showing clipping.

If, when the mike gain is reduced to zero, the scope pattern shows you still have some output, you may be transmitting carrier. Adjustment of the balanced modulator, which is covered later, will be necessary.

A sideband transmitter should be a linear device from mike jack to output connector — for each audio frequency put in you should get out an rf frequency, with no distortion of the wave-form. The basis of a two-tone test is that you inject two audio signals, from which you should get out only two rf signals. No tube is ever perfectly linear, so some mixing of the two tones will occur, but all of the new signals produced should be so weak in comparison with the main output of the transmitter that you cannot detect their presence in a scope pattern. What you will see is the pattern of two sine-wave signals as they add and subtract, forming peaks and valleys.

A two-tone test's main advantage is that it will produce a stationary pattern that my be examined for defects. It is not easy to tell with your eye exactly what is a

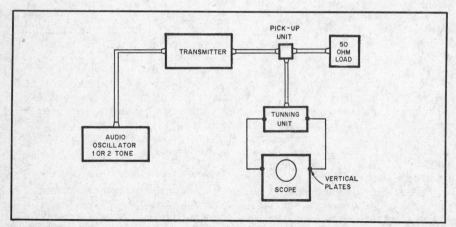

Fig. 96 — A typical test setup for a sideband transmitter.

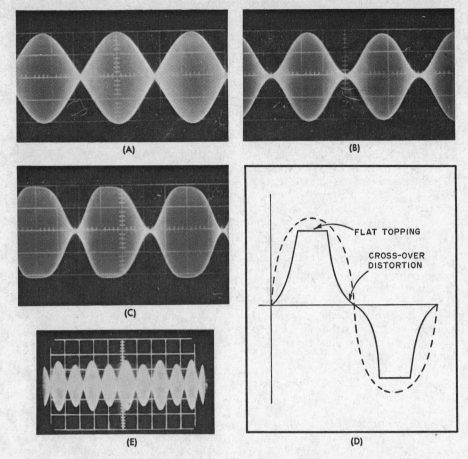

Fig. 98 — Sideband two-tone test patterns: (A) a correctly adjusted transmitter, (B) mild peak clipping and (C) severe peak clipping caused by excessive drive or underloading of the amplifier, (D) incorrect amplifier bias causing rounding of the crossover points, (E) pattern with modulation caused by carrier leak-through.

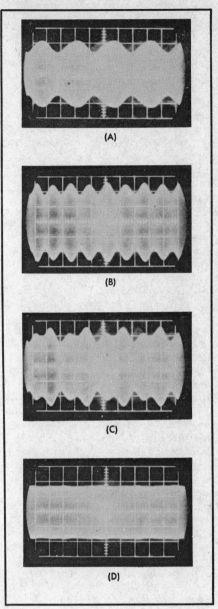

Fig. 99 — Phasing-type exciter patterns with single-tone input and constant oscilloscope sweep frequency: (A) carrier leak-through, (B) insufficient unwanted-sideband suppression, (C) both carrier leak-through and unwanted sideband, (D) correct pattern for single-tone input.

pure sine wave on a scope. Complex patterns are even more difficult, so it is a good idea to draw the correct pattern carefully on a piece of tracing paper, which then may be placed over the actual pattern on the scope face for comparison. Remember that this test will show major defects in the transmitter only.

To make the test, apply the output of the two-tone generator to the mike jack, set the 'scope sweep for about 200 Hz, and check the pattern to see that both tones are of equal level. If they are not equal level, the valleys of the waveform will not meet at a single point on the zero line. Fig. 98A shows the correct pattern; note that the crossover is in the form of an X. Another way to obtain a two-tone test signal is to use a single audio tone and unbalance the carrier to the point where it forms the pattern shown in Fig. 98A.

Examine closely Fig. 98A — this is the correct pattern. Note the clean rounded peaks and straight sides of the envelopes, and again how an X is formed at the crossover. Fig. 98B shows mild flattening of the peaks, and 98C severe flattening. The cause is the same: an amplifier stage being overdriven or underloaded. Cutting the drive level or increasing the loading should result in the Fig. 98A pattern.

Incorrect bias adjustment can also cause a stage to be nonlinear. This defect will show up as rounding of the crossover points as in Fig. 98D. The manufacturer's instruction manual should be consulted for the proper bias value and the location of the bias control. This control should be adjusted for the proper operating bias. Incorrect bias will also show up as high or low values of resting plate current. If a correct resting current and pattern cannot be obtained the tube may be bad and should be replaced.

Fig. 98E indicates what happens when an external two-tone generator is used and carrier leak-through is also present. The carrier causes the peaks of the two-tone pattern to have different heights. If this happens, you should first null out the carrier, then go back to the two-tone testing.

For carrier balance adjustments only one tone is used. The pesky carrier shows up as a sine-wave modulation, similar to what you may have seen in a-m. The carrier-balance control(s) should be adjusted until the sine-wave modulation disappears. Fig. 99D shows the pattern after the carrier has been balanced out.

The location of the carrier-balance controls may be found in the instruction manual if they are not located on the front panel. Phasing rigs usually have two controls, while the filter types have one control and a variable capacitor. In either case the action of these adjustments is somewhat interlocking. The first should be adjusted, then the second, repeating in turn until the carrier is nulled out.

Carrier balance may also be adjusted with the aid of a communications receiver if it has an S meter. The receiver should be coupled to the transmitter so you have a strong, S9 signal. Then adjust the balanced modulator as before for the least amount of indicated signal on the S meter. During this test the mike gain should be reduced to zero, so no modulation appears on the carrier.

Operating Procedures

Slow-Scan Television

Commercial TV signals take up more than 5 MHz of bandwidth. Since this is more kHz than in all the amateur bands below 6 meters, it is obvious that if we want to work TV-DX on the hf bands we will have to modify the TV signal a bit.

Slow-scan TV (SSTV) is, just as its name implies, a TV signal with a very slow scan rate. While a regular fast-scan TV signal produces 30 frames per second, it takes 8 seconds to send one SSTV frame. Thus, motion pictures are impossible. If you consider that ATV is like watching home movies by radio, then SSTV resembles a photographic slide show on the air. In addition, SSTV picture definition is four times less than with fast-scan TV.

But these disadvantages are more than balanced by the fact that SSTV can be used in any amateur phone band above 3.5 MHz. Anyone you can work with a good signal on ssb can be worked via slow scan. Many DX stations are now equipped for picture transmission, and more than one amateur has worked over 100 countries on SSTV!

The signal that comes out of an SSTV camera is a variable frequency audio tone — high tones for bright areas and low tones for dark. To send SSTV over the air, you just feed this tone into the microphone jack of any ssb transmitter. (SSTV on double sideband a-m or fm is illegal on the hf bands.) To receive, you tune in the signal on an ssb receiver and feed the audio into the SSTV monitor.

All you need to get started is an ssb station, a monitor (the slow-scan "TV set") and a camera. You don't even need the camera if you already have a tape recorder. Since a SSTV signal is just an audio tone, it can be recorded on any tape recorder (high fidelity *not* necessary). You can have a friend prerecord some pictures from his camera onto your recorder and use these for your on-the-air transmissions. Note that, like RTTY, SSTV is a 100-percent full power transmission — most ssb transmitters will have to be run considerably below their normal power ratings to avoid ruining the final amplifier or power supply.

SSTV Camera Procedures

It takes time to focus a slow-scan picture because you can't see the effects of readjusting the focus right away. It helps to have a high-contrast vertical line in the picture. As the screen is scanned from top to bottom, you can keep your eye on the vertical line while you adjust the focus. It is possible to electronically convert a fast scan TV signal to slow scan. Such fast-scan to slow-scan converters make it possible to see the results of camera adjustments immediately by watching the screen of a TV set. The camera can then be switched back to the slow-scan mode for transmission.

Lighting is critical with SSTV because the reproducible range of brightnesses is limited. You should adjust the brightness and contrast controls on the camera so that the darkest area of a screen comes out black while the brightest areas just reach maximum brightness on the monitor screen. This assumes that the monitor contrast and brightness controls are set correctly. The easiest way to do this is to use a test tape either obtained directly or recorded from another station off the air. These tapes typically have several vertical bars of various shades of gray. Proper monitor calibration is achieved when the darkest bar is just dark enough to blacken the screen completely while the brightest bar just reaches maximum brightness.

Your subjects don't all have to be either "live" or on tape. Some SSTVers find it convenient to mount the camera in front of an easel into which various prepared cards can be inserted. These cards can be photographs, drawings or lettered signs. A kitchen-type noteboard with press-on removable letters is handy for making headings. You can also buy or build a keyboard-operated device that prints characters on the SSTV screen. It sends the same message over and over until you erase it or type something else. A simple way to avoid the expense of a camera is to build a flying-spot scanner. This is a device that sends pictures by scanning a slide transparency (with a "flying spot" of light). Even many of the SSTVers who do own cameras have an "FSS" because you can build a large library of slides, any one of which can be selected for on-the-air showing almost instantly. In addition to this convenience, having an FSS frees the camera for other uses — no need constantly to be readjusting the lighting and focus when you move the camera from subject to subject.

What do you make pictures of? The selection of subjects is endless, but you will find that high-contrast black-and-white pictures that aren't cluttered with too much detail work best. Some possibilities are a close-in shot of you in front of the operating position, cartoons (commercial or homemade) or a couple of frames with your call and perhaps name and QTH.

SSTV Operating Procedures

It's customary to send two or three frames of each subject to ensure that the other station gets at least one good quality picture. Many ops like to send a couple of frames followed by voice comments concerning the picture just sent. Some of the more elaborate setups are equipped to send video and audio simultaneously with the voice on one sideband and the picture on the other! These "ISB" (independent sideband) signals can be copied with two receivers or a single receiver with two i-f filters, detectors and audio ampifiers.

SSTV has good potential for rendering service to the public by means of third-party traffic. For example, the scientists working on the Antarctic ice pack often don't see their families for months — except by amateur slow-scan TV. Anyone can write or call almost anywhere in the world these days, but how often can grandma and grandpa talk to (and see instant photos of) the kids from 3000 miles away — without a toll charge!

SSTV is legal anywhere in the Advanced and Extra Class voice segments of the 75, 40, 20 and 15-meter bands, and all voice bands above 28 MHz. The standard calling frequencies are 3845, 7171, 14,230, 21,340 and 28,680 kHz, with 75 and 20 meters being the most popular bands.

An SSTV signal must be tuned in properly so that the picture will come out with the proper brightness and so that the 1200-Hz synchronization pulses will be detected. If the signal is not "in sync" the picture will appear wildly skewed. The easiest way to tune SSTV is to wait for the transmitting operator to say something on voice and then tune him in while he is talking. With experience you may find you are able to zero in on an SSTV signal by listening to the sync pulses and by watching for proper synchronization on the screen. Many SSTV monitors are equipped with tuning aids of various kinds.

If you want to record slow-scan pictures off the air, there are two ways of doing it. One is to tape record the audio signal for playback later. The other is to take a picture of the image right from the SSTV screen. Polaroid cameras equipped with a closeup lens enable you to see the results shortly after the picture is taken. If you want to do this without darkening the room lights, you'll have to fabricate a light-tight hood to fit between the camera and monitor screen.

On any amateur transmission, the legal identification must be made by voice or cw. Sending "This is WA0XYZ" on the screen is *not* sufficient. Most stations intersperse the pictures with comments anyway, so voice i-d is not much of a problem. Otherwise SSTV operating procedures are quite similar to those used on ssb.

Facsimile

Facsimile is transmission of pictures by radio. "FAX" is similar to SSTV except that the picture definition is much better, and the image comes out on paper rather than on the face of a picture tube. Using inexpensive surplus facsimile machines, good newspaper quality photographs can be sent on any of the amateur vhf/uhf bands. Many amateurs and other experimenters use FAX to receive government weather satellite photographs beamed direct from the satellite. On a clear day you can see forever — or a good-sized piece of North America, anyway!

Facsimile standards depend on the particular machine in use. All FAX machines make their copies on current- or light-sensitive paper wrapped around a drum. As the drum revolves, the marking device moves slowly down the side, etching a close-spaced series of parallel lines from top to bottom of the paper. The darkness of the mark depends on the strength of the signal as it is received. For transmission, a similar mechanical arrangement is used except that instead of a marking device, a photo-sensitive pickup unit scans the copy. Thus variations in lightness and darkness of the picture are transformed into variations in amplitude of the output signal. Typical standards call for 60, 120 or 180 lines per minute and 72 or 96 lines per inch. The popular Western Union Telefax unit rotates at 180 lines per minute with 72 lines per inch and produces an amplitude-modulated, 2400-Hz signal that can be fed into the microphone input of any vhf a-m transmitter. (Fm FAX is not legal on the 6 and 2 meter bands.) Drum synchronization is tied to the ac house current.

Rules and Regulations

The FCC expects every amateur to know and abide by its rules. Therefore, it should not be surprising to find a list of rules to be learned in the FCC's Advanced class study outline. Every Advanced class license applicant can expect to be tested on the rules found in this section. The numbers in parentheses refer to the section of Part 97 of the Commission's Rules. Part 97 is printed in its entirety in Chapter 9 of this *License Manual.*

Frequency Bands Available to the Advanced Class Amateur (§97.7(a))

The only amateur frequencies not permitted Advanced class amateurs are those reserved for the Amateur Extra class. This simplifies matters because the only amateur frequencies *not* permitted Advanced class operators are as follows:
3500-3525 kHz and 3775-3800 kHz
7000-7025 kHz
14,000-14,025 kHz
21,000-21,025 kHz and 21,250-21,270 kHz
Refer to the frequency chart on page 00, and you will see that we are talking about the bottom 25 kHz of the 80-, 40-, 20-, and 15-meter bands, plus the bottom 25 kHz of the 80- and 15-meter *phone* bands. The Advanced class licensee is permitted on any other amateur frequency.

Limitations on Use of Frequencies (§97.61)

Applicants for the Advanced class license should read rule §97.61 and be familiar with the frequency and emission limitations of the amateur bands. A chart in chapter 9 summarizes most of the mode limitations for the hf bands. Take special note of cw-only portion of the bands.

You should also know that the amateur 160-meter band has power and frequency restrictions dependent on the amateur's location and the time of day (daytime or nighttime). In addition, some amateur bands are shared with other services. For example, in Region 2 (North and South America), some countries allow their mobile services to operate on the 80-meter band. If you hear one of these stations, you should not interfere with it because the basic principle is the equality of opportunity to operate. See §97.61(b)(3).

Other frequency and power limitations apply when operation is conducted on certain frequencies from some areas. See §97.61(b)(4-13). Also, you should know that *repeater operation* is permitted on the following frequencies:
52-54 MHz
144.5-145.5 MHz and 146-148 MHz
420-431 MHz and 433-435 MHz
All amateur frequencies above 438 MHz
Auxiliary operation is permitted on all frequency bands above 220.5 MHz, except for 431-433 and 435-438 MHz.

Automatic Retransmission of Amateur Radio Signals and Signals From Other Radio Services (§97.3(x), 97.113 and 97.126)

Automatic retransmission means retransmission of signals by an Amateur Radio station whereby the retransmitting station is actuated solely by the presence of a received signal through electrical or electromechanical means. (In other words, there is no direct, positive action by the control operator.) Only stations in repeater, auxiliary or space operation may automatically retransmit the signals of other Amateur Radio stations, and no amateur station may automatically retransmit programs or signals emanating from any class of station other than amateur. For example, a repeater station may not automatically rebroadcast a NOAA weather station transmission.

Amateur Radio Stations in Repeater Operation (§97.3(l), 97.85 and 97.61(c))

Repeater operation is defined in the rules as radiocommunication, other than auxiliary operation, for retransmitting automatically the radio signals of other Amateur Radio stations. You should also know that a repeater's "squelch tail" should be no longer than five seconds. In other words, when a user station stops transmitting through a repeater, it usually takes a few seconds for the repeater to stop transmitting. The rules require that the repeater operation be discontinued within *five seconds*.

A repeater may not have more than one output frequency on the same band from the same location. Thus, it would be illegal for W1XX/R to have an input frequency on 146.34 MHz and output frequencies on 146.94 MHz *and* 146.78 MHz.

You must know the frequency bands on which repeater operation is permitted. See the section above on *Limitations on Use of Frequencies.*

Amateur Radio Stations in Auxiliary Operation (§97.3(l), 97.86 and 97.61(d))

An Amateur Radio station is said to be in *auxiliary* operation if it is being used to do any of the following:
1) remotely control another Amateur Radio Station;
2) automatically relay the radio signals of other Amateur Radio stations in a system of stations;
3) intercommunicate with other Amateur Radio stations in a system of stations.
Note: An Amateur Radio station used to remotely control a model craft or other object *is not* auxiliary operation. The object being radio-remotely controlled must be another Amateur Radio station for it to be auxiliary operation. We will talk a little more about the remote control of Amateur Radio stations in the next section of this chapter.

A station in auxiliary operation may communicate only with the stations shown in the system network diagram entered in the station log. A station in auxiliary operation may, itself, be remotely controlled by another station in auxiliary operation as long as it is part of the system shown in the system network diagram. A station in auxiliary operation must use the amateur frequencies above 220.5 MHz (except 431-433 and 435-438 MHz), but if the auxiliary station is replaying a repeater station's signals, it would be permitted to use an input (receiving) frequency located in a repeater band.

Remote Control of Amateur Radio Stations (§§97.3(m)(2), 97.88)

As we have mentioned before, it is legal for an Amateur Radio station to be controlled by another Amateur Radio station. The station doing the controlling is in auxiliary operation. If you are remotely controlling a repeater station using another radio station (station in auxiliary operation), you may not use the input frequency of the repeater to effect control. An Amateur Radio station may also be remotely controlled by a means other than radio signals. For example, a telephone wire may be used to carry the signals controlling the remotely controlled station. In this situation, you would have no auxiliary operation, just a remotely controlled station. FCC defines remote control as manual control, with the control operator monitoring the operation on duty at a control point located elsewhere than at the station transmitter, such that the associated operating adjustments are accessible through a control link.

Now let's turn our attention to the station being remotely controlled. FCC requires that the remotely controlled station have a provision designed to limit its transmission to a period of no more than *three minutes* in case the control link fails.

At the remotely controlled station site, you must post, in a conspicuous place, a photocopy of the station's license. You must also post the name, address and telephone number of the station licensee and the same information for at least one control operator. Unless the remotely controlled station is operating under automatic control, the control operator must be on duty at all times of operation and monitor the station's emissions. The control operator shall terminate all transmissions upon any deviation from the rules.

Automatic Control of Amateur Radio Stations (§97.3(m)(3))

Automatic control means the use of devices and procedures for control so that a control operator does not have to be present at the control point at all times. (Only rules for automatic control of stations in repeater operation have been adopted.) Examples of devices and procedures: automatic identification, access to the station limited by a locked door, education of users and frequent "on-site" inspections by a control operator. A station in auxiliary operation, either locally controlled or remotely controlled, may also be operated by automatic control when it is operated as part of a system of stations in repeater operation operated under automatic control.

Control Link (§97.3(n))

A control link is apparatus for effecting remote control between a control point and a remotely controlled station. A control link could use a radio link or wire link.

System Network Diagram (§97.3(u))

A system network diagram shows each station and its relationship to the other stations in a network of stations, and to the control point(s). See the section below, "Station Log Requirements," to see when a system network diagram must be entered in a station log.

Station Identification (§97.84(c), (d) and (e))

An Amateur Radio station in repeater operation or a station in auxiliary operation used to relay automatically the signals of other stations in a system of stations shall be identified by radiotelephony or radiotelegraphy at a level of modulation sufficient to be intelligible through the repeated transmission at intervals not to exceed 10 minutes.

Repeater Operation

When identifying by radiotelephony, a station in repeater operation shall transmit the word "repeater" at the end of the station call sign. When identifying by radiotelegraphy, a station in repeater operation shall transmit the fraction bar $\overline{DN}$, followed by the letters RPT, or R at the end of the station call sign. (The requirements of this subparagraph do not apply to stations having call signs prefixed by the letters WR.)

Auxiliary Operation

When identifying by radiotelephony, a station in auxiliary operation shall transmit the word "auxiliary" at the end of the station call sign. When identifying by radiotelegraphy, a station in auxiliary operation shall transmit the fraction bar $\overline{DN}$, followed by the letters AUX or A. A station in auxiliary operation may be identified by the call sign of its associated station as long as one of the aforementioned procedures indicating auxiliary operation is used.

Station Log Requirements (§97.103 (c), (d), (e), (f) and (g).

FCC used to require separate licenses for repeaters and auxiliary stations; presently, however, all amateurs (except Novices) may now operate their stations in repeater or auxiliary operation without having to file anything with the FCC. But additional entries are required in your *station log*.

Remotely Controlled Station

The log of a remotely controlled station must have the names, addresses and call signs of all authorized control operators. It must also contain a functional block diagram of the control link as well as a technical explanation sufficient to describe its operation. In addition, the log must contain descriptions of (1) the measures taken for protection against unauthorized operation, (2) the measures taken for shutting down the station in case the control link fails and (3) the means used for monitoring the transmitting frequencies.

One or More Associated Stations

Whenever a station has one or more associated stations; that is, stations in repeater or auxiliary operation, a *system network diagram* shall be entered in the station log.

Repeater Operation Logging

Depending on the frequency band and effective radiated power (erp) used, the FCC may require that additional information be entered in a station log for repeater operation. This additional information is required if: (1) a 6-meter repeater exceeds 25 watts (erp); (2) a 2-meter or 220 MHz repeater exceeds 100 watts (erp); or (3) a 420-MHz band repeater exceeds 400 watts (erp). If a repeater station using the bands mentioned above exceeds the specified power, the station log must contain the following:

1) the location of the transmitting antenna marked on a topographic map

2) the transmitting antenna's height above average terrain (HAAT)

3) the station's maximum power output (erp) calculation of the main lobe of the antenna pattern

4) transmitter output power

5) the loss (in decibels) in the transmission line

6) the transmitting antenna gain and

7) the horizontal and vertical radiation patterns of the transmitting antenna with reference to true North.

Auxiliary Operation Logging

The FCC also requires that additional information be entered in a station log for auxiliary operation. You must enter the following:

1) a system network diagram

2) the station transmitting band(s)

3) the transmitter output power and

4) details of its remote control if it is being operated by remote control.

Height Limitations for Amateur Radio Station Antenna Structures, Including FAA Notification Criteria, and Calculation of Height Above Average Terrain (§97.45, 97.67(c) and Appendix 5)

Before an amateur puts up an antenna, he should be aware of height limitations designed to avoid interference to air traffic. Generally, an amateur does *not* have to notify the Federal Aviation Administration (FAA) if (1) the antenna is shielded by existing structures of a permanent and substantial character or by natural terrain or topographic features of equal or greater height, and would be located in a congested area of a city, town or settlement where it is evident beyond all reasonable doubt that the structure so shielded will not adversely affect safety in air navigation, or (2) the antenna is 20 feet or less in height.

You will have to notify the FAA and FCC of your antenna (and possibly be required to get special approval) if your antenna (1) exceeds 200 feet in height above ground level, (2) is located near an airport or heliport (see §97.45(a) for minimum heights and distances), or (3) is located at an airport.

Study Questions

1) During periods of minimal solar activity, what is the most likely mechanism for propagating a 50-MHz signal over a 2000-km path?
A) Extended ground wave.
B) Knife-edge diffraction.
C) Sporadic E-layer refraction.
D) F2-layer refraction.

2) Which of the following effects is *not* attributable to selective fading?
A) Garbled teleprinter signals on the 3.6-MHz band when no interference is present.
B) Occasional severely distorted a-m voice signals in the 160-meter band.
C) Enhanced long-distance reception of television signals in the 420-450 MHz band.
D) Occasional loss of some of the frequency components of a modulated wave.

3) Which of the following is *not* an effect of the aurora borealis?
A) Blackout of ionospheric propagation in the hf spectrum.
B) F-layer refraction in the 10.0-10.5 GHz band.
C) All long-distance vhf signals arrive from a polar direction.
D) Long-distance vhf signals are distorted from spectrum spreading.

4) If the geometric horizon is 100 km from a point above smooth earth, what is a typical maximum range for "line of sight" radio communication from that point?
A) 114 km
B) 92 km
C) 100 km
D) 287 km

5) A certain frequency counter has a known accuracy of ±(10 ppm + 1 digit) and a resolution of 1 Hz. What is the lowest reading that can be accepted to ensure that a cw transmitter having a 40-dB keying bandwidth of 100 Hz is within the 40-meter amateur band?
A) 7.000001 MHz
B) 7.004706 MHz
C) 6.999998 MHz
D) 7.000121 MHz

6) Which of the following devices can be used to measure the frequency of a microwave signal?
A) Cavity wavemeter
B) Lecher wires
C) Slotted line
D) All of the above

7) What instrument might be used to detect spurious resonances in an rf choke?
A) Wouff hong
B) Dip oscillator
C) Time-domain reflectometer
D) Distortion analyzer

8) An oscilloscope can be used to
A) Check the linearity of an ssb transmitter.
B) Ensure that all spurious emmissions from a transmitter comply with §97.73 of the amateur rules.
C) Measure the period and peak-to-peak voltage of an audio-frequency signal.
D) A and C.

9) Two signals having frequencies of 144.098 and 144.174 MHz are applied to the input of a receiver that tunes the 2-meter amateur band. If the input stage exhibits high third-order intermodulation distortion, the receiver will produce outputs when tuned to
A) 144.098 and 144.174 MHz.
B) 144.022, 144.098, 144.174 and 144.250 MHz.
C) 144.090, 144.098, 144.174 and 144.182 MHz.
D) 144.098, 144.174, 145.098 and 145.174 MHz.

10) Cross modulation
A) is a likely cause of interference between two fm stations.
B) is the superimposition of one a-m signal's modulation envelope on another signal's carrier.
C) is a receiver defect resulting from nonlinear operation of an rf amplifier or mixer stage.
D) B and C

11) Receiver desensing
A) can occur if the agc bandwidth is greater than the signal bandwidth.
B) may be an indication of poor dynamic range.
C) can occur in a repeater station having insufficient isolation between the transmitter and receiver.
D) All of the above.

12) The capture effect
A) causes a well-designed fm receiver to respond only to the stronger of two signals having the same frequency.
B) is a result of excessive hysteresis in a receiver agc loop.
C) is of academic interest only and has no practical application to radio communications.
D) causes a receiver to respond only to ssb signals.

13) The efficiency of an antenna
A) depends on the feed line SWR.
B) is the ratio of the power radiated to the power delivered by the feed line.
C) is important for receiving purposes only.
D) None of the above.

14) The velocity factor of a transmission line
A) is the ratio of physical length to the electrical length.
B) is the reciprocal of the square root of the dielectric constant.
C) is the ratio of the speed of the rf wave in the line to the speed of light in free space.
D) All of the above.

15) The radiation resistance of an antenna system
A) is the ratio of voltage to current at the feedpoint if the system is resonant and lossless.
B) is a measure of the system's ability to withstand long exposure to the ultra-violet component of sunlight.
C) is always independent of height above ground for a horizontal radiator.
D) should be zero for maximum efficiency.

16) A 6-element Yagi array on a single boom most typically would have
A) four driven elements in phase and two "dummy" elements to absorb energy beamed to undesired directions.
B) a half-wavelength dipole driven element, a reflector and four directors.
C) 12 dB gain over a reference rhombic.
D) 6 m^2 of wind-loading area.

17) What is the purpose of traps in a multiband antenna?
A) To establish resonance in each of the desired bands.
B) To allow greater element length, thus enhancing efficiency.

C) To prevent the radiation of harmonics or other spurious emissions.
D) To double the receiving efficiency by preventing any reradiation of the impinging wavefront.

18) How are antenna gain and beamwidth related?
A) They are independent.
B) For a constant efficiency, gain increases with decreased beamwidth.
C) Gain is proportional to the square root of the beamwidth.
D) Beamwidth is the ratio of gain to boom length.

19) Describe the voltage and current distribution on a quarter-wavelength vertical antenna fed against ground.
A) The current is maximum at the feedpoint and minimum at the top.
B) The voltage is minimum at the base and maximum to the free end.
C) The voltage and current are constant along the radiator.
D) A and B

20) Of the following antennas, which is the most reasonable compromise between electrical performance and mechanical practicality for 75-meter mobile operation?
A) A 3-foot whip with a capacitive top hat.
B) An 8-foot whip with center or base loading.
C) A helical dipole.
D) A conical monopole.

21) What is the most suitable time base element for a frequency counter requiring a long-term accuracy of 1 ppm?
A) A series-tuned Colpitts oscillator.
B) A temperature-compensated crystal oscillator (TCXO).
C) An oven-controlled crystal oscillator.
D) B or C

22) Which of the following factors does *not* influence the frequency stability of a well-buffered oscillator?
A) Variation of the load impedance.
B) Mechanical shock.
C) Ambient temperature.
D) Tank-circuit heating from rf current.

23) In an a-m transmitter the class-C final amplifier _____ varies in step with the modulating waveform.
A) power input
B) efficiency
C) A and/or B
D) filament temperature

24) In amplitude modulation
A) the carrier amplitude does not vary.
B) the intelligence is contained in the sidebands.
C) the rf output envelope takes the shape of the modulating waveform.
D) All of the above.

25) What type of amplifier is suitable for increasing the amplitude of an a-m signal?
A) A linear amplifier.
B) A class-C amplifier.
C) A saturated amplifier.
D) None of the above.

26) A reactance modulator is used in
A) an ssb transmitter.
B) an fm transmitter.
C) an a-m receiver.
D) a video sync generator.

27) The carrier suppression of an ssb signal generated by the phasing method is controlled by
A) The balanced modulator.
B) the audio preemphasis network.
C) the linearity of the frequency multiplier stages.
D) the power supply ripple voltage.

28) An ssb signal can be demodulated by
A) an envelope detector.
B) a phase detector.
C) a product detector.
D) a metal detector.

29) What circuit in a transmitter or receiver would be used to heterodyne a signal to a different frequency for processing?
A) an rf amplifier.
B) an i-f amplifier.
C) a buffer amplifier.
D) a mixer.

30) What section of a superheterodyne receiver establishes the dominant gain and selectivity?
A) The beat frequency oscillator.
B) The i-f amplifier.
C) The noise blanker.
D) The r-f amplifier.

31) If a composite video signal from a television camera is applied to a varactor diode in an oscillator tank circuit, what emission type will result?
A) A5
B) A4
C) F4
D) F5

32) Which of the following components is likely to be used in a receiver agc circuit?
A) Hot-carrier diode.
B) PIN diode.
C) Zener diode.
D) Varactor diode.

33) What do tunnel diodes, unijunction transistors and neon lamps have in common?
A) They can be used in relaxation oscillator circuits.
B) They must be operated with negative base-to-collector bias.
C) Nothing.
D) They can be used as pilot lights.

34) When minimum saturation voltage is required of a power transistor, what semiconductor material should be used?
A) Gallium arsenide.
B) Germanium.
C) Silicon.
D) Lead sulphide.

35) Silicon-controlled rectifiers and triacs are the solid-state analogs of
A) latching relays.
B) stepping relays.
C) voice-operated relays.
D) mercury-wetted relays.

36) A crystal-lattice filter
A) uses silicon crystals for thermal stability.
B) uses crystal pairs having an approximately 2-kHz frequency difference.
C) is designed using the same crystal frequencies as a ladder filter having the same bandwidth.
D) has too narrow a passband for cw reception.

37) Which of the following is *not* a characteristic of a class-C amplifier?
A) Can be used as a frequency multiplier.
B) Can be used to amplify fm signals.
C) Conducts current over small intervals of the excitation cycle.
D) None of the above.

38) State the resonant frequency, 3-dB bandwidth and Q of the circuit in Fig. 1.
A) f_o = 16.24 MHz, BW = 2.98 MHz, Q = 5.4
B) f_o = 1624 kHz, BW = 20.8 kHz, Q = 54.5
C) f_o = 14.1 MHz, BW = 250 kHz, Q = 56.4
D) f_o = 141 MHz, BW = 2.5 MHz, Q = 56.4

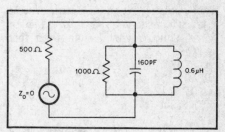

Fig. 1

39) What determines the color generated by a light-emitting diode?
A) The type of semiconductor material used.
B) The array multiplexing frequency.
C) The reverse bias voltage.
D) The forward bias current.

40) What capacitance value is required to cause maximum voltage drop across the resistor in Fig. 2? What is the approximate bandwidth of the circuit?

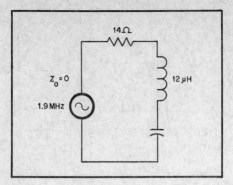

Fig. 2

A) C = 410 pF, BW = 81 kHz.
B) C = 585 pF, BW = 186 kHz.
C) C = 58.5 pF, BW = 18.6 kHz.
D) C = 41 pF, BW = 810 kHz.

41) A certain transmitter uses a 5-element Chebyshev low-pass filter. What could be done to improve the harmonic attenuation without compromising the impedance match seen by the transmitter?
A) Change the filter to a 5-element half-wave design.
B) Redesign the filter for a higher ripple value.
C) Change the end sections from constant-k to m-derived.
D) Replace the filter with one having 7 elements and the same ripple value.

42) What type of filter could best suppress an unwanted fixed-frequency spurious emission near a desired output frequency band?
A) A Butterworth filter.
B) A notch filter.
C) A pi-section filter.
D) A T-section filter.

43) The sharpness of resonance of a pi-network output tank circuit in a linear rf power amplifier depends on
A) the impedance transformation ratio.
B) the excitation to the final stage.
C) the peak-to-average power ratio of the operator's voice.
D) none of the above.

44) A spectrum analysis of a square wave having a fundamental frequency of 1 kHz would show strong components at:
A) 111, 143, 200, 333 and 1000 Hz.
B) 62, 125, 250, 500 and 1000 Hz.
C) 1000, 2000, 4000, 8000 and 16000 Hz.
D) 1000, 3000, 5000, 7000 and 9000 Hz.

45) How is the peak voltage of a sine wave related to the rms value?
A) Peak = rms × $\sqrt{2}$
B) Peak = rms × $1/\sqrt{2}$
C) Peak = $\sqrt{3}$ /rms
D) Peak = rms + π/rms + $2\pi/rms^2$ + $3\pi/rms^3$ + . . .

46) Two cw signals, each isolated from the other, are applied to a load resistor.

What is the peak envelope power if each tone has a power of 200 watts? What is the average power taken by the resistor?
A) PEP = 800 watts, average = 100 watts.
B) PEP = 400 watts, average = 400 watts.
C) PEP = 200 watts, average = 100 watts.
D) PEP = 800 watts, average = 400 watts.

47) What is the polarity (with respect to the earth) of the electric field in the vicinity of a quarter-wavelength Marconi antenna erected perpendicular to the surface of the earth?
A) elliptical
B) right-hand circular
C) vertical
D) random

48) If a dipole driven element in a parasitic array shows a resistive impedance of 12 ohms, what would the impedance be if the driven element were replaced with a folded dipole having three equal-diameter conductors?
A) 12 ohms
B) 52 ohms
C) 300 ohms
D) 108 ohms

49) How is the signal-to-noise ratio of an fm communications system related to the modulation index?
A) S/N increases with modulation index.
B) S/N decreases with modulation index.
C) S/N increases with modulation indices up to 0.6.
D) S/N is not related to modulation index.

50) What is the deviation ratio for an fm transmitter having a maximum frequency swing of ± 5 kHz and accepting a maximum modulation rate of 3 kHz?
A) 0.6
B) 1.67
C) 15
D) 8

51) How does the modulation index of a phase-modulated emission vary with the modulating frequency?
A) The modulation index increases with the modulating frequency.
B) The modulation index decreases with the modulating frequency.
C) The modulation index does not vary with the modulating frequency.
D) Modulation index has no meaning in phase modulation.

52) Of the following antennas, which would respond best to the magnetic field near a horizontal dipole?
A) A small loop in a plane perpendicular to the dipole.

B) A short vertical whip.
C) A quadrifilar helix.
D) A terminated rhombic.

53) A Zener diode is used to establish a reference voltage at the base of a silicon emitter follower transistor. What Zener voltage should be chosen to produce 13.2 volts at the emitter?
A) 13.2 volts.
B) 12.6 volts.
C) 13.8 volts.
D) 14.9 volts.

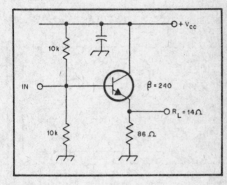

Fig. 3

54) What is the low-frequency input impedance of the circuit shown in Fig. 3?
A) 14 ohms
B) 20 k ohms
C) 1831 ohms
D) 1479 ohms

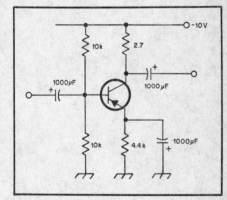

Fig. 4

55) In the circuit of Fig. 4, how much output voltage will a 1000-Hz, 24-mV input signal produce?
A) 4.8 V
B) 2.5 V
C) 78 mV
D) 240 mV

56) What phenomenon other than self resonance will cause the Q of an inductor to increase with frequency, peak, and then decline with further frequency increase?
A) Gunn effect
B) Miller effect
C) Doppler effect
D) skin effect

57) How long can an electrostatic charge be stored in an ideal capacitor?
A) Indefinitely
B) One second per volt-Farad of energy stored.
C) One second per coulomb of charge.
D) One second per ampere of charging current.

58) In the circuit of Fig. 5, state the phase angle of the voltage with respect to the current in the generator, the power factor seen by the generator, the apparent power delivered by the generator and the power consumed by the load resistor.
A) 18.7°, 0.947, 439.5 VA, 416.2 W
B) 24.2°, 0.864, 501.1 VA, 489.6 W
C) 13.4°, 1.234, 114 VA, 972 W
D) 364°, 2.718, 24 VA, 619 W

59) What is the effective radiated power from the main lobe of the antenna shown in Fig. 6?
A) 90 W
B) 900 W
C) 72 W
D) 720 W

60) The network feeding the load in Fig. 7 can be replaced by
A) a 5-volt battery in series with a 43.4-ohm resistor.
B) a 9-volt battery in series with a 24.8-ohm resistor.
C) a 3.7-volt battery.
D) None of the above.

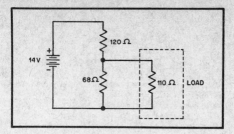

Fig. 7

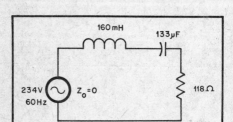

Fig. 5

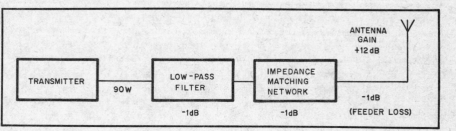

Fig. 6

Chapter 7

The Amateur Extra Class License

The Amateur Extra Class is the highest class license available to the radio amateur and carries with it *all* amateur privileges. For this reason, the Amateur Extra Class examination is the most comprehensive of the FCC amateur tests. The material contained in this chapter, therefore, is intended solely as a study guide, not as a definitive text. In addition to this book you should have a copy of the ARRL *Radio Amateur's Handbook*.

You can expect questions on the examination to be worded in such a manner that the correct answer can be determined only on the basis of a thorough understanding of the principles involved. Simple memorization of a few questions and answers is no longer sufficient.

Printed below is the FCC's study outline, which lists the subjects the test will cover. This chapter does not follow the same subject *order* as the FCC's outline; we've rearranged the subjects in a different order to make studying a little easier. However, we recommend that you constantly refer to the FCC outline printed here and check off each topic as you cover it. If you have trouble with a certain subject, make a note of it on the outline so that you can come back to it.

Federal Communications Commission Study Guide
Amateur Extra Class Amateur Radio Operator License Examination

(Element 4B Syllabus)

A. Rules and Regulations

1) Frequency bands available to the U.S. Amateur Radio operator and limitations on their use including variations for Regions 1 & 3 97.61; 97.95
2) Space Amateur Radio stations 97.3(i)
3) Purity of emissions 97.73
4) Mobile operation aboard ships or aircraft 97.101
5) RACES operation Part 97, Subpart F
6) Points of communications 97.89

B. Operating Procedures

1) Use of Amateur Radio satellite
2) Amateur fast-scan television

C. Radio Wave Propagation

1) EME; "Moonbounce"
2) Meteor Burst
3) Trans-equatorial

D. Amateur Radio Practice

Use of test equipment:
1) Spectrum analyzer; interpret display; display of transmitter output spectrum, such as commonly found in new product review articles in Amateur Radio magazines
2) Logic probe; indication of high or low state, pulsing state

Electromagnetic compatability:
3) Vehicle-noise suppression; ignition noise, alternator whine, static
4) Direction-finding techniques; methods for location of source of radio signals

E. Electrical Principles
Concepts:

1) Photoconductive effect
2) Exponential charge/discharge

Mathematical relationships; calculations:

3) Time constant for R-C and R-L circuits (including circuits with more than one resistor, capacitor or inductor)
4) Impedance diagrams; basic principles of Smith Chart
5) Impedance of R-L-C networks at a specified frequency
6) Algebraic operations using complex numbers; real, imaginary, magnitude, angle

F. Circuit Components

Physical appearance, types, characteristics, applications, and schematic symbols for:
1) Field-effect transistors; enhancement, depletion, MOS, CMOS, n-channel, p-channel
2) Operational amplifier and phase-locked loop integrated circuits
3) 7400 series TTL digital integrated circuits
4) 4000 series CMOS digital integrated circuits
5) Vidicon; cathode ray tube

G. Practical Circuits

1) Digital logic circuits; flip-flop, multivibrator, AND/OR/NAND/NOR/ gates
2) Digital frequency divider circuits; crystal marker, counters
3) Active Audio Filters using integrated operational amplifiers

High-performance receiver characteristics
4) Noise figure, sensitivity

5) Selectivity
6) Dynamic range

Calculation of voltages, currents, and power in common Amateur Radio-oriented circuits:
7) Integrated operational amplifier; voltage gain, frequency response
8) FET common-source amplifier; input impedance

Circuit design; selection of circuit component values
9) LC preselector with fixed and variable capacitors to tune a given frequency range
10) Single-stage amplifier to have desired frequency response by proper selection of bypass and coupling capacitors

H. Signals and Emissions

1) Pulse modulation; position, width
2) Digital signals
3) Narrow-band voice modulation
4) Information rate vs. bandwidth
5) Peak amplitude of a signal
6) Peak-to-peak values of a signal

I. Antennas and Feedlines

1) Antennas for space radio communications; gain, beamwidth, tracking
2) Isotropic radiator; use as a standard of comparison
3) Phased vertical antennas; resultant patterns, spacing in wavelengths
4) Rhombic antennas; advantages, disadvantages
5) Matching antenna to feedline; delta, gamma, stub
6) Properties of 1/8-, 1/4-, 3/8-, and 1/2-wavelength sections of feedlines; shorted, open

A Review of Some Needed Fundamentals

Before we delve into the specific subjects on which you will be tested, a quick review of some basic circuit theory is in order.

Time Constant

When a voltage is applied to a series RC (resistance-capacitance) or RL (resistance-inductance) circuit, the current through the circuit and the voltage across the inductor or capacitor do not reach the final value instantaneously. Rather, they change value over a period of time determined by the component values. This period is defined in terms of the *time constant*. The time constant is the time required for the current or voltage to die down to 36.8 percent of the initial value or to build up to $100 - 36.8 = 63.2$ percent of the final value. Time constant is expressed as $TC = RC$ or L/R.

In the example of Fig. 1A, the time constant is equal to 1 megohm $\times$ 1 microfarad $= (1 \times 10^6) \times (1 \times 10^{-6}) = 1$ second. When the switch is thrown to the "shorting" position, current flows from the capacitor through the resistor. After a period of time equal to one time constant (1 second in this case), the voltage across the capacitor will have discharged to 36.8 volts. After 2 seconds, the voltage will be reduced to 0.368^2 times the initial value or 13.5 volts. During the third time constant, the voltage will die down to 36.8 percent of 13.5 or 5 volts. This process continues forever with the voltage across the capacitor decreasing by 63.2 percent each time constant.

If the capacitor is initially discharged and the switch is then thrown to the "charging" position, the voltage across the capacitor will reach $100 \times (1 - 0.368) = 63.2$ volts in one second. During the next second, this voltage will build up to $100 \times (1 - 0.368^2) = 100 - 13.5 = 86.5$ volts. Eventually (after about 5 time constants) the voltage will be very close (within less than 1 percent) to its final value.

As can be seen from the above discussion, the rate of change in voltage across the capacitor decreases with increasing time. The change in voltage per unit time (the *voltage gradient*) thus gets smaller the longer the time lapse from the instant the switch was thrown. The graph of voltage or current versus time follows what is known as an *exponential* curve, as shown in Fig. 1B.

Chapter 2 of the ARRL *Handbook* gives additional information about time constants.

AC Circuit Theory

In Chapter 7 it was explained how to calculate the impedance of a circuit consisting of coils, capacitors and resistors in series. This is reviewed in the *impedance diagram* of Fig. 2. By the Pythagorean theorem of right triangles, impedance is given by

$$Z = \sqrt{R^2 + X_t^2} \qquad \text{(Eq. 1)}$$

where
R = the total series resistance
X_t = the total series reactance
Since inductive and capacitive reactances are of opposite sign, $X_t = X_L - X_C$ where X_L and X_C are inductive and capacitive reactance, respectively. An example of the total impedance calculation is shown in Fig. 2.

In Fig. 2, the *phase angle* between the voltage and the current is indicated by the angle between the resistance and impedance vectors. If the impedance vector is *above* the resistance on the diagram (Fig. 3B), the phase angle is *positive* (meaning the voltage leads the current), and if the impedance vector is below the resistance (Fig. 3C), the phase angle is *negative* (meaning the voltage lags the current). The phase angle will always be between plus and minus 90 degrees since the resistance is never negative. If you are familiar with trigonometry, you can see that the phase angle, θ, between the voltage and current is given by

$$\tan \theta = \frac{X_t}{R} \qquad \text{(Eq. 2)}$$

where
X_t = the total reactance ($X_L - X_C$)

or

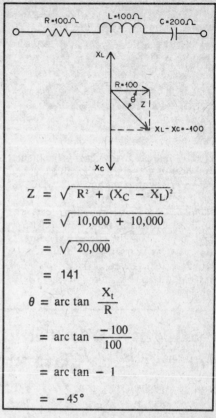

$$Z = \sqrt{R^2 + (X_C - X_L)^2}$$
$$= \sqrt{10,000 + 10,000}$$
$$= \sqrt{20,000}$$
$$= 141$$
$$\theta = \text{arc tan} \ \frac{X_t}{R}$$
$$= \text{arc tan} \ \frac{-100}{100}$$
$$= \text{arc tan} \ -1$$
$$= -45°$$

Fig. 2 — By the Pythagorean Theorem, total impedance is the square root of the sum of the squares of the resistance and reactance.

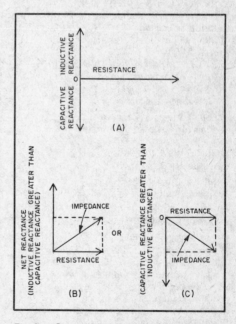

Fig. 3 — Conventional method of representing resistance and inductive and capacitive reactance on an impedance diagram (A). Impedance is the vector sum of reactance and resistance (B,C). (See text.)

$$\theta = \text{arc tan} \ \frac{X_t}{R} \qquad \text{(Eq. 3)}$$

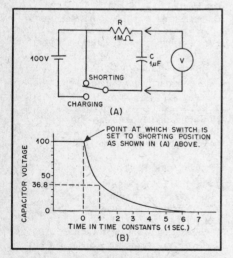

Fig. 1 — In the circuit at A, when the switch is in the charging position, current flows from the 100-volt supply through resistor R to charge capacitor C. When the switch is set to the shorting position the capacitor discharges through the resistor. At B is a graph of capacitor voltage as a function of time.

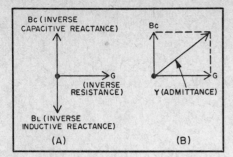

Fig. 4 — The admittance diagram (A) is similar to the impedance diagram of Fig. 3A. For this reason, total admittance (B) is calculated in a similar manner. (See text.)

When components are in parallel, their resistances and reactances do not combine in any simple way; however, their *admittances* do. Admittance is inverse *impedance* so it is measured in *mhos*, or inverse ohms. ("Mho" is "ohm" spelled backward!) A 50-ohm resistor has 1/50 or 0.02-mhos admittance. A capacitor with a reactance of 20 ohms has an admittance of 1/20 or 0.05 mhos.

On an admittance diagram (Fig. 4), inverse resistance is indicated by a horizontal vector pointing to the right, inductive admittance by a vector pointing vertically downward, and capacitive admittance by a vector pointing upward. Total admittance Y is calculated using the Pythagorean theorem

$$Y = \sqrt{G^2 + B_t^2} \qquad \text{(Eq. 4)}$$

where

G = the sum of all the inverse resistances in the circuit (G = 1/R1 + 1/R2 +...
B_t = the total inverse reactance

Since inverse inductive and capacitive reactances are of opposite sign, $B_t = B_C - B_L$ where B_C and B_L are the sum of all the inverse inductive and capacitive reactances are of opposite sign, $B_C = 1/X_{C1} + 1/X_{C2} +...$and $B_L = 1/X_{L1}, + 1/X_{L2} +...$). The total circuit impedance is then given by $Z = 1/Y$.

The example of Fig. 5 should make this more clear. The sum of the inverse resistances is G = 1/5 + 1/10 = 0.1 + 0.2 = 0.3 ohms. The two coils in parallel have a total inverse reactance of 1/20 + 1/20 = 0.05 + 0.05 = 0.1 mhos. The inverse reactance of the capacitor is 1/2 =

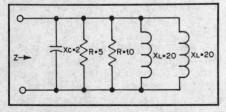

Fig. 5 — A circuit in which total impedance is most readily calculated using admittances. (See text.)

0.5 ohms. Total inverse reactance is thus $B_t = 0.5 - 0.1 = 0.4$, and the total admittance is

$$Y = \sqrt{0.3^2 + 0.4^2} = \sqrt{0.09 + 2.16}$$

$$= \sqrt{0.25} = 0.5 \text{ mhos} \qquad \text{(Eq. 5)}$$

Thus Z = 1/Y = 1/0.5 = 2 ohms.

Phase angle is calculated in the same way as for series circuits, substituting admittance for impedance

$$\tan \theta = \frac{B_t}{G} \text{ or} \qquad \text{(Eq. 6A)}$$

$$\theta = \text{arc tan } \frac{B_t}{G}$$

where

B_t = the total inverse reactance ($B_C - B_L$)
G = the inverse resistance

When θ is positive, the current leads the voltage and when θ is negative, the current lags the voltage. Note the difference between this and the phase relationship in a series circuit mentioned above.

If the inductors and capacitors had been specified by their component values instead of by their reactances, we would first have had to convert using the reactance formulas.

$$X_C = \frac{1}{2 \pi f C} \qquad \text{(Eq. 7A)}$$

and

$$X_L = 2\pi f L \qquad \text{(Eq. 7B)}$$

Ohm's Law for Complex Impedance

No matter how complicated any two terminal network may be, the relationship between the magnitudes of voltage and current can always be reduced to the simple formula

$$E = IZ \qquad \text{(Eq. 8)}$$

where

E = the voltage across the two circuit terminals
I = the current through the network
Z = the impedance

Resonant Circuits

In a series-*resonant* circuit, inductive and capacitive reactances cancel so that total impedance is just equal to the series resistance of the circuit. Impedance of a series-resonant circuit is *minimum* at the resonant frequency.

Similarly, in a parallel-resonant circuit, inverse inductive and capacitive reactances are equal ($B_c - B_L$) so that the total inverse reactance is zero ($B_t = B_C - B_L = 0$). Total admittance is just the inverse resistance

$$Y = \sqrt{0 + G^2} \qquad \text{(Eq. 9)}$$

so that the impedance is equal to the total

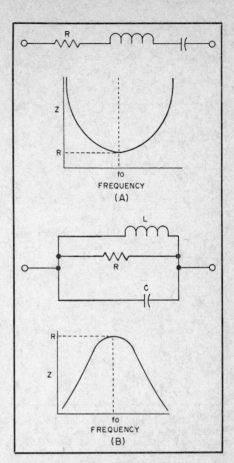

Fig. 6 — Impedance of a series-resonant circuit (A) is minimum at resonance while the impedance of a parallel-resonant circuit (B) is maximum at resonance.

resistance in parallel with the tuned circuit ($Z = 1/Y = 1/G = R$). Total impedance of a parallel-resonant circuit is *maximum* at the resonant frequency.

Since in either a series- or parallel-resonant circuit resonance occurs when the capacitive and inductive reactances are equal, the following relationship holds.

$$X_L = 2\pi f L = X_C = \frac{1}{2\pi f C}$$

$$1 = \frac{1}{(2\pi f L)(2\pi f C)}$$

$$f^2 = \frac{1}{(2\pi)^2 LC}$$

$$f = \frac{1}{2\pi \sqrt{LC}} \qquad \text{(Eq.10)}$$

If you don't want to memorize this formula, you can always figure it out again as we have just done. In any case, this is an equation you should know.

Note that since inductive and capacitive reactance (or inverse reactance) change in opposite directions as the frequency is changed, there will be only *one* frequency at which a coil and capacitor will have the

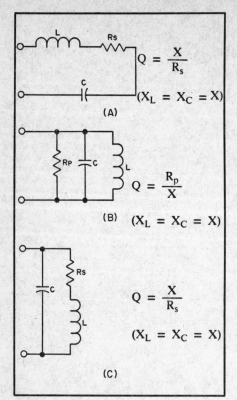

$$Q = \frac{X}{R_s}$$

$$(X_L = X_C = X)$$

(A)

$$Q = \frac{R_p}{X}$$

(B)

$$(X_L = X_C = X)$$

$$Q = \frac{X}{R_s}$$

$$(X_L = X_C = X)$$

(C)

Fig. 7 — The Q-factor of a tuned circuit is a measure of how much it is affected by resistance. The higher the Q, the sharper the selectivity (i.e. the narrower the bandwidth). X is the reactance of either the coil or capacitor at resonance R_s is the series resistance, and R_p is the parallel resistance.

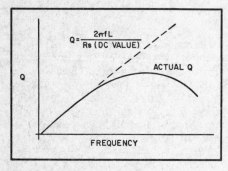

Fig. 8 — For low frequencies, the Q of an inductor is proportional to frequency. At high frequencies, increased losses in the coil cause the Q to decrease.

same reactance. In other words, a tuned circuit is resonant on only one frequency.

The more a resonant circuit is affected by resistance, the higher its Q factor. A series-resonant circuit with zero series resistance or a parallel-resonant circuit with infinite parallel resistance (zero resistive admittance) has infinite Q. More exactly, in a series-resonant circuit:

$$Q = \frac{X}{R_s}$$

(Eq. 11)

and in a parallel-resonant circuit:

$$Q = \frac{R_p}{X}$$

(Eq. 12)

where

> X = the reactance at resonance of either the coil or capacitor
> R_s = the series resistance
> R_p = the parallel resistance

Thus the Q-factor of a tuned circuit is a measure of how much it is affected by resistance (Fig. 7A and B).

Just to complicate matters a little, we should also point out that in a *parallel-resonant* circuit, resistance in series with either the coil or capacitor can also lower the Q (Fig. 7). The *unloaded* Q of a resonant circuit is its Q when it is not connected to anything and is determined by the series resistance of the inductor. (Usually the capacitor's series resistance is negligible.) The *loaded* Q is the Q of a tuned circuit when it is loaded down by the resistance of the circuit in which it is used.

It is often convenient to speak of the unloaded Q of a coil even when it is not being used in a tuned circuit. The formula is $Q = X_L/R_s$ where X_L is the reactance of the coil and R_s is its series resistance. Since inductive reactance is proportional to frequency ($X_L = 2\pi fL$), the Q of a coil also increases proportional to frequency. This assumes that the series resistance is the same at all frequencies. Actually, however, at high frequencies, the series resistance increases due to skin effect and losses in the core material (if any). At very high frequencies, the resistive losses increase faster than the coil reactance and the Q begins to decrease with increasing frequency (see Fig. 8).

RC Differentiation and Integration

The word *differentiation* is derived from the same root as the word *difference*. The *derivative* of something is its rate of change. For example, the rate of change of distance is velocity. Thus we say that the derivative of distance is velocity.

If a battery is connected to a previously discharged capacitor, the capacitor will charge quickly to the full battery voltage. The current that flows the instant the battery is connected is very high, depending upon the amount of resistance in the wires and battery. If the voltage changes instantaneously from one voltage to another, its rate of change (or current) is very high. In the case of a square wave, every time the voltage changes from one value to another, a very high current flows through the capacitor, first in one direction, then the other (Fig. 9A). Theoretically, if we had a circuit that had no resistance, the current pulses at these instantaneous voltage change times would be infinite.

If a sine-wave voltage is applied to the capacitor, the current will be maximum when the sine wave is changing value most rapidly, and the current wil be zero when the sine wave is not changing (that is, when it is at a positive or negative peak). The current through a capacitor is thus a

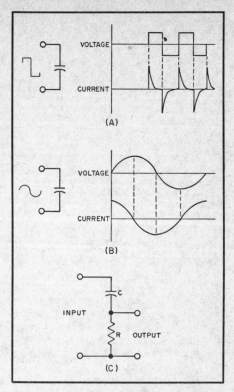

Fig. 9 — The current through a capacitor is proportional to the rate of change (derivative) of the voltage. Since the rate of change of a square wave is nearly infinite each time the signal flips from one voltage level to another, the current through the capacitor is nearly infinite at these times (A). The derivative of a sine wave is another sine wave that is phase-shifted 90 degrees (B). At C is a practical RC differentiator. (R must be small compared to the reactance of C at the highest frequency of interest.)

sine wave that leads the voltage by 90 degrees (Fig. 9B).

The circuit of Fig. 9C is a practical differentiator. So long as resistor R is small, it has little effect on the current through capacitor C. Thus since the voltage drop across R is proportional to the current through C, the output voltage is approximately the derivative of the input voltage. This circuit is known as an *RC differentiator*.

Integration is the converse of differentiation. An integrator takes a continuous sum of the signal at its input.

If you travel 5 feet per second for 10 seconds, you end up 50 feet from your starting point. If you then slow down to 1 foot per second and remain at that speed for 10 seconds, you move another 10 feet for a total of 60 feet (Fig. 10A). Since distance traveled is a continuous sum of the velocity, we say that distance is the integral of velocity.

Likewise in a capacitor, voltage is the integral of current. If 5-mA dc is passed through a 0.001-farad (1000 μF) capacitor for 10 seconds, the capacitor will charge to 50 volts. If the current is then reduced to 1 mA for another 10 seconds the voltage will rise another 10 volts to 60 volts.

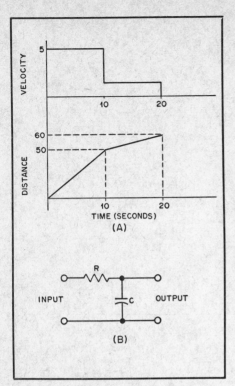

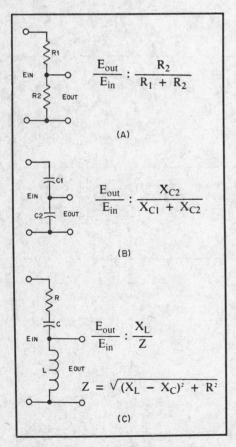

Fig. 10 — Distance is the integral of velocity, as illustrated at A. Since voltage across a capacitor is the integral of the current, the circuit at B can be used as an integrator (if R is large compared to the reactance of C at the lowest frequency of interest).

Fig. 11 — Voltage dividers that use only components of the same type (A and B) divide an ac voltage proportional to the component impedances. Circuits that use components of different types (C) are slightly more complex.

The circuit of Fig. 10B is a practical integrator. If resistor R is large enough, capacitor C will have little effect on current through R. Thus, since the current through C is proportional to the input voltage, output voltage is approximately the integral of the input voltage. This circuit is known as an *RC integrator*.

AC Voltage Division

A voltage divider consisting entirely of resistances as shown in Fig. 11A, divides the applied dc voltage directly proportional to the resistance values. In the case of ac voltage dividers, the process is similar. The voltage will divide proportionally to the value of reactance if the divider elements are all of the same type, as shown in Fig. 11B. However, if the divider consists of combinations of resistors, capacitors and inductors, the voltage across any element or elements is equal to the ratio of the impedance of that element to the total divider impedance (Fig. 11C).

Nonsinusoidal Waves

Most ac-circuit theory is based on the use of a pure sinusoidal waveform. Voltages, for example, are given as rms values unless otherwise specified. While the peak voltage of a sine wave is equal to 1.41 times the rms value, this is not usually true for nonsinusoidal waves. In addition, while nonsinusoidal waves contain a variety of frequency components, an unmodulated sine wave contains energy at only a single frequency.

A *sawtooth wave*, as shown in Fig. 12A, is so named because it closely resembles the teeth on a saw blade. It is characterized by a rise time significantly faster than the fall time (or vice versa). A sawtooth wave is made up of a sine wave at the fundamental frequency and sine waves at all the harmonic frequencies as well. When a sawtooth voltage is applied to the horizontal deflection plates of an oscilloscope, the electron beam sweeps slowly across the screen during the slowly changing portion of the waveform and then flies quickly back during the rapidly changing portion of the signal. This is what is desired to obtain a linear sweep in an oscilloscope.

A *square wave* is one which abruptly changes back and forth between two voltage levels and which remains an equal time at each level (Fig. 12B). (If it spends an unequal time at each level, it is known as a rectangular wave.) A square wave is made up of sine waves of the fundamental and all the *odd* harmonic frequencies.

Filters

A *filter* is an electrical circuit designed to have a specified frequency response — that is, to attenuate specific frequencies by given amounts. A *low-pass filter* permits low frequencies to pass through relatively unimpeded but attenuates all

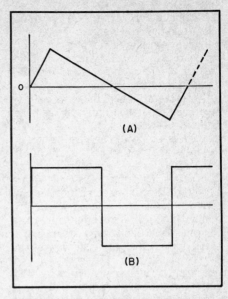

Fig. 12 — Any waveform that is not a pure sine wave contains harmonics. Sawtooth waves (A) consist of both odd and even harmonics as well as the fundamental. Square waves consist of only fundamental and odd-harmonic frequencies.

signals above a specified *cutoff frequency*. The high-pass filter does just the opposite — it passes high frequencies but attenuates signals below the cutoff frequency. A *band-pass* filter allows only frequencies in a specified passband to go through, attenuating all higher and lower frequencies. A tuned circuit is a simple type of band-pass filter. A *band-stop* filter attenuates frequencies in a specified band while allowing all others to pass. A tuned wave trap is an example.

The *constant-k filter*, Fig. 13A, is so called because the product of the impedances of the series and shunt elements equals a constant (k^2) at all frequencies. This filter has only a gradual transition between the passband and stopband, but it does maintain high attenuation for frequencies far removed from the passband.

M-derived filters make use of a parallel or series-tuned trap to attenuate undesired frequencies that are too near the cutoff frequency to be properly eliminated by a constant-k filter. As shown in Fig. 13B, however, m-derived filters have poor attenuation at frequencies far from the cutoff frequency. These filters are called m-derived because a parameter m is used in the design to specify the ratio between the trap frequency $f\infty$ and the cutoff frequency f_C.

More than one filter sction may be connected in tandem to improve the filtering action, as shown in Fig. 13C. Of course, the two parallel components shown would be combined into a single unit in a practical circuit. K- and m-derived sections are always combined into a single filter to obtain the best characteristics of each type — that is, good attenuation both near and far away from the cutoff frequency (Fig. 13D).

It is important that these filters be terminated in the proper values of input and output resistance. Knowing this resistance, the cutoff frequency and, in the case of m-derived filters, the frequency of infinite attenuation (trap frequency), you can determine the exact component values from the formulas in chapter 6 of the ARRL *Handbook*.

A power-supply *ripple filter* is a type of low-pass filter. In this instance, the cutoff frequency is set as low as is practicable to give as much attenuation to the 60- or 120-Hz ripple voltage as possible. In the case of the simple, single-capacitor filter of Fig. 14A, this is done by making the capacitor large enough that its reactance at the ripple frequency is much lower than the load resistance. (To compute load resistance, divide ouput voltage by load current.) Series choke inductors are often added to further reduce ripple (Fig. 14B and C). Specific design information can be found in chapter 5 of the ARRL *Handbook*.

The Thyristor

The *thyristor*, also known as the silicon-controlled rectifier (SCR), is a diode whose forward conduction from cathode to anode is controlled by a third terminal, the gate. Specifically, the diode will not conduct until the voltage exceeds the forward-breakdown voltage, a value that is determined by the gate current. Once the rectifier begins to conduct, the gate no longer has any control, and the device behaves as a low-forward-resistance diode. This condition persists until the voltage drops to zero again at which time the forward-breakdown voltage barrier is re-established, and the gate regains control.

Fig. 15A shows a typical motorspeed control/light-dimmer circuit using a thyristor. During each positive half cycle, the SCR will not conduct until the 0.1-μF capacitor has charged up to the conduction voltage of the neon bulb. When the bulb fires, sufficient gate current flows to trigger the thyristor, and it conducts for the remainder of the half cycle. The percentage of the half cycle that SCR conducts is determined by the RC time constant and can be varied by adjusting the 100-kΩ resistor. Since this circuit will only conduct in one direction, two thyristors are often used (Fig. 15B) to allow up to nearly full 360-degree conduction time. The same thing can be done using a *triac*, a type of bi-directional thyristor. Electrically, a triac is equivalent to two SCRs connected back-to-back (anode-to-cathode) with their gates tied together. A practical triac circuit is described in chapter 17 of the ARRL *Handbook*.

Power Supplies

So-called *electronic voltage regulation* is a technique of providing a very steady power-supply voltage by means of a *pass*

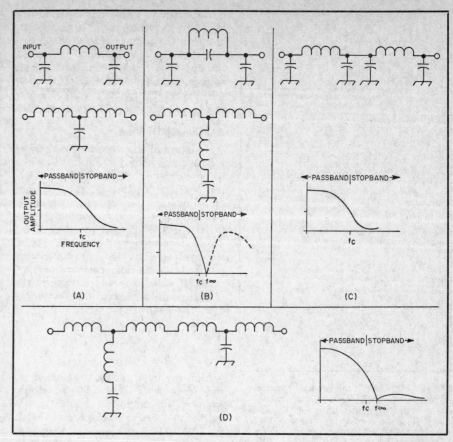

Fig. 13 — Constant-k (A) and m-derived (B) filters and their frequency responses. While these are all low-pass filters, they may be transformed into high-pass filters by replacing each coil with a capacitor whose reactance is the same at the cutoff frequency and by replacing each capacitor with a coil with the same reactance at the cutoff frequency.

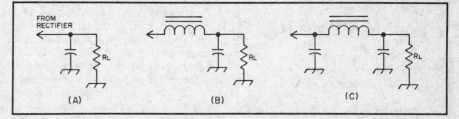

Fig. 14 — Power-supply ripple filters. The capacitor-input filters of A and C usually have an output voltage somewhat higher than the transformer rms output voltage, depending on transformer and rectifier series resistance and load current. The choke input filter at B will produce an output voltage that is very near .9 times the rms voltage for all load currents above a certain minimum value.

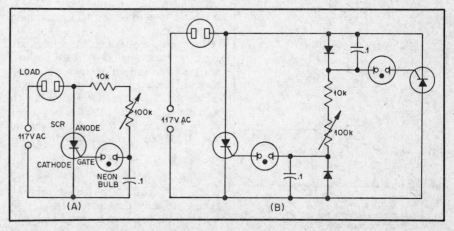

Fig. 15 — A pair of thyristor (SCR) light-dimmer/motor-speed control circuits. The circuit at A conducts only on half cycles while the circuit at B has up to nearly 360-degree conduction.

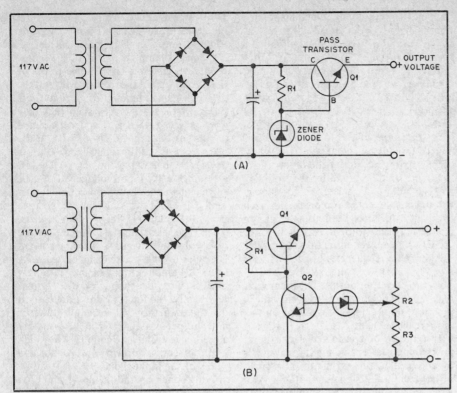

Fig. 16 — Electronic voltage-regulator circuits. The circuit at A is suitable for fixed output voltages. At B the output voltage may be adjusted by varying the setting of potentiometer R2.

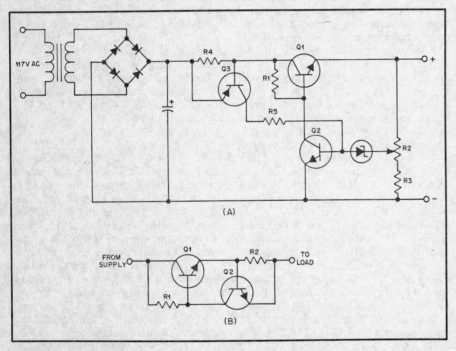

Fig. 17 — At A, a current-limiting transistor Q3 has been added to the circuit of Fig. 16B. The two-terminal current limiter at B may be added to any power-supply circuit.

transistor or *series control tube* in series with the unregulated voltage source. The conduction of the control device is controlled in such a way that a nearly constant voltage appears at the output no matter how much load current is drawn. The simplest implementation of this idea uses only three components in addition to the rectifier and filter (Fig. 16A). This circuit may be viewed as an emitter follower —

the output voltage at the transistor emitter closely follows the voltage at its base. Since the voltage across the zener diode is nearly constant, then so will be the output voltage. Resistor R1 provides operating current for the Zener diode and bias current for the transistor.

The circuit of Fig. 16B has an adjustable output voltage. Under normal conditions, the voltage at the wiper-arm

terminal of R2 is equal to the Zener-diode voltage plus the transistor base-emitter forward voltage drop, hereafter referred to as the reference voltage. If the output voltage starts to increase, Q2 base current will increase, and Q2 will draw more current. This will cause a greater voltage drop across R1 so the Q1 base voltage will decrease and thus force the output voltage down again. Similarly, if the output voltage tries to decrease, Q2 will conduct less, Q1 base voltage will increase, and the output voltage will be brought back up. Now, the adjustment of R2 sets the percentage of the output voltage that appears across the Zener diode and Q2 base-emitter junction, but as we have just shown, the regulator circuit automatically adjusts the output potential so that the voltage on the wiper arm of R2 just equals the reference voltage. Thus the setting of R2 determines the output voltage. Note that the lowest voltage attainable with this circuit is the reference voltage. The highest voltage is the reference voltage times the ratio (R2 + R3)/R3.

One disadvantage that both of these circuits have is that if you accidentally short the output, the regulator will pass a very large current in an attempt to keep up the output voltage. This, of course, will cause the pass transistor to self-destruct. In Fig. 17A, Q3 acts as a *current limiter*. As the load current rises, the voltage drop across R4 increases until it reaches the base-emitter forward conduction voltage of Q3. When that happens, Q3 conducts and feeds a relatively large current (limited only by R5) into the base of Q2. This causes Q2 to conduct, the voltage drop across R1 increases, and the output voltage goes down. Output current is thus limited to a value determined by R4 and the base-emitter conduction voltage of Q3.

Fig. 17B shows a two-terminal current limiter usable in any power-supply circuit. R1 normally provides enough bias current so that Q1 is biased on and current flows freely through the limiter. When the current is high enough that the voltage drop across R2 equals the base-emitter conduction voltage of Q2, it conducts. This removes bias from Q1 so that it stops conducting, and the limiter cuts off power to the load. While this device may be placed either on the load side or the supply side of the regulator, it is usually placed on the power-supply side since the resistance of R2 in series with the regulator output can degrade its performance.

Voltage regulation is covered in chapter 5 of the ARRL *Handbook*.

Amplifiers

A *power amplifier* is an amplifier whose purpose is not only to amplify a signal, but to provide enough output power to drive a utilization device, such as a loudspeaker or antenna system. The final amplifier in a radio transmitter is a type of

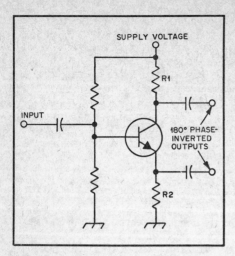

SUPPLY VOLTAGE

R1

INPUT

180° PHASE-
INVERTED
OUTPUTS

R2

Fig. 18 — A transistorized phase inverter. If R1
and R2 are equal, then the two output signals
will be of nearly equal amplitude.

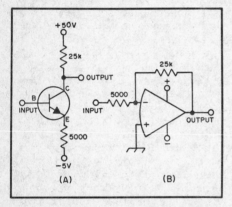

+50V

25k

OUTPUT

C

B
INPUT

E

5000

−5V

(A)

25k

5000

INPUT

−

+

OUTPUT

(B)

Fig. 19 — Two representative dc amplifiers.
The circuit at A has a 25-volt output offset
voltage, while the operational amplifier design
at B has nearly zero offset voltage. Voltage
gain of both amplifiers is 5.

power amplifier, and for this reason, it is
often referred to as the "PA." High-
frequency amplifiers are covered later in
this section.

A *phase inverter* (also called a *phase
splitter*) is an electrical device that takes a
single signal and produces two equal-
amplitude output signals, each 180
degrees out of phase with the other. Fig.
18 shows the most common circuit configuration. These devices are most frequently used to drive push-pull audio
amplifiers which require two phase-
inverted inputs.

A *dc amplifier* is able to amplify continuous, slowly varying voltages. There
must be no dc blocking (coupling)
capacitors in series with either the input or
the output of the amplifier. Fig. 19 shows
two representative circuits.

Additional phase inverter and dc
amplifier circuits are given in chapter 6 of
the *Radio Handbook* published by
Editors and Engineers, New Augusta, Indiana 46268.

High-Frequency Transmitting Circuits

There is a fundamental misunder-

standing among many amateurs as to
what is meant by the term "linear" when
applied to radio-frequency amplifiers. At
audio frequencies, any amplifier that
distorts the *rf envelope* is considered to be
nonlinear. Since a tuned circuit or filter is
invariably used between the rf amplifier
and the antenna, the rf waveform is
always restored to a fairly pure sine wave,
so if the shape of the rf envelope is retained, the output signal will be a nearly
perfect representation of the input.

When an audio amplifier is amplifying
a sine wave, it must be conducting
throughout the entire 360 degrees of each
cycle in order to be linear. Such an
amplifier is said to be operating in *Class
A*. Class A power amplifiers are rarely
used at radio frequencies because of their
low efficiency in converting dc supply
power to rf output power. The theoretical
maximum efficiency is 50 percent and in
practical amplifiers, 20 to 30 percent is a
more realistic figure.

In order to be considered linear, an rf
power amplifier must amplify all signals
by an equal factor, no matter how small
or large the input signal amplitude. With
large input signals, the amplifier must
begin to conduct as soon as the input rf
voltage begins a positive half cycle, and it
must continue to conduct so long as the
instantaneous input voltage remains
positive (negative for pnp transistors). In
other words, it must amplify over at least
half a cycle, or 180 degrees. If the
operating angle is exactly 180 degrees, the
amplifier is said to be operating *Class B*.
A *Class AB* amplifier operates for more
than 180 degrees but less than 360 degrees
of each cycle. Both Class AB and B operation is satisfactory for rf linear amplifiers.
Theoretical efficiency of a true Class B
amplifier is about 68-1/2 percent and of a
Class AB amplifier, between 50 and
68-1/2 percent. A well designed Class AB
amplifier typically would have about
60-percent efficiency.

A *Class C* amplifier has an operating
angle of less than 180 degrees. Such
amplifiers distort the modulation
envelope of a voice signal and are thus
usable only for continuous-wave applications. In fact, if fixed grid bias is used, a
Class C stage will even distort the wave
shaping of a keyed cw signal, a condition
that can cause key clicks. This does not
occur if a continuous signal is available at
the input and the amplifier itself is keyed.
There is no specific theoretical limit to the
efficiency of a Class C amplifier, but in
practice a figure between 65 and 85 percent is typical.

For Class B operation the amplifying
device should be biased at *cutoff*; that is,
bias should be adjusted to the point where
the device just starts to draw current from
the power supply. Since even a slight
positive voltage on the control element
(grid, base or gate) will cause the device to
draw current, it will, therefore, have a

180-degree conduction angle, the essential
requirement for Class B operation. A
Class A amplifier must draw current all
the time, so enough positive bias is provided so that even on negative peaks of
the input signal the device will still be
drawing a small amount of current. Class
AB amplifiers are biased such that they
draw a steady current under no-signal
conditions but are still cut off during the
negative peaks of the input signal. Class C
devices are biased beyond cutoff. That is,
a small positive input voltage will not be
sufficient to cause them to conduct; current will be drawn only on the positive
peaks of relatively large input signals.
Tube-type Class B and C amplifiers are
nearly always adjusted so that grid current
is drawn during positive signal peaks. A
Class AB amplifier may or may not draw
grid current, depending on the design.
Frequently, the figures 2 and 1 are used to
designate whether grid current is drawn or
not, respectively. Thus a Class AB2
amplifier is a Class AB amplifier in which
grid current is drawn during positive
peaks of the input signal.

For proper operation, an rf amplifier
must be terminated in the correct value of
load resistance. As a rule of thumb, a
Class A power amplifier should be terminated in a resistive impedance equal to
the ratio of plate voltage to current. Load
resistance for a Class AB amplifier should
be about 2/3 this value, and a Class B or C
amplifier should be terminated in a
resistance about half this ratio.

Specific circuits and techniques to implement these design principles can be
found in chapters 3, 4 and 6 of the ARRL
Handbook.

Transistors

The first solid-state component ever to
come into general use was the galena
detector, a type of *point-contact diode*. It
consisted of a hunk of galena crystal connected to one terminal and a thin "cat
whisker" wire connected to the other.
Modern point-contact diodes use a germanium or silicon crystal and the entire
unit is enclosed in a small glass or plastic
case so that there is no longer any need to
tediously adjust the cat whisker for the
most sensitive spot on the crystal surface.
Point-contact diodes are distinquished by
their low forward-voltage drop and by
their very low junction capacitance (on
the order of 1 pF or less). Many diodes of
this type are useful in rf applications up
into the microwave region of the spectrum.

The junction capacitance of any
semiconductor diode decreases as the
reverse bias voltage is increased. *Varac-
tors*, or voltage-variable-capacitance
diodes, are especially constructed to emphasize this property. They may be used
in place of variable capacitors when supplied with a well-regulated adjustable bias
voltage. When an rf voltage is applied

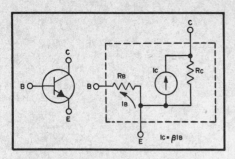

Fig. 20 — Mathematical model of a bipolar transistor. The circle with the arrow inside represents a constant-current source in which the amount of current depends on the input base current. While current flow in a vacuum tube is controlled by grid voltage, current flow in a transistor is controlled by base current.

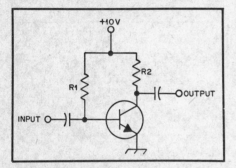

Fig. 21 — A simple transistor amplifier. Determination of resistor values and gain is explained in the text.

across a varactor, the capacitance varies in step with the rf and distorts the waveform. This nonlinearity can be used to good effect as a high-efficiency vhf/uhf frequency multiplier, as explained in chapter 4 of the ARRL *Handbook*. Use of these devices in parametric amplifiers was discussed in the previous section of this chapter.

A simple but very useful model of the bipolar transistor is illustrated in Fig. 20. The base-emitter junction is modeled as a resistor equal to the base-emitter impedance of the transistor. The collector-emitter path is modeled as a current generator in parallel with the transistor collector resistance R_c. Since the transistor grounded-emitter current gain is beta (β), the current generator generates a current $I_c = \beta \times I_b$, or putting it in words, the collector current equals the current gain times the base current.

Let us design a simple transistor amplifier using the circuit of Fig. 21. Assume $\beta = 100$, $R_c = 100K$, $R_b = 1k$. Assume also that we desire the amplifier to have an output impedance of 2k. Thus the parallel combination of R2 and R_c should be 2000 ohms. Since R_c is so much greater than this value, we can ignore its contribution to the output resistance and set R2 = 2 kΩ. If we set the dc voltage drop across R2 to be half the supply voltage (5 V), then the ac output voltage will be able to swing plus or minus 5 volts, and maximum output-voltage capability

will be achieved. Since current through R2 is the same as I_c, we have $I_c = V/2\ k\Omega = 2.5$ mA. Now the base current is the collector current divided by the beta so $I_b = 2.5$ mA/100 = 0.025 mA. Base current flows through R1 and R_b in series, but since R_b is very small in relation to R1, we can say from Ohm's Law that R1 = 10V/0.025 mA = 400 kΩ. Note that as far as dc biasing is concerned, one can usually ignore the collector and base impedances (that is, assume $R_b = 0$ and $R_c = \infty$).

To obtain the voltage gain of the circuit, assume a one-millivolt ac signal is applied to the base. One mV across the 1k-base resistance will cause 1 μA of ac base current to flow. This will generate a collector current of 100 μA flowing through R2. From Ohm's Law, the output voltage will be 100 μA $\times$ 2 kΩ = 200 mV. The voltage gain is thus 200 mV/1 mV = 200. In general, voltage gain is the current gain times the ratio of output to input impedances.

$$VG = \beta \frac{R_{out}}{R_{in}} \qquad \text{(Eq. 13)}$$

What is the *power gain*? The input power is E_{in}^2/R_{in}, and the output power is E_{out}^2/R_{out}. Power gain is thus

$$\frac{P_{out}}{P_{in}} = \frac{E_{out}^2/R_{out}}{E_{in}^2/R_{in}} \qquad \text{(Eq. 14)}$$

or

$$PG = (VG)^2 \frac{R_{in}}{R_{out}} = \beta^2 \frac{R_{out}}{R_{in}} \text{(Eq. 14B)}$$

Power gain is the current gain squared times the ratio of output to input impedance. R_{in} and R_{out} include the effects of both circuit resistance and transistor input and output resistances.

Solid-state devices are covered further in chapter 4 of the ARRL *Handbook*.

Oscillators

Crystal and variable frequency oscillator circuits are discussed in chapter 6. It would be wise to be able to identify the different types by looking at the schematic diagrams.

Frequency Multipliers

Any amplifier that does not perfectly reproduce the input waveform (that is, anything but a properly adjusted Class A amplifier) generates harmonics. A *frequency multiplier* is a device intentionally adjusted to maximize the harmonic output. Amplifier conduction angle has a profound effect on harmonic generation — in general, the higher the harmonic, the narrower the optimum conduction angle. For example, optimum conduction angle for a frequency doubler is about 110 degrees, for a tripler, about 100 degrees, and for a quadrupler, about 80 degrees. Since only Class C amplifiers have con-

duction angles of less than 180 degrees, Class C stages make the most efficient frequency multipliers. The *push-push* frequency multiplier of Fig. 22A is a very efficient even-harmonic generator but has very little odd-harmonic output.

The *push-pull* circuit, Fig. 22B, on the other hand, has very little even-harmonic output, but makes a good odd-harmonic generator. More detailed information appears in chapter 6 of the ARRL *Handbook*.

Above 1215 MHz

At frequencies up to 100 MHz or so, we can usually assume that the electrons in a vacuum tube travel from cathode to plate instantaneously. However, one of the factors that renders most conventional tubes unusable in the microwave region is *transit time*, the amount of time it takes an electron to traverse the space between cathode and anode. As the operating frequency is increased, this transit time becomes an appreciable portion of an rf cycle and tube performance rapidly deteriorates.

The *klystron* is a type of transmitting tube that takes advantage of this characteristic by employing *velocity modulation* of an electron beam to amplify microwave signals. The electrons are emitted from a cathode and directed across a gap (called the *buncher*) in a cavity resonator. The input signal is coupled to this cavity which causes an axial electric field across the gap that alternately aids and opposes the electron beam on the successive half cycles of the input signal. Thus some electrons are speeded up and some slowed down. From the buncher, the beam enters a *drift space* which gives the faster electrons time to catch up with the slower electrons just ahead, so that gradually the beam forms itself into *bunches*. The bunched-up electrons then pass across another gap (called the *catcher*) in a second cavity. The stream of electron bunches acts much like a modulated current and as such can set up a voltage in the scond cavity from which the output signal is extracted. If the power induced in the output cavity is greater than the input power, the device has gain and can be used as an amplifier.

By coupling power from the output back to the input, the device can also be used as an oscillator. The *reflex klystron* uses the same cavity for both input and output. After passing through the cavity gap, the electron beam is reflected back through again by a negatively charged *repeller* electrode. The reflex klystron will act only as oscillator. Usually, there is a method of adjusting cavity dimensions to coarse-tune the frequency, and fine tuning can be controlled by varying the repeller voltage. For a diagram of the device and an alternative explanation of its operation, see chapter 3 of the ARRL *Handbook* or chapter 13 of the *VHF Manual*.

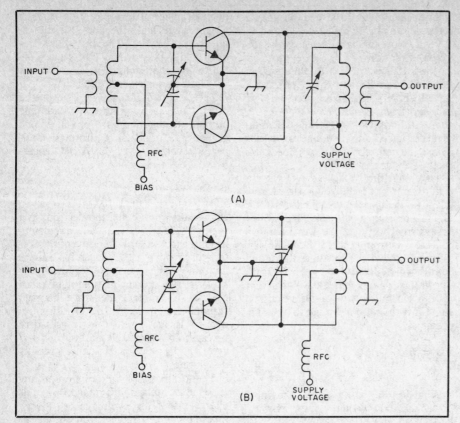

(A)

(B)

Fig. 22 — The "push-push" frequency multiplier at A is used most often as a frequency doubler or quadrupler and is useful where low odd-harmonic output is desired. The "push-pull" circuit at B discriminates against even harmonics and is most often used as a frequency tripler. Bias is adjusted for Class C operation at the optimum conduction angle for the harmonic multiple desired.

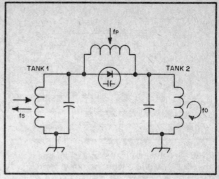

Fig. 23 — A parametric amplifier. The input signal is coupled to tank 1. The amplified output signal may be taken from tank 1 or a frequency-shifted version of it may be coupled out of tank 2.

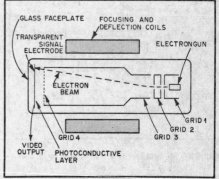

Fig. 24 — A vidicon TV camera tube.

Most radio-frequency amplifiers operate by converting dc supply current into rf energy. The *parametric amplifier* (par-amp), on the other hand, uses *rf* energy pumped into the circuit to amplify an rf signal at another frequency.

An essential component in most par-amps is a *varactor* or variable-capacitance diode. The varactor is basically a diode whose junction capacitance varies with applied voltage. This voltage-variable capacitance characteristic can be used to modulate an rf signal with another rf signal of a different frequency (the *pump* signal). If the pump signal is of high enough frequency, it can be made to modulate the lower frequency in such a way as to cause amplification.

In the circuit of Fig. 23, if the pump frequency f_p is higher than the signal frequency f_s and the output frequency f_o, then the circuit will be regenerative. Thus the output will not only be frequency-converted according to the formula $f_o = f_p - F_s$, but it will be amplified as well. Similarly, if both the input and output are coupled to tank 1, the circuit will function as a regenerative amplifier, much in the fashion of a Q-multiplier.

Parametric amplifiers are frequently used as low-noise amplifiers at uhf and microwave frequencies where many tube and transistor amplifiers become unusable. Lowest noise figures are obtained with highest pump frequencies. More information appears in chapter 13 of the ARRL *VHF Manual*.

Vacuum Tubes

The *vidicon* is a relatively simple, inexpensive TV camera pickup tube. It is the type employed in closed-circuit applications in banks and factories because of its small size and low cost. It is the type used almost exclusively by radio amateurs for both fast- and slow-scan television.

The vidicon is illustrated schematically in Fig. 24. The photoconductive layer and signal electrode can best be thought of as an array of leaky capacitors. As the electron beam scans the photoconductor, it charges each minicapacitor to the cathode voltage (usually about − 20 V with respect to the signal electrode.) As soon as each capacitor is charged, it starts discharging through its leakage resistance, the rate of discharging depending on the amount of light reaching it. On the next scan of the area, the electron beam will redeposit enough electrons to recharge the capacitor to cathode potential. In the instant that it does this, a net current flows through the cathode/signal electrode circuit with an amplitude proportional to the amount of discharge of the capacitor. Since this discharge depends on the amount of light hitting that portion of the screen, the beam current that flows as the beam sweeps by that area is proportional to the light intensity. The output beam current is very low (a fraction of a microamp), and its impedance is very high so that the video preamp must be designed with care to reduce hum and noise problems. Focusing and horizontal and vertical deflection of the electron beam are done with magnetic fields generated by external coils in the same manner as in a TV picture tube.

The *lighthouse tube* is a type of uhf triode designed for low lead inductance. Conventional tubes use cylindrically shaped tube elements, each stacked concentrically inside the other, with all leads brought out through the tube base. The lighthouse tube uses flat elements stacked one atop another. The plate lead is brought out to a metal cap on the top, and the grid and cathode are brought out to low-inductance metal rings encircling the tube envelope. The bottom ring is larger than the middle one which is larger than the plate cap so that the tube looks vaguely like a lighthouse, from which it gets its name.

Cathode ray tubes, such as those used in TV sets and oscilloscopes, should be handled with care. Because of the high vacuum inside, they can implode if scratched or cracked. The resulting flying glass can cause severe injury, especially if the tube implodes in close proximity to someone's face.

Chapter 3 of the ARRL *Handbook* has further information on vacuum tubes.

Amateur Extra Class Concepts

Operational Amplifiers

Operational amplifiers (op-amps) are so called because a host of operations can be performed with them by altering the feedback parameters. In simple terms an op-amp is a device which is capable of very high gain. It is characterized further by its differential-input dc amplifier arrangement. Basically, it can be thought of as a very precision push-pull type of amplifier. It was used at its beginning in analog computer circuits — the vacuum-tube era. The operational amplifier is perhaps the most versatile IC in the amateur and commercial field today. It would take an entire book to illustrate the many uses to which op-amps can be put. Here we will show some basic examples. The reader is referred to Jung, *IC Op-Amp Cookbook,* published by Howard Sams and Co., for an in-depth treatment of op-amp theory and practical applications.

Op-Amp Basics

A theoretically perfect (ideal) op-amp would have some outstanding characteristics: (1) high input impedance (infinite); (2) low output impedance (zero); (3) infinite voltage gain; (4) flat frequency response within its frequency range; and (5) with zero input signal the output is zero. These criteria can be approached in a practical situation, but not realized entirely.

Three of the more common op-amp configurations are the inverting amplifiers, noninverting amplifiers and difference amplifiers. These modes are compared in Fig. 25. The phase relationships are compared in the example.

Voltage gain and voltage output for an op-amp can be determined easily by means of the equations in Fig. 26. The determining elements are R1 and Rf. This illustrates clearly that the op-amp gain is determined by the resistors rather than by the op-amp characteristics and power supply voltage.

Fig. 27 shows the gain relationship for a noninverting op-amp. A theoretical gain of 10^9 is attainable from the circuits of Figs. 26 and 27.

Fig. 28 illustrates a difference amplifier. A reference voltage can be applied to one of the op-amp inputs while the remaining input is fed a changing dc level (such as that which might occur across the source resistor of an FET dc amplifier). The difference in the two input voltages will appear at the op-amp output. An equation is given in Fig. 26 for determining the output voltage of this circuit.

Op-Amps as Audio Filters

One of the more common uses to which op-amps are put can be seen in the RC ac-

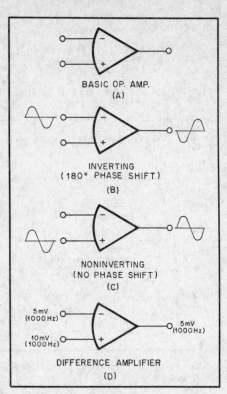

Fig. 25 — Various modes of op-amp utilization.

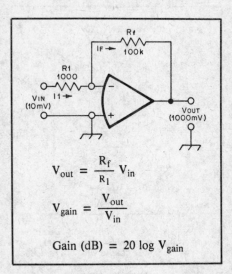

$$V_{out} = \frac{R_f}{R_1} V_{in}$$

$$V_{gain} = \frac{V_{out}}{V_{in}}$$

Gain (dB) = 20 log V_{gain}

Fig. 26 — Resistance values determine the op-amp gain.

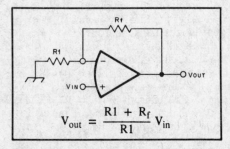

$$V_{out} = \frac{R1 + R_f}{R1} V_{in}$$

Fig. 27 — Voltage output versus voltage input for a noninverting op-amp.

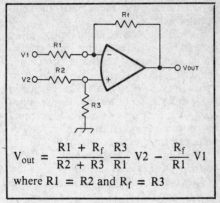

$$V_{out} = \frac{R1 + R_f}{R2 + R3} \frac{R3}{R1} V2 - \frac{R_f}{R1} V1$$

where R1 = R2 and R_f = R3

Fig. 28 — Voltage relationship for a difference amplifier.

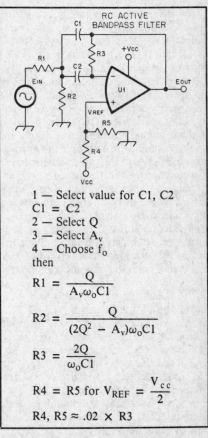

1 — Select value for C1, C2
C1 = C2
2 — Select Q
3 — Select A_v
4 — Choose f_o
then

$$R1 = \frac{Q}{A_v \omega_o C1}$$

$$R2 = \frac{Q}{(2Q^2 - A_v)\omega_o C1}$$

$$R3 = \frac{2Q}{\omega_o C1}$$

$$R4 = R5 \text{ for } V_{REF} = \frac{V_{cc}}{2}$$

R4, R5 ≈ .02 × R3

Fig. 29 — Basic circuit for an RC active bandpass filter. One pole is shown with the fundamental equations for finding the resistance values needed.

tive audio-filter field. Op-amps have the distinct advantage of providing gain and variable parameters when used as audio filters. Passive filters that contain L and C elements are generally committed to some fixed-value frequency, and they exhibit an insertion loss.

Although RC active filters can be built with bipolar transistors, the modern approach is to utilize op-amps. The use of an op-amp IC, such as a type 741, results in a compact filter pole that will provide stable filter operation. Only five connections are made to the IC, and the gain of the filter sections, plus the frequency characteristic, is determined by the choice of components external to the IC.

Fig. 29 shows a single band-pass-filter pole and gives the equations for obtaining the desired values for the resistors once the gain, Q, F_o and C1-C2 capacitor values are chosen. C1 and C2 are equal in value and should be high-Q, temperature-stable components. R4 and R5 are equal in value and are used to establish the op-amp reference voltage. This is $V_{cc}/2$.

Single pole filter sections can be cascaded for greater selectivity. A practical limit of four poles would be typical for the style of filter presented.

Phase-Locked Loop

A phase-locked loop (PLL) is basically an electronic servo loop consisting of a phase detector, a low-pass filter and a voltage-controlled oscillator. Its controlled oscillator phase makes it capable of locking or synchronizing with an oncoming signal. If the phase changes, indicating that the incoming frequency is changing, the phase detector output voltage increases or decreases just enough to keep the oscillator frequency the same as the incoming frequency, preserving the locked condition. Therefore, the average voltage applied to the controlled oscillator is a function of the frequency of the incoming signal. In fact, the low-pass filter voltage is the demodulated output when the incoming signal is frequency modulated (provided the control oscillator has a linear voltage-to-frequency transfer characteristic). A block diagram of a phase-locked loop circuit is shown in Fig. 30.

The actual PLL circuit shown in Fig. 31 makes use of the Signetics NE565. This circuit is configured as an fm demodulator. The free-running frequency of the voltage-controlled oscillator is set by C1 and the loop filter consists of just C2. Phase-locked loops are also used for frequency synthesis, frequency synchronization, signal conditioning, a-m demodulation, fsk demodulation and a host of other applications.

Photovoltaic Conversion

Sunlight can be converted directly into electricity by a process known as photovoltaic conversion. A solar cell is used for this purpose. These cells rely on the photoelectric properties of a semiconductor. Practically, the solar cell is a large area p-m junction diode. The greater the area of the cell, the higher the output current will be. A dc voltage of approximately 0.5 is obtained from a single cell. Numerous cells are normally connected in series and parallel to provide the required voltage and current ratings.

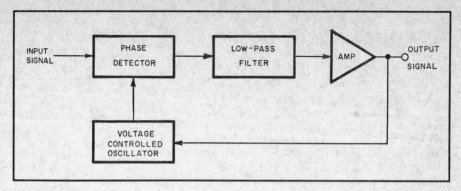

Fig. 30 — Block diagram of a phase-locked-loop system.

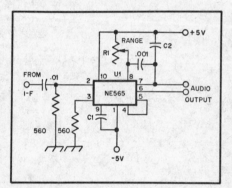

Fig. 31 — Diagram of a practical phase-locked-loop fm demodulator.

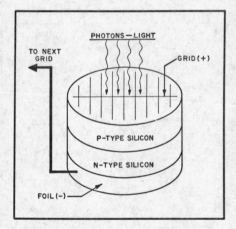

Fig. 32 — a solar-energy diode cell. Electrons flow when light strikes the upper surface. The bottom of the cell is coated with foil to collect current for the load, or for the succeeding cell in series-connected arrays of cells.

The solar diode cell is built so that light can penetrate into the region of the p-n junction, as in Fig. 32. Most modern solar cells use silicon material. Impurities (doping) are introduced into the silicon material to establish excess positive or negative charges, which carry electric currents. Phosphorous is used to produce n-type silicon. Boron is used as the dopant to produce p-type material.

Light is absorbed into the silicon to generate excess holes (one hole/electron pair for each photon absorbed). When this occurs near the p-n junction, the electric fields in that region will separate the holes from the electrons. This causes the holes to increase in the p-type material. At the same time the electrons will build up in the n-type material. By making direct connections to the p and n regions by means of wires, these excess charges generated by light (and separated by the junction) will flow into an external load to provide power. Additional information on this subject can be found in chapter 4 of *The Radio Amateur's Handbook*.

DIGITAL ELECTRONICS

The fundamental principle of digital electronics is that a device can have only two logical states: on and off. This system is perfectly suited to binary (base or radix two) arithmetic, which only has two numerals, zero and one. The simplest digital devices are switches and relays. Some pre-1950 computers were built almost entirely of relays. Low speed and rapid wear were the objections to mechanical devices, so the next generation of digital instruments used electron tubes as the switching elements. Physical size and power consumption were the factors that limited the complexity of digital circuits using tubes. Modern semiconductor technology allows digital systems of tremendous complexity to be built at a small fraction of the cost of previous methods.

Gates

The three logical operations are AND, OR, and NOT. An AND gate may be assembled with two relays as shown in Fig. 33.

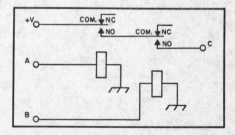

Fig. 33 — AND gate. In order to have a voltage at C, A and B must be energized.

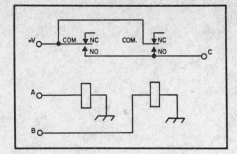

Fig. 34 — OR gate. Energizing A or B will produce voltage at C.

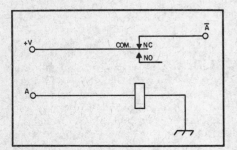

Fig. 35 — NOT gate. If we apply voltage at A there will be no voltage at $\overline{A}$ (read not A), and vice versa.

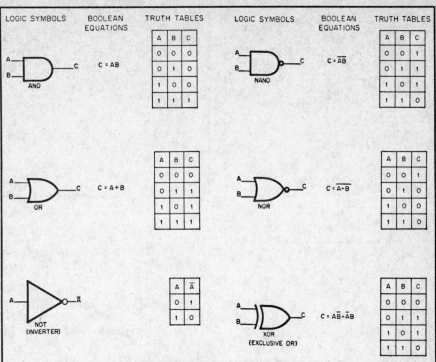

LOGIC SYMBOLS	BOOLEAN EQUATIONS	TRUTH TABLES

AND $C = AB$

A	B	C
0	0	0
0	1	0
1	0	0
1	1	1

NAND $C = \overline{AB}$

A	B	C
0	0	1
0	1	1
1	0	1
1	1	0

OR $C = A + B$

A	B	C
0	0	0
0	1	1
1	0	1
1	1	1

NOR $C = \overline{A + B}$

A	B	C
0	0	1
0	1	0
1	0	0
1	1	0

NOT (INVERTER)

A	$\overline{A}$
0	1
1	0

XOR (EXCLUSIVE OR) $C = A\overline{B} + \overline{A}B$

A	B	C
0	0	0
0	1	1
1	0	1
1	1	0

Fig. 36 — Boolean equations and truth tables.

If we connect the contacts in parallel rather than in series, an OR gate results. See Fig. 34.

The NOT, COMPLEMENT, or INVERSE function may be implemented with a normally closed relay contact. See Fig. 35.

With the proper system of AND and NOT gates or OR and NOT gates, any logical or arithmetic function may be synthesized. AND and OR gates are often combined with inverters in IC packages and called NAND and NOR gates.

A special combination of gates called an EXCLUSIVE OR has an output only if the two inputs are different. This combination is used frequently enough to be packaged specially and assigned a fundamental symbol.

Logic systems have polarity. If the highest voltage level represents a zero, the logic is said to be positive. If the opposite representation is used, the logic is negative.

Since each input or output of a digital system can have only two possible states, it is possible to list all of the input combinations and their corresponding outputs, thus completely characterizing the operation. Such a list is called a truth table.

Each type of gate is assigned a distinctive schematic symbol. The AND gate symbol has a straight edge on the input side and a blunt convex edge on the output side. The OR gate is characterized by a concave edge on the input side and a sharp cusp on the output side. A small circle at the output of a gate signifies that an inversion has taken place.

Digital systems may be designed with Boolean algebra. Circuit functions may be defined by equations. The symbology and laws of Boolean algebra are somewhat different from those of ordinary algebra. The "+" symbol is used to indicate the OR function. AND is represented by "." or juxtaposition of the variables. A bar over a variable indicates that it has been inverted. The chart at Fig. 36 shows the symbols for the common logic functions with their associated Boolean equations and truth tables. With the exception of the EXCLUSIVE OR, all of the gates may be expanded to any number of inputs. There is no universally accepted definition for an EXCLUSIVE OR gate with more than two inputs.

Multivibrators

The oscillator circuit shown in Fig. 37 is a free-running or astable multivibrator. It is called astable because the output oscillates between two distinct states, and is stable in neither. The resulting square wave can be used to time or synchronize parts of a digital system. In this capacity, the circuit would be referred to as a "clock." The frequency of the square-wave output is approximately equal to 0.7/RC.

Another type of multivibrator is referred to as monostable, as it has only one stable state. Monostable multivibrators are useful for generating pulses of a specific duration for use in digital circuits. The output rests in the stable state until a trigger pulse is applied to the input. The output goes temporarily to the unstable state and then returns to the stable state.

Sequential Logic

A circuit in which the output state is a function not only of the input levels but

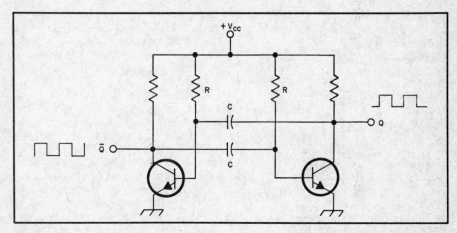

Fig. 37 — An astable multivibrator circuit. The point labeled Q is the output. An inverted output is available from the point labeled $\overline{Q}$.

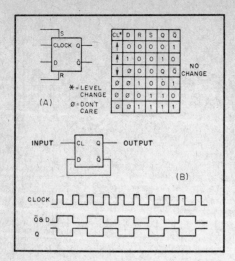

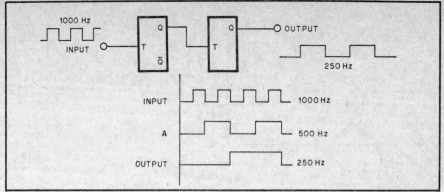

Fig. 40 — Two T flip-flops connected to form a divide-by-four circuit.

Fig. 38 — A D flip-flop. In A, set and reset ("jam") inputs are provided. Note that the functional truth table shows Q and $\bar{Q}$ both in the high state for one combination of R and S. While this appears contradictory, it is the standard way of defining the operation of this type of flip-flop.

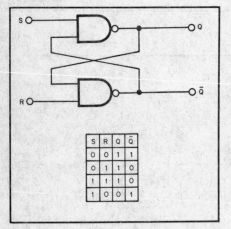

Fig. 39 — A regenerative switching circuit called an RS flip-flop. The circuit could be implemented with NOR gates, in which case the first defined input state would be 11.

also of past output states is a *sequential* logic circuit. Conventional truth tables are not generally applicable to sequential circuits because a certain input condition may not have a unique output state. The simpler sequential circuits are sometimes defined by a modified truth table showing input transitions and output state progressions. State tables, flow diagrams and timing charts are the tools used to design complex sequential machines.

The dependence on previous output states implies a requirement for *memory*. The simplest memory element is a special type of bistable multivibrator (flip-flop) called a latch. A D (for data) flip-flop is often used as a latch. A flip-flop can store one bit (binary digit) of information. A typical D flip-flop with its truth table is shown in Fig. 38A. The logic level at D is transferred to Q on the positive transition of the clock pulse. The Q output will re-

tain this logic level regardless of any changes at D until the next positive clock transition. The D throughout is said to be *synchronous* because it is actuated by the clock signal. The flip-flop shown also has set and reset (S and R) inputs. These inputs are *asynchronous* because they are independent of, and in fact overide, the clock and data inputs.

Fig. 38B shows a common application for a D flip-flop, a modulus-two frequency divider. The sequency of events is illustrated by the timing diagram. Several of these flip-flops may be cascaded in a single IC package and called a counter. The states of the Q outputs can be read as a binary code, indicating the number of clock pulses received in an interval.

An RS flip-flop is shown in Fig. 39. Two inverting gates connected in this fashion form a *regenerative* switching circuit. The accuracy of the accompanying truth table depends on the input states occuring in the order given. The output corresponding to an input of 11 could easily be the complement of that shown if it followed a 00 input state. An important rule in the design of sequential logic circuits is that the simultaneity of events cannot be depended upon.

The RS flip-flop is the simplest type. Its outputs change directly as a result of changes at its inputs. The type T flip-flop "toggles," "flips," or changes its state during the occurrence of a T pulse, called a clock pulse. The T flip-flop can be considered as a special case of the J-K flip-flop. Although there is some disagreement in the nomenclature, a J-K flip-flop is generally considered to be a toggled or clocked R-S flip-flop. It may also be used as a storage element. The J input is frequently called the "set" input and the K is called the "clear" input (not to be confused with the clock input). The clock input is called c. A clear-direct or C_D input which overrides all other inputs to clear the flip-flop to 0 is provided in most J-K flip-flop packages.

In Fig. 40 two T flip-flops that trigger on negative-going transition are shown connected together. Since each flip-flop waits until a negative-going transition oc-

curs at its input before changing state, the output frequency is half of the input frequency. Thus, the 1000-Hz square-wave signal applied to the input of this circuit is divided by a total of four, to 250 Hz at the output. Any number of flip-flops could be cascaded in this manner to obtain larger divisors. Generally, the divisor is equal to 2^n, where n is the number of flip-flops cascaded together. In the example of Fig. 40, two flip-flops divide by 2^2, or 4. If for example, 10 flip-flops were cascaded, they would divide an input signal by 2^{10}, or 1024. To obtain 25-kHz frequency markers, flip-flops could be used to divide a 100-kHz crystal-calibrator signal by 4.

Cascaded flip-flops can also be used to "count" numbers of pulses or triggers. But to understand how this is done one must first learn the base-2 number system that is frequently used in digital circuitry. The base-2 number system has only two numbers, 0 and 1. Counting using just these two numbers follows the same rules as the base-10 number system. Fig. 41A illustrates the base-10 number 2943, which is read as "two thousand nine hundred and forty three." The number gets its value according to the weight that we assign to each column. Starting from the right and working to the left, the numeral 3 is in the 10^0, or units, column and has a value of three. The numeral 4 is in the 10^1, or tens, column and has a value of 40. The numeral 9 is in the 10^2, or hundreds, column and has a value of 900. The numeral 2 is in the 10^3, or thousands, column and has a value of 2000. Accordingly, $3 + 40 + 900 + 2000$ results in the value of 2943.

Fig. 41B shows the binary, or base-2, number 1101. The columns are now worth 2^0, 2^1, 2^2 and 2^3, instead of 10^0, 10^1, 10^2 and 10^3 as in the base-10 system. The numeral 1 in the right-most column has a value of one, the 0 in the 2^1 column has a value of zero, the numeral 1 in the 2^2 column has a value of four (because $2^2 = 4$) and the numeral 1 in the 2^3 column has a value of eight. Therefore the binary number 1101 has a total value of $1 + 0 + 4 + 8$, or 13. The largest four-digit binary number would still be 1111, and would

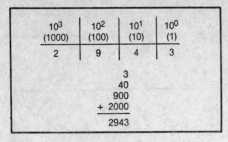

10^3 (1000)	10^2 (100)	10^1 (10)	10^0 (1)
2	9	4	3

$$3$$
$$40$$
$$900$$
$$+\ 2000$$
$$\overline{2943}$$

Fig. 41A — The base-10 number 2943. Each numeral is assigned a specific value, or weight, depending on its column.

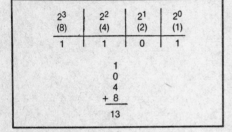

2^3 (8)	2^2 (4)	2^1 (2)	2^0 (1)
1	1	0	1

$$1$$
$$0$$
$$4$$
$$+\ 8$$
$$\overline{13}$$

Fig. 41B — The base-2 number 1101. Again, each numeral is weighted according to the column.

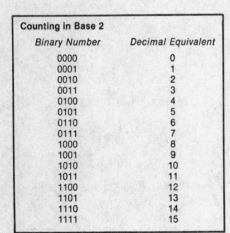

Counting in Base 2

Binary Number	Decimal Equivalent
0000	0
0001	1
0010	2
0011	3
0100	4
0101	5
0110	6
0111	7
1000	8
1001	9
1010	10
1011	11
1100	12
1101	13
1110	14
1111	15

Fig. 42 — Counting in base 2 for the numbers 0 through 15.

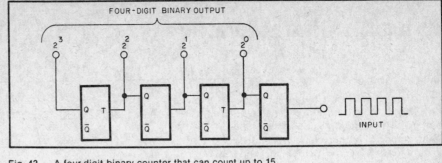

Fig. 43 — A four-digit binary counter that can count up to 15.

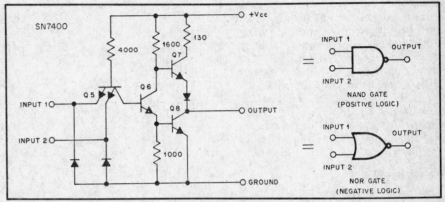

Fig. 43A — A TTL circuit and its equivalent logic symbols. Indicated resistor values are typical. Identification of transistors is for reference only; these are *not* discrete components.

have a value of 15 (1 + 2 + 4 + 8). Fig. 42 illustrates all the binary numbers from 0 to 15 and their decimal equivalents.

A four-digit binary counter can be constructed by adding two additional flip-flops to the circuit of Fig. 40. Such a circuit is shown in Fig. 43. If the input signal to this circuit were a series of pulses as shown, the four outputs would be a tally of how many pulses (up to 15) that the circuit has counted. This simple counter circuit is called a "ripple" counter because pulses move through it from flip-flop to flip-flop like waves through water. If it were necessary to count higher numbers, additional counters would have to be added to the string.

Digital-Logic IC Families

There are several families or types of ICs that are seeing widespread use. Each family has its own inherent advantages and disadvantages. Each is geared to its own particular market, meeting a specific set of needs RTL (resistor-transistor logic) and DTL (diode-transistor logic) are obsolete and are no longer used in new designs. They are manufactured for exact replacement purposes only.

Transistor-Transistor Logic — TTL

TTL is one of the bipolar logic families. Also known as T^2L (T squared L), this family has a variety of circuit configurations. Some devices have "open collector" outputs, and these may be "wire ORed." Open collector outputs are useful for interfacing with other logic families or discrete components. Although + 5 volts is the recommended power supply for TTL, open collectors can be connected to a different voltage through the external load resistor, within the limits specified for the device. Most TTL devices have "totem pole," or "active pull-up" output stages, and these cannot be wire ored. Typically, the outputs are capable of sinking more current than they can source. This situation is of importance only when interfacing devices outside a particular TTL subfamily. TTL devices have a fanout (number of inputs that can be driven by a single output) of 10 within a subfamily. If TTL inputs are left open, they assume a "high" logic state, but greater noise immunity will be realized if pull-up resistors are used. When operated with a + 5-volt supply, any input voltage level between 2.0 and 5.5 is defined to be high. A voltage less than 0.8 is an input low. TTL ICs output a minimum high level of 2.4 volts, and a maximum low level of 0.4 volts. The switching transients generated by TTL devices appear on the supply line and can cause false triggering of other devices. For this reason, the power bus should have several bypass capacitors per pc board.

"Plain" TTL ICs are identified by 5400- or 7400-series numbers and operate at speeds up to 35 MHz. A commonly used TTL device is represented schematically in Fig. 43A. High-speed ICs (50 MHz) are identified by 54H00- or 74H00-series numbers. These ICs consume more power than their ordinary counterparts. The 54L00- and 74L00-series of devices are designed for lower power consumption than the standard types. These ICs typically dissipate one milliwatt per gate, or about one-tenth of that dissipated by standard TTL. Operating speed is the tradeoff for the lower power, and the maximum speed for this subfamily is 3 MHz.

The subfamilies discussed so far operate as saturated switches. The 54S00- and 74S00-series has Schottky diode clamps that keep the transistors out of saturation. Some ICs of this series are useful up to 125 MHz. The power dissipation is about twice that of standard TTL. A commonly used subfamily combining low power dissipation with fairly high speed is the 54LS00- and 74LS00-series. The dissipation and speed for this series are 2 mW and 45 MHz, respectively.

Emission Characteristics

Low-Level Modulation

Low-level modulation is any modulation applied to the transmitted signal at a point in the transmitter preceding the final power amplifier output circuit. Included in this category are grid modulation and screen modulation of the final power amplifier, which were covered in the Advanced and General class chapters of this book. The definition is a little hazy in the case of a "transmitter" consisting of an exciter and a separate power amplifier. The exciter may in fact use high-level plate modulation. However, with the addition of a separate linear power amplifier, the *system* is considered to be low-level modulated. This is because the power-amplifier input is already modulated; the final amplifier stage merely amplifies the modulated signal.

Modulation Limiting

The human voice contains many amplitude peaks that are of higher intensity than the average level of speech as shown in Fig. 44A. If an a-m transmitter is adjusted so that the peak speech intensity is at 100-percent modulation, then the average value of modulation will be considerably less (Fig. 44B). If you try to increase the average modulation level simply by turning up the microphone gain, the modulation peaks will exceed 100 percent. When the negative-going peaks cause the final amplifier to reach cutoff or the positive peaks cause saturation, then high-level clipping occurs. The result will be a squaring of the wave shape, as shown in Fig. 44C, with the resulting generation of audio harmonics or splatter.

The average modulation level can be increased without the corresponding splatter, however, by clipping off the peaks of the speech at a low-level stage of the modulator. The resultant harmonics can then be greatly reduced by using a well-designed audio low-pass filter as shown in Fig. 45.

Another method of improving the average modulation level is *speech compression* (Fig. 46). This system uses a fast-acting form of automatic gain control to reduce modulator gain on voice peaks. Although speech compression is useful in ensuring a fairly constant average modulation level, it improves the peak-to-average power ratio only a little. It is often used in ssb transmitters, however, since it creates much less distortion than does audio clipping.

Rf speech clipping can be a very effective method of reducing the peak-to-average power ratio of an ssb transmission. The output from the crystal filter (or phasing-type ssb generator) is clipped and

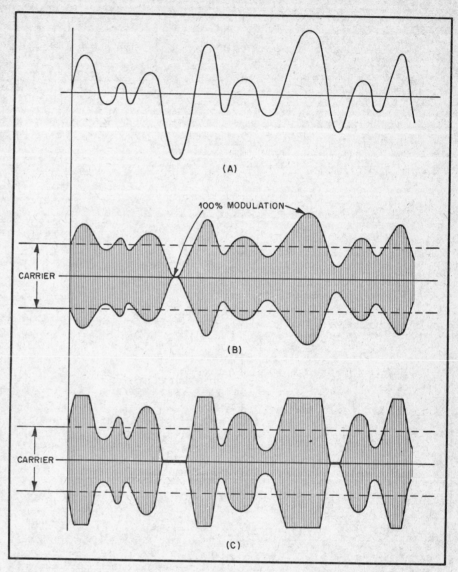

Fig. 44 — The audio signal at A is shown amplitude modulating an rf carrier at B. If peak modulation level is increased further (C), the resulting sharp-cornered peaks and valleys cause out-of-band emissions known as splatter.

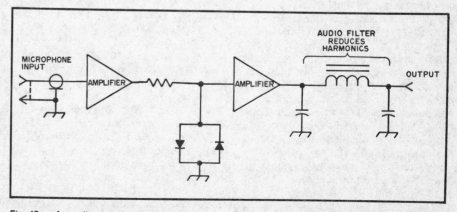

Fig. 45 — An audio speech clipper that uses a pair of reverse-connected diodes to limit the maximum amplitude of the audio signal. By clipping at a low-level stage in the modulator and filtering the out-of-band audio harmonics before they are applied to the modulated stage, a high average modulation level can be achieved with little splatter.

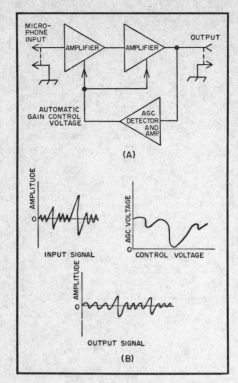

Fig. 46 — A speech compressor or automatic-gain-control system. The agc detector and amplifer lower audio amplifier gain in proportion to signal level in order to reduce variations in volume.

then passed through another filter to remove the out-of-band distortion products (splatter). Although both audio limiting and rf clipping increase audio distortion (Fig. 47), they nevertheless increase intelligibility during weak-signal conditions if they are properly implemented.

For more information about speech compression and clipping, refer to chapter 12 of the ARRL *Handbook* or chapter 9 of *Single Sideband for the Radio Amateur.*

Phase Modulation

As mentioned in the Advanced class chapter, in an fm system equal-amplitude audio tones always produce the same deviation, no matter what their frequency. However, the frequency deviation of a pm signal is proportional to the modulating audio frequency. If a 1-kHz modulating tone causes 5kHz frequency deviation, then a 2-kHz tone of the same amplitude will cause 10-kHz deviation. If you pass an audio signal through a filter with a 6-dB per octave rising-frequency characteristic (that is, every time you double the frequency, the output amplitude doubles) and if the resulting audio is routed to an fm modulator, the output signal will be indistinguishable from phase modulation. Likewise, if an audio filter with a 6-dB per octave *falling*-frequency characteristic is used in the speech amplifier of a pm transmitter, the output

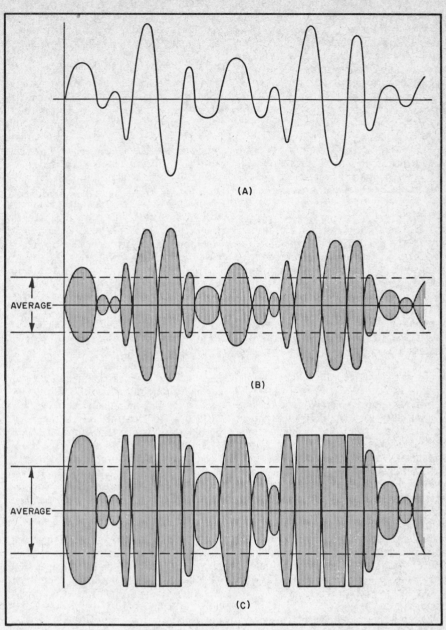

Fig. 47 — An audio signal (A) and the resulting double sideband from the balanced modulator (B). When rf speech clipping is used (C), the signal must subsequently be filtered to remove splatter. Normally rf clipping is used with a single-sideband signals: The clipper is placed after the ssb filter and before the splatter filter.

signal will be indistinguishable from true fm.

Practical phase modulators have a maximum modulation index of less than about 0.5. Since the highest modulating frequency used is generally about 3 kHz, the maximum deviation is thus less than about 1.5 kHz. If a pm signal is passed through a frequency multiplier however, the deviation will increase by the same factor as the frequency. For this reason, phase modulation is usually accomplished at a low-frequency stage in a transmitter and then multiplied up to the output frequency. For example, consider a 144-MHz transmitter that uses 12-MHz crystals. If the phase modulator (operating at 12 MHz) is capable of 1-kHz maxi-

mum deviation, then the output signal can have a deviation of up to 12 kHz.

In designing a phase modulator, the desire to generate large amounts of phase deviation must be weighed against the generation of odd-harmonic distortion. As mentioned before, if a phase modulator is used to generate fm, then an audio-frequency correcting network with a 6-dB per octave falling-frequency characteristic is needed. The lower the frequency, the greater the amplitude of the signal applied to the phase modulator. Since the greatest amount of phase deviation is obtained at the lowest audio frequency of the modulating signal, it is at this frequency where maximum distortion occurs. As mentioned before, the maximum frequency deviation that can be generated in a phase modulator with acceptable odd-harmonic distortion is about 0.5 times the modulating frequency. If the lowest audio frequency in use is, say, 400 Hz, then the maximum fm deviation possible is about 200 Hz. To get 2.4-kHz deviation (deviation ratio of about 0.8), the frequency must be multiplied by at least 13 times.

For more information about phase modulation, refer to chapter 13 of the ARRL *Handbook* or chapter 4 of *FM and Repeaters for the Radio Amateur*.

Facsimile

Facsimile is the transmission of printed pictures by radio. The picture to be sent is attached to a drum which rotates under a photo-sensitive pickup unit. The pickup device moves slowly down the rotating drum in a direction parallel to the axis so that the image is "read" as a series of horizontal lines from top to bottom of the paper. At the receiving end, a similar mechanical arrangement moves a marking device over current-sensitive or light-sensitive paper to reproduce the transmitted image.

The variations in picture brightness and darkness are converted into variations in the dc output voltage of the facsimile machine. This voltage is then applied to a modulator. In some systems, 100-percent modulation represents black with 0 percent representing white, while in other systems the reverse is true. In either case, the signal can be transmitted as either amplitude modulation (A4) or frequency modulation (F4). Frequency-modulated facsimile may not be used below 220 MHz. A4 may be used in the bands 50.1-54 MHz and 144.1-148 MHz as well as 220 MHz and up. Refer to §97.61 in chapter 9 for details.

Facsimile is discussed further in chapter 4 of *Specialized Communications Techniques*.

Pulse Modulation

Under current regulations, pulse modulation (P) is restricted to the microwave region. Because of this it is not in common usage among amateurs. As the name implies, pulse-modulated signals are usually sent out as a series of short pulses separated by relatively long stretches of time with no signal being transmitted. (A typical pulse transmission might use 1-microsecond pulses with a 1000-Hz pulse rate.) For this reason, the peak power of a pulse-transmission is usually much greater than its average power. The two most common types of pulse-modulating systems are the pulse-width and pulse-position methods. For the purposes of the Amateur Extra examination, be familiar with the alphabetic classification of the mode, the letter P, and the frequencies where pulse modulation is permitted (§97.61 in chapter 9). For more

general information about this communications mode, refer to chapter 7 of *Specialized Communications Techniques*.

ASCII Data Rates and Bandwidth

ASCII data rates are commonly specified as a baud rate, although a character-per-second (cps) or word-per-minute (wpm) rate may also be given. The lowest standard ASCII data rate in common usage is 110 baud. ASCII characters sent at 110 baud are usually sent with a 2-unit-wide stop pulse, although a 1-unit stop pulse may also be found in some applications. Above 110 baud, it is common to make the stop pulse one unit pulse in length. The standard ASCII data rates commonly used with asynchronous serial transmission are shown in Fig. 48.

The ASCII data rates up to 300 baud are authorized for U.S. amateur use on frequencies between 3.500 and 21.250 MHz. Data rates up to 1200 baud are permitted between 28 and 225 MHz; up to 19,600 baud may be used above 420 MHz. The 110-baud rate is by far the most practical for 3.5- to 21.25-MHz use because of the increased susceptibility of the higher data rates to noise and static interference. Vhf fm amateur activity finds 110 and 300 useful for terminal-to-terminal communications, and 300 and 1200 baud for such computer-related activities as exchanging programs. The very high data rates (1800, 2400, 4800 and 9600 baud) find their best application in high-speed, computer-terminal data links. The 150 and 600 baud are recognized ANSI and Electronic Industries Association (EIA) standards, but have seen limited use to date. Some home computer systems are also using 250, 500 and 1100 baud for cassette interfaces, not necessarily with ASCII encoding of the data. FCC regulations (§97.69) specify maximum baud rates for each frequency range, but do not require the use of standard rates.

The approximate bandwidth of an ASCII-encoded signal can be determined by multiplying the baud rate in cps by 2. This would represent the minimum bandwidth necessary for proper transfer of data.

Narrow-Band Voice Modulation (NBVM)

This technique, now implemented and in the production stage, works at baseband (audio) rather than at intermediate or radio frequencies (i-f or rf). Thus it is applicable to virtually all types of analog and digital transmission systems. The system includes the newly developed frequency compandor and the well-known, but not extensively used, amplitude compandor. Use of both devices within the same baseband system offers significant improvements in adjacent-channel rejection and signal-to-noise ratio (SNR).

The transceive baseband system operates on the audio waveform just after the microphone but before the speaker.

ASCII Data Rates				
Baud Rate	Data Pulse (ms)	Stop Pulse (ms)	CPS	WPM
110	9.091	9.091	11.0	110
	9.091	18.182	10.0	100
150	6.667	6.667	15.0	150
300	3.333	3.333	30.0	300
600	1.667	1.667	60.0	600
1200	0.8333	0.8333	120	1200
1800	0.5556	0.5556	180	1800
2400	0.4167	0.4167	240	2400
4800	0.2083	0.2083	480	4800
9600	0.1041	0.1041	960	9600
19200	0.0520	0.0520	1920	19200

CPS = characters per second

$$= \frac{1}{START + 8 (DATA) + STOP}$$

WPM = words per minute = $\frac{CPS}{6} \times 60$

= number of 5 letter-plus-space groups per minute.

Fig. 48 — ASCII data rates for popularly used speeds.

The frequency compandor filters the essential parts of speech and down converts this information electronically on transmission, thus providing a significant reduction in transmitted bandwidth. A narrower bandwidth signal causes less interference to others operating in the same band. It also allows the use of a sharper and narrower receive filter, which greatly reduces adjacent-channel interference.

One can better understand how the frequency compandor works by considering the composition of speech. Acoustically, human speech consists predominantly of two types of sounds — voiced and unvoiced.

Voiced sounds originate by passing air from the speaker's lungs through the larynx (voice box), a passage in the human throat with the opening obstructed by vocal cords. As air is passed by these cords, they vibrate, causing puffs of air to escape into the aural cavity, which consists of the throat, nasal cavity and mouth. Studies indicate that the acoustic waveform produced by the vocal cords has many harmonics of the fundamental vibration. Because of the irregular shape of the aural cavity, the spectral-amplitude distribution of the harmonics tends to show peaks at distinct points. As speech is produced, changes occur in the aural cavity shape, thus changing the spectral location of these peaks.

Fig. 49 shows a spectrogram, or voice print, of the utterance "digital communication." The vertical axis represents frequency (80 to 8000 Hz), and the horizontal axis represents time (0 to 1.5 s). Darkness of the bands indicates amplitude or voice strength. The fine structure of amplitude peaks that are very close

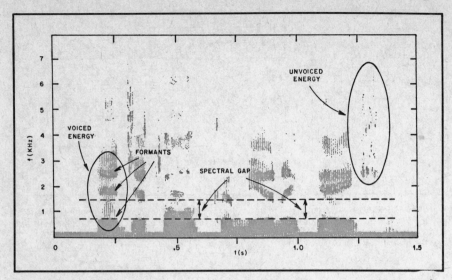

Fig. 49 — A spectogram or voice print of the utterance "digital communication." The vertical axis represents frequency (80 to 8000 Hz), and the horizontal axis represents time (0 to 1.5 s).

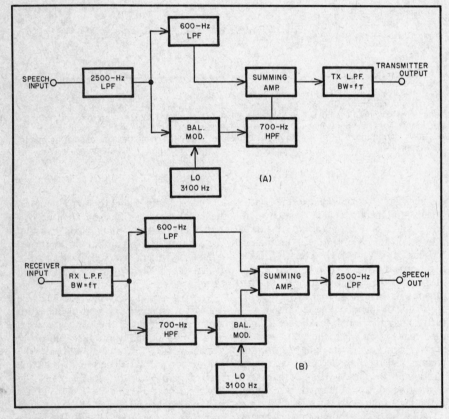

Fig. 50 — Block diagram of the basic frequency compandor scheme. The circuit at A is used to compress the audio bandwidth on transmit. The circuit at B expands this signal for receive.

together in the horizontal dimension is a measurement of vocal-cord vibration (fundamental frequency).

Notice the rather strong amplitude concentrations below 4000 Hz. These are the spectral peaks referred to above and are called formants. The first three formants are shown in Fig. 49 at the beginning of the utterance. Proper processing of these three formants is a major concern of bandwidth conservation in speech.

Unvoiced sounds occur when there is no vocal-track excitation. Sounds such as clicks, hisses and popping are caused by the speaker using his tongue, lips and teeth. These sounds, or evidence of their occurrence by formant extensions into or from a voiced sound, are very important to the intelligibility of speech. Spectral-amplitude distributions of unvoiced sounds are generally above 1500 Hz and are "noise-like," in that very little

periodic structure is present (see Fig. 49).

One other important aspect of speech is the pause between acoustic sounds. Juncture pauses carry meaning and cannot be eliminated without impairing intelligibility. Some long pauses can, however, be shortened and thereby reduce message length.

Briefly, speech is the continuous production of voiced and unvoiced sounds, with appropriate pauses to add clarity and distinctness. Measurements performed on voices from different speakers indicate that the first three formants lie predominantly below 2500 Hz. Speech consisting of these three formants is of good quality, both from an intelligibility and "listenability" standpoint. Sufficient information as to the existence of some unvoiced sounds appears to lie in this range. For example, to produce an "s" sound, the frequency range must extend to approximately 4000 Hz, but this is not usually required for intelligibility since contextural clues provide sufficient evidence for the listener to "hear" an "s."

Evidence from theory and that gained through practice (amateur communications) indicate a bandwidth of 300 to 2500 Hz is adequate for good quality speech.

How can we take advantage of the structure of speech and transmit it more efficiently, and yet preserve the essentials to allow acceptable-sounding speech with high intelligibility? Let us first consider bandwidth conservation and then power. Bandwidth can be conserved at rf and baseband. Rf-bandwidth conservation involves the choise of modulation type such as a-m, fm, ssb or dsb. Amateur users have played a significant role in popularizing ssb which is the most efficient with respect to bandwidth. Rf modulation types more efficient than ssb are not known. Thus to conserve even greater signal bandwidth it appears that audiobandwidth reduction prior to rf modulation and transmission is the last possibility.

To explain the approach taken consider the spectrogram in Fig. 49. Notice that there are natural gaps between the first and second, and second and third formants. There is little energy present in these gaps.

After extensive listening tests and consideration of various filtering and mixing combinations it was found that the first formant is not as essential to intelligibility as the second and third. Furthermore, the gap between the first and second formants is wider then between the second and third and it is more constant with time. As a result the system shown in Fig. 50 was developed.

To understand how the system works note that two bands of speech are preserved, the first from dc to 600 Hz (most communications transceivers limit the low end to 350 Hz) and second from f_1 to 2500

Hz; f_1 corresponds to the low end of the second formant and is variable depending on the transmission and reception low-pass filter (LPF) cutoff frequency f_T. In equation form

$$f_1 = 3100 - f_T \qquad \text{(Eq. 15)}$$

For example, the two filter options provided by the first commercial system will be $f_T = 1600$ Hz and $f_T = 2100$ Hz. Both the transmission and reception filters have a 1.3 shape factor. Thus the narrow system with a transmission bandwidth of 1600 Hz is designed to preserve speech from 350 to 600 Hz, which is the first formant approximation, and from 1500 to 2500 Hz, which is the band of contiguous second and third formants. The wider system with a 2100-Hz transmission bandwidth preserves speech from 350 to 600 Hz system, but also preserves the region from 1000 to 2500 Hz which includes more of the lower end of the second formant.

Operationally, the first formant, 350 to 600 Hz, passes essentially straight through the system. The second and third formants are inverted and down converted for transmission, then reinverted and up converted on reception. Use of the 700-Hz high-pass filter (HPF) aids in eliminating potential distortion products caused by high frequencies mixed low on transmit and low frequencies mixed high on receive.

Amateur Television

A block diagram of a complete ATV station is shown in Fig. 51. The fm modulator is used only if the standard 4.5-MHz fm audio subcarrier is being used. Since the TV video is amplitude modulated, the audio may simultaneously frequency modulate the video carrier if this method of transmitting the voice signal is desired. The audio can also be sent on another frequency band using a separate transmitter and receiver.

Coaxial cable is used for transmission line in most amateur installations, while balanced "twin lead" is used on most TV sets. For this reason, it is necessary to connect a 4:1 balun between the TV receiver and the uhf converter to match the TV set's 300-ohm balanced input to the converter 75-ohm unbalanced output. If the converter is a type designed for home TV set use and has 300-ohm input and output, the balun should be connected between the preamplifier and the converter. The preamp is needed since most uhf TV converters have inadequate sensitivity for serious amateur work.

Technical standards used in amateur television transmission closely resemble those used in commercial TV broad-

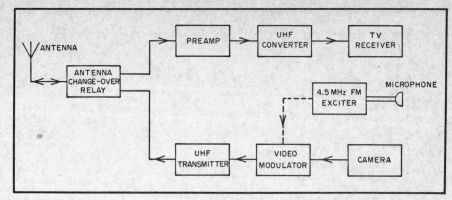

Fig. 51 — Block diagram of an amateur television station. Most common video modulators use grid modulation of the transmitter final-amplifier tube. Because of grid modulation requires little driving power from the video modulator, it is usually a simple one- or two-transistor device built into the transmitter cabinet.

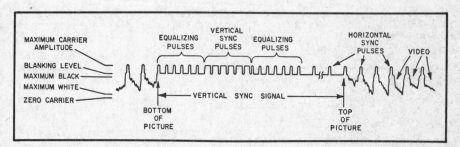

Fig. 52 — A composite TV video signal. The horizontal sync pulses, superimposed on the video (picture information) signal "tell" the TV receiver when to start a new horizontal line. The vertical sync signal is sent at the bottom of each vertical sweep to tell the TV set to go to the top of the screen to start a new field. Since high-amplitude signals come out dark on the screen, the electron beam in the receiver is automatically blanked while it is flying back across the screen to start a new sweep.

casting. The electron beam in the picture tube simultaneously scans from top to bottom (at a 60-Hz rate) and from side to side (at a 15750-Hz rate) to produce a 525-line *raster* on the TV screen. (It takes two vertical scans to sweep out all 525 lines.) As the beam scans, its instantaneous intensity is controlled by the amplitude of the incoming video signal — the stronger the signal, the darker the picture. Now, in order for the light and dark areas to come out in the right places in the picture, the receiver electron beam must be scanning the same portion of the screen as the transmitter TV camera is scanning at the same time. This is why the horizontal and vertical sweeps in the receiver must be synchronized with those in the TV camera.

At the end of each horizontal line, the TV camera sends a high-amplitude sync pulse superimposed on the video (picture) signal. This is the receiver's cue to start the next horizontal line. In addition, at the end of each vertical sweep, a vertical sync pulse is sent. This consists of a series of elongated pulses that the receiver can

recognize as the signal to start a new vertical scan (see Fig. 52). Note that the sync pulses are "blacker than black" so that the electron beam is automatically turned completely off or *blanked* during retrace (when the beam returns to start a new sweep).

The TV sound frequency-modulates a 4.5-MHz *subcarrier* which in turn amplitude-modulates the picture carrier. This would normally produce subcarrier sidebands 4.5 MHz above and below the picture carrier, but since the TV signal is filtered before transmission, most of the lower sideband is removed. The resultant *vestigial sideband* TV signal has video and sync signal frequencies extending to about 4.2 MHz above the carrier and a single fm voice subcarrier 4.5 MHz above. In the TV receiver, the sound subcarrier is heterodyned against the picture carrier to produce a 4.5-MHz fm signal which is amplified and detected in the same manner as in a regular fm receiver. Television techniques are further explained in chapter 14 of the 1981 *Radio Amateur's Handbook*.

High-Performance Receiver Concepts

Some fundamentals of receiver design were presented in earlier chapters of this volume. However, there was minimal discussion of noise figure, bandwidth and dynamic range. These topics will be covered in this section.

The critical portion of the receiver is the front end, that part which precedes the main selectivity-determining elements. Distortion effects in the front end will lead to blocking, intermodulation products and cross modulation. Careful design is necessary if these problems are to be minimized.

Dynamic Range

One of the basic specifications for receivers is noise figure. Implicit in the noise figure concept is the fact that the minimum discernable signal (MDS) of a receiver depends not only on the amount of noise generated by the transistors in the receiver, but on the bandwidth of the system.

While sensitivity is of major significance to the DXer, a receiver must be able to function in the presence of strong signals. This has a twofold meaning. First, the gain-control mechanisms in the receiver, manual or automatic, must have a range that will permit signals with wide strength variations to be received. However, this can be realized easily — in the extreme case, attenuators in the antenna line can be used to decrease the signal level to a point where intelligence can be recovered.

The second and more subtle figure for dynamic range is a number that provides a measure of the range of signals that may be present at the antenna terminals of a receiver while no undesired responses are created in the output.

First, let's consider the measurement of noise figure of an amplifier (or receiver). By definition, the noise factor of the amplifier is the input signal-to-noise ratio divided by the output signal-to-noise ratio.

$$ NF = \frac{S_{in}/N_{in}}{S_{out}/N_{out}} = \frac{S_{in} \, N_{out}}{S_{out} \, N_{in}} $$

(Eq. 16)

The terms in the equations are noise or signal powers, and the noise factor is an algebraic ratio. If the ratio is expressed in decibels, as is often done with other power ratios, the result is the noise figure.

As presented, the noise figure is a nebulous number, for the input (and hence, the output) noise power depends on what is hooked to the input of the amplifier. To attach some meaning that will make a noise figure number a standard measure of the "noisiness" of an amplifier or receiver, the input noise is

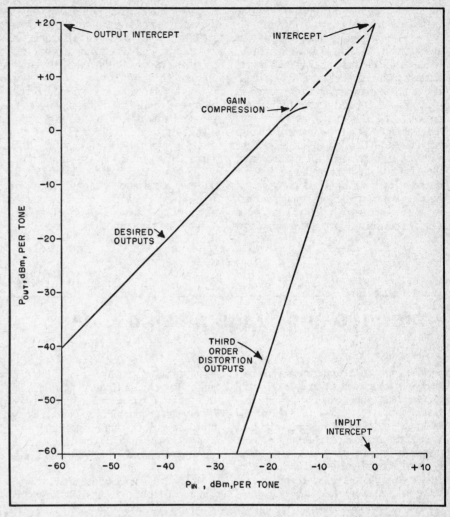

Fig. 53 — Plot example showing signal power versus distortion products as a function of input power of two identical input signals.

assumed to be the noise power available from a resistor at a temperature of 290 kelvins. Using this value for T_o, the noise power is given as

$$ P_n = kT_oB $$

(Eq. 17)

where T_o = 290 kelvins, B is bandwidths in Hz and k is Boltzmann's constant, 1.38 $\times$ 10^{-23} watts/degree. It is convenient to use logarithmic units and to note that in a bandwidth of 1 Hz, P_n = −174 dBm.

Consider a receiver with a bandwidth of 500 Hz. The bandwidth is greater than 1 Hz by a factor of 500, or 27 dB. Hence, in a 500-Hz bandwidth, the power available from this resistor would be −174 dBm + 27 dB = −147 dBm. If the noise output from this receiver with the input terminated in a 50-ohm resistor corresponds to the output that would result from a signal of −140 dBm, the noise figure of the receiver is then the difference, or 7 dB. The MDS, or noise floor of the receiver, is −140 dBm.

The question might arise as to why noise figure is even specified. The same essential information is contained in a specification of the MDS of a receiver. However, such is not the case for an amplifier. Here, the MDS is not specified — it will depend not only on the noise contribution of the amplifier but on the bandwidth of the system using the amplifier. Noise figure is independent of bandwidth.

Consider now the case where two relatively strong signals are injected simultaneously to the input of a 20-dB-gain amplifier. Assume that two input signals of −50 dBm are placed at the input of the amplifier at frequencies f_1 and f_2. Analysis of the amplifier will show that distortion in the amplifier will give rise to outputs not only at the desired input frequencies of f_1 and f_2, but at $(2F_1 - f_2)$ and $(2f_2 - f_1)$. For example, if the input frequencies were 14,040 and 14,050 kHz, the distortion products would appear at

14,030 and 14,060 kHz. In the amplifier the desired outputs would be 20 dB above the −50-dBm input signals, or −30 dBm, and the third-order distortion products might be at −130 dBm. In this case the distortion will be 100 dB down from the desired outputs.

The interesting and significant characteristic of Class A linear amplifiers is that while the desired outputs will vary linearly with changes in the input signals, the dominant (third order) distortion products will vary as the cube of the input powers. Hence, if the signals driving the input are increased to −40 dBm, the output power of the desired signals will be −20 dBm for each of the desired input tones. While the level of the desired frequencies increased by 10 dB, however, the output power of the distortion products will have increased by 30 dB to −100 dBm. The distortion products are now only 80 dB below the desired signals.

Shown in Fig. 53 is a plot for the hypothetical amplifier under discussion, showing the power of the desired output signals and the output power of the distortion products as a function of the level of the input power of the input tones. Eventually, the levels of the input signals will be large enough so that the desired outputs will cease to follow the input power linearly. This effect, called *gain compression*, is the phenomenon in a receiver that ultimately leads to "blocking" (desensitization of a signal caused by a strong signal nearby in frequency). It is not viable to plot the data for the amplifier much beyond this compression point.

The linear portion of the curves may be extended or extrapolated to higher powers even though the amplifier is not capable of operating at these levels. If this is done as shown in the dashed line in the figure, eventually the two curves will cross each other. That is, at some usually unattainable output power, the level of the distortion products equals that of the desired outputs. This point is commonly referred to as the amplifier intercept. More specifically, the output power where the curves intersect is called the output intercept of the amplifier. Similarly, the input power corresponding to the point of intersection is called the input intercept. This brings us to the concept of dynamic range.

The two-tone dynamic range of a receiver is defined as the ratio of the noise floor (MDS) of the receiver to the level of one of two identical input signals which will cause distortion products at the noise floor level. Additional information on receiver dynamic range can be found in Chapter 6 of *Solid State Design For the Radio Amateur.*

Antennas and Transmission Lines

Transmission Lines at VHF and UHF

Both *parallel-conductor* and *coaxial* feed lines are used at vhf and uhf. Coaxial cable is much more popular because it is easy to use, is relatively impervious to the weather, and readily matches the low-impedance unbalanced output of most transmitters and receivers. Inexpensive types of coaxial cable tend to have high power loss factors at vhf and above, however. The more expensive semiflexible "hardline" which uses a solid aluminum outer conductor is often used when low line loss is important. Open-wire feed line has very low loss if the spacing between the wires is very small with respect to the operating wavelength (less than 1/50 wavelength or so), but care must be taken to prevent the wires from becoming tangled. Additionally, if an unshielded balanced transmission line comes close to a metal object, or if for any other reason the rf currents in the two wires are not balanced, the feed line will radiate. This can upset the radiation pattern of the antenna. Antennas fed with coaxial feed line can have the same problem if feed-line radiation exists. This is most often caused by connecting the unbalanced coaxial line directly to a balanced antenna. "Twin-lead" is a type of parallel-conductor feed line with a solid dielectric material between the two wires. Twin-lead is easier to work with than open-wire feed line, but many types develop prohibitive losses at vhf when they get wet. Also this type of feed line is intrinsically more lossy than the open-wire type, although good-quality twin-lead generally has less loss than flexible coaxial cable.

The Smith Chart

Named after its inventor, Phillip H. Smith, the Smith Chart was originally described in *Electronics* for January 1939. They are an invaluable tool for calculating impedances along transmission lines and many types of matching networks, both for antennas and other electronic circuitry.

Although its appearance may at first seem formidable, the Smith Chart is really nothing more than a specialized type of graph, with curved, rather than rectangular, coordinate lines. The coordinate system consists simply of two families of circles — the resistance family and the reactance family. The resistance circles (Fig. 54) are centered on the resistance axis (the only straight line on the Chart), and are tangent to the outer circles at the bottom of the Chart. Each circle is assigned a value of resistance, which is indicated at the point where the circle crosses the resistance axis. All points along any one circle have the same resistance value.

The values assigned to these circles vary from zero at the top of the Chart to infinity at the bottom, and actually represent a ratio with respect to the impedance value assigned to the center point of the Chart, indicated 1.0. This center point is called prime center. If prime center is assigned a value of 100 ohms, then 200 ohms of resistance is represented by the 2.0 circle, 50 ohms by the 0.5 circle, 20 ohms by the 0.2 circle, and so on. If a value of 50 is assigned to the prime center, the 2.0 circle now represents 100 ohms, the 0.5 circle 25 ohms and the 0.2 circle 10 ohms. In each

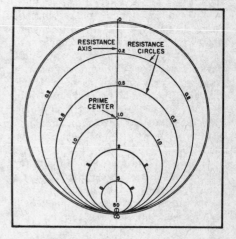

Fig. 54 — Resistance circles of the Smith Chart coordinate system.

case it may be seen that the value on the Chart is determined by dividing the actual resistance by the number assigned to prime center. This process is called normalizing. Conversely, values from the Chart are converted back to actual resistance values by multiplying the Chart value times the value assigned to prime center. This feature permits the use of the Smith Chart for any impedance values, and therefore with any type of uniform transmission line.

Now consider the reactance circles (Fig. 55), which appear as curved lines on the Chart because only segments of the complete circles are drawn. These circles are tangent to the resistance axis, which itself is a member of the reactance family (with a radius of infinity). The centers are dis-

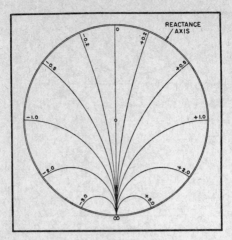

Fig. 55 — Reactance circles (segments) of the Smith Chart coordinate system.

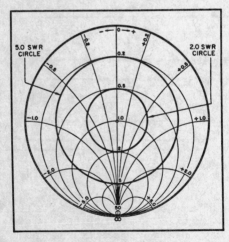

Fig. 56 — The complete coordinate system of the Smith Chart. For simplicity, only a few divisions are shown for the resistance and reactance values.

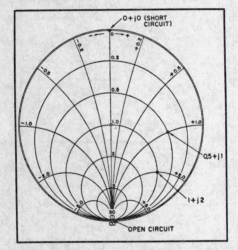

Fig. 57 — Smith Chart with SWR circles added.

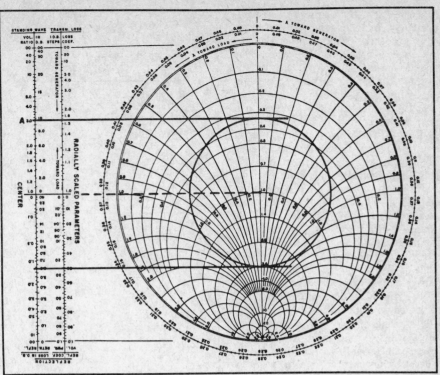

Fig. 58 — Example discussed in the text.

placed to the right or left on a line tangent to the bottom of the Chart. The large outer circle bounding the coordinate portion of the Chart is the reactance axis.

Each reactance circle segment is assigned a value of reactance, indicated near the point where the circle touches the reactance axis. All points along any one segment have the same reactance value. As with the resistance circles, the values assigned to each reactance circle are normalized with respect to the value assigned to prime center. Values to the right of the resistance axis are positive (inductive), and those to the left of the reactance axis are negative (capacitive).

When the resistance family and the reactance family of circles are combined, the coordinate system of the Smith Chart results, as shown in Fig. 56. Complex series impedances can be plotted on this coordinate system.

Impedance Plotting

Suppose we have an impedance consisting of 50 ohms resistance and 100 ohms inductive reactance (Z = 50 + j100). If a value of 100 ohms is assigned to prime center, normalize the above impedance by dividing each component of the impedance by 100. The normalized impedance would then be

$$\frac{506}{100} + j\frac{100}{100} = 0.5 + j1.0$$

This impedance would be plotted on the Smith Chart at the intersection of the 0.5 resistance circle and the +1.0 reactance circle, as indicated in Fig. 57. If a value of 50 ohms had been assigned to prime center, as for 50-ohm coaxial line, the same impedance would be plotted at intersection of the 1.0 resistance circle and

the +2.0 reactance circle (also indicated in Fig. 57).

From these examples, it may be seen that the same impedance may be plotted at different points on the Chart, depending on the value assigned to prime center. It is customary when solving transmission-line problems to assign to prime center a value equal to the characteristic impedance, or Z_o, of the line being used.

Short and Open Circuits

On the subject of plotting impedances, two special cases deserve consideration. These are short circuits and open circuits. A true short circuit has zero resistance and zero reactance, or 0 + j0. This impedance would be plotted at the top of the Chart, at the intersection of the resistance and reactance axes. An open circuit has infinite resistance, and would therefore be plotted at the bottom of the Chart, at the intersection of the resistance and reactance axes. These two special cases are sometimes used in matching stubs.

Standing Wave Ratio Circles

Members of a third family of circles, which are not printed on the Chart but which are added during the process of problem solving, are standing-wave ratio (SWR) circles. See Fig. 57. This family is centered on prime center, and appears as concentric circles inside the reactance axis. During calculations, one or more of these circles may be added with a drawing compass. Each circle represents a value of SWR, every point on a given circle may be determined directly from the Chart coordinate system by reading the resistance value where the SWR circle crosses the resistance axis, below prime center. (The reading where the circle crosses the resistance axis above prime center indicates the inverse ratio.)

Consider the situation where a load mismatch in a length of line causes a 3:1 SWR to exist. Disregarding line losses, it may be said that the SWR remains constant throughout the length of the line. This is represented on the Smith Chart by drawing a 3:1 constant-SWR circle (a circle with a radius of 3 on the resistance axis), as in Fig. 57. The design of the Chart is such that any impedance encountered anywhere along the length of this mismatched line will fall on the SWR circle, and may be read from the coordinates merely by progressing around the SWR circle by an amount corresponding to the length of the line involved.

This brings into use the wavelength scales, which appear in Fig. 58 near the outer perimeter of the Smith Chart. These scales are calibrated in terms of portions of an electrical wavelength along a transmission line. One scale, running counterclockwise, starts at the generator or input end of the line and progresses toward the load, while the other scale starts at the load and proceeds toward the generator in a clockwise direction. The complete circle represents one half wavelength. Progressing once around the perimeter of these scales corresponds to progressing along a transmission line for a half wavelength. Because impedances will repeat themselves every half wavelength along a piece of line, the Chart may be used for any length of line by disregarding or subtracting from the line's total length an integral, or whole number, or half wavelengths.

Also shown in Fig. 58 is a means of transferring the radius of the SWR circle to the external scales of the chart, by drawing lines tangent to the circle. Or the radius of the SWR circle may be simply transferred to the external scale by placing the point of a drawing compass at the center, or 0, line and inscribing a short arc across the appropriate scale. It will be noted that when this is done in Fig. 58, the external standing-wave voltage-ratio scale indicates the SWR to be 3.0 (at A) — the condition for initially drawing the circle on the Chart. Complete information on how to solve problems with the Smith Chart is given in Chapter 3 of *The ARRL Antenna Book*.

Properties of Open and Shorted Coaxial Lines

The diagrams shown in Figs. 59 and 60 illustrate the relationships of impedance, voltage and current for open and shorted sections of line or various lengths. The impedance that the generator "sees" for various lengths of line are indicated direct-

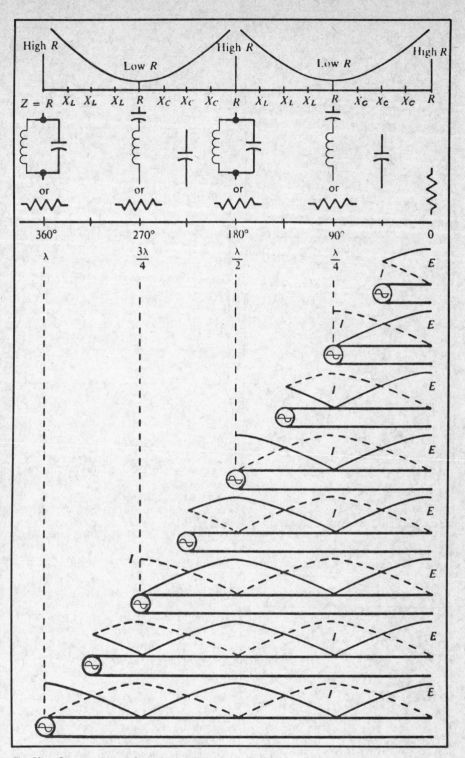

Fig. 59 — Characteristics of an open-ended transmission line.

ly above on the chart. Curves above the axis marked with R, X_L and X_C indicate the relative value of the impedance presented to the generator. Circuit symbols indicate the equivalent circuits for the lines at that particular length. Standing waves of voltage (E) and current (I), whose quotient is impedance (Z), are shown above each line.

Considering the open ended line, at all odd quarter-wave points (1/4, 3/4 and so on) measured from the output end, the current is maximum and the impedance is minimum. At all even quarter-wave points (1/2 λ, 1 λ, 3/2 λ, and so on), the voltage is maximum and the impedance is maximum (infinite). At points in between quarter-wave marks, the impedance seen by the generator is either capacitive or inductive. For example, between 0 and 1/4 λ the impedance is capacitive. At exactly the 1/8 λ point, the impedance seen by the generator is capacitive and is equal to the impedance of the line. Between 1/4 λ and 1/2 λ the impedance is inductive. At exactly the 3/8 λ point, the impedance is induc-

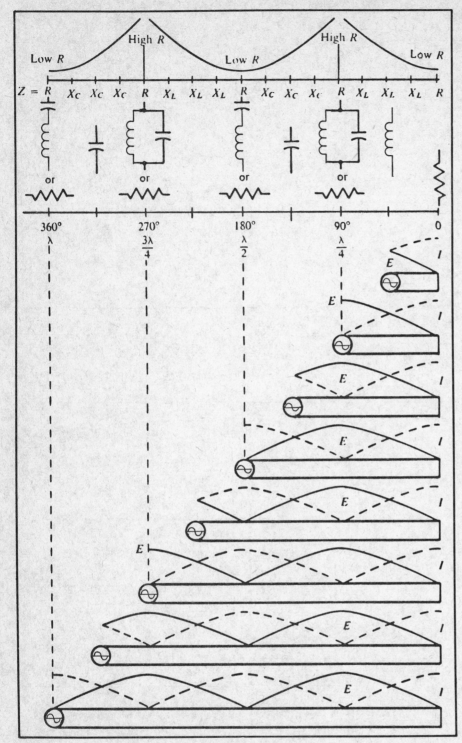

Fig. 60 — Characteristics of a short-circuited transmission line.

tive and equal to the impedance of the line. As can be seen on the graph, the impedance alternates between capacitive and inductive.

The shorted line can be considered in a similar manner. See Fig. 60. For additional information on transmission lines, consult Chapter 3 of *The ARRL Antenna Book*.

SWR

When any transmission line is terminated in other than its characteristic im-

pedance, reflection of rf energy will occur from the termination point. At any point along the line, the reflected waves will combine with the outgoing incident signal to produce an rf voltage that depends on the line impedance, load impedance, and distance from the load. If, for example, the end of the line is shorted, then the reflected signal is just as strong as the incident one, and at locations where the two are 180 degrees out of phase, no net voltage will be present. Thus the ratio between the voltages at locations where the

voltage is maximum and minimum respectively (that is, the *standing-wave ratio* or SWR) is infinity. See chapter 19 of the ARRL *Handbook* or chapter 3 of the *Antenna Book* for a further discussion.

SWR can be measured directly by alternately placing an rf voltmeter or ammeter (voltage SWR and current SWR are identical) at points of maximum and minimum voltage or current along the transmission line (assuming the line is at least a quarter wavelength long). More common practice is to use a directional coupler and appropriate detectors ("SWR meter") which measures the incident and reflected power directly. The SWR may be computed from these two figures using the formula

$$SWR = \frac{1 + \sqrt{P_r/P_f}}{1 - \sqrt{P_r/P_f}} \qquad \text{(Eq. 18)}$$

where

P_f = forward power
P_r = power reflected from the load

It is also possible to measure SWR with an *impedance bridge* (covered in the next section of this chapter). If the load impedance is a pure resistance, the SWR is

$$SWR = \frac{Z_r}{Z_o} \text{ or } \frac{Z_o}{Z_r} \qquad \text{(Eq. 19)}$$

whichever is greater. Here Z_o = the line impedance and Z_R = the resistance of the load. If the load is a complex impedance, the SWR is most easily computed with a Smith Chart. (See chapter 3 of *The ARRL Antenna Book*.)

The feed-point resistance of a half-wave dipole antenna varies with height above ground, but for heights above about a quarter wavelength, the radiation resistance will be reasonably near the free-space value of about 73 ohms. Thus a dipole may be fed directly with 75-ohm twin-lead with low SWR on the feed line. Twin-lead of other impedances or open-wire feed line may also be used if the line in question can stand the higher peak voltages and currents caused by the high SWR.

If an unbalanced line, such as coaxial cable, is used to feed directly a balanced antenna, such as a dipole, then current may be induced on the outside of the coax outer conductor (shield), which will cause the feed line to radiate. While this may not be a problem with a dipole antenna, since the radiation pattern of a dipole is often of little importance, with directional beams feed-line radiation will upset the radiation pattern and (usually) reduce the gain. A *balun* ("*bal*anced-to-*un*balanced" transformer) may be used to decouple the antenna current from the coax shield. The *broadband balun* is basically a transformer designed to work at radio frequencies (see Fig. 61A and B). Each of the two or three sections of the coil is bifilar or trifilar wound with the other sections for maximum coupling. The windings may be in the conventional solenoid (cylinder) shape or the two ends of the coil may be bent around until they meet to form a circular *toroidal* (doughnut-shaped) coil. Frequently in the latter case, a toroidal core of high-permeability material is used. Coax cable or parallel-conductor transmission line is often used for the windings. See chapter 5 of *The ARRL Antenna Book* or chapter 19 of the *Handbook* for more details.

The so-called *linear balun* works only on a single frequency band and makes use of the properties of a quarter- or half-wavelength section of transmission line. The two most commonly used arrangements appear in Fig. 61 C and D.

Three methods of matching low-impedance feed line to a half wave dipole element are shown in Fig. 62. The *T match* (A) and *delta match* (C) are for balanced feeders. The latter is adjusted for proper matching by varying dimensions A and B. The effective lengths of the two matching rods of the T match are changed by moving the shorting bars, and the reactance of the bars is tuned out with two variable capacitors. The *gamma match* (B) is useful for coax feed line, and operation is similar to that of the T match. These three matching devices are covered in more detail in chapter 3 of *The ARRL Antenna Book*.

Antenna Coupling

An antenna coupling circuit has two purposes: (1) to provide the proper resistive load for the power-amplifier tube or transistor, and (2) to reduce unwanted emissions (mainly harmonics) to a very low value.

One of the coupling methods used in early transmitters was *variable-link coupling* to the power amplifier tank circuit (Fig. 63). The coupling between the tank coil L1 and its link L2 is usually varied by rotating the link; maximum coupling occurs when the two coils are parallel. The center tap of the link is grounded for balanced feed lines, and one end is grounded for coaxial feed. Frequently, a variable capacitor is used in series with the output to cancel link inductance. Not only does this facilitate good coupling, but it provides better harmonic rejection as well.

Most modern transmitters use *pi-network coupling* (Fig. 64). Because of the series coil and parallel capacitors, this circuit acts as a low-pass filter to reduce harmonics as well as an impedance-matching device. As with the link-coupled circuit the circuit Q will be equal to the plate load impedance divided by the reactance of the tuning capacitor C1. Coupling is adjusted by varying C2, which generally has a reactance somewhat less than the load resistance (usually 50 ohms). Circuit design information for pi- and link-coupled networks appears in chapter 6 of the ARRL *Handbook*.

Harmonic radiation can always be

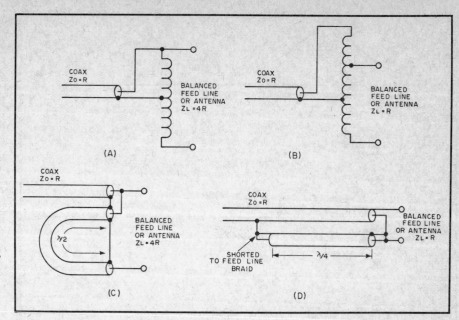

Fig. 61 — Balanced-to-unbalanced (balun) coils are pictured at A and B. Figures C and D show single-band baluns made with resonant lengths of coaxial cable. A and C match low-impedance coaxial line with a balanced load of four times the line impedance. These are thus called "4 to 1 baluns." The 1:1 baluns at B and D match coaxial cable to a balanced load of the same impedance.

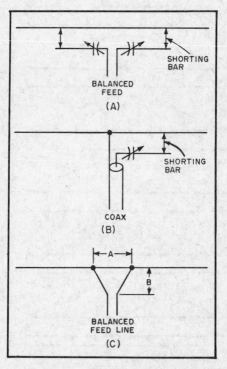

Fig. 62 — Illustrated above are (A) T-match, (B) gamma-match and (C) delta-match methods of coupling transmission line to the antenna. All of these methods are useful for beam antennas in which it is not convenient to electrically insulate the driven element from the supporting boom.

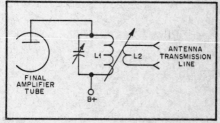

Fig. 63 — A variable-link coupling circuit.

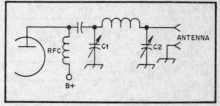

Fig. 64 — A pi-network coupling circuit. Capacitor C2 is the coupling (loading) control, and C1 is for adjusting the tuning.

reduced to any desired level by sufficient shielding of the transmitter, filtering of all external power and control leads, and inclusion of a low-pass filter (of the proper cutoff frequency) connected with shielded cable to the transmitter antenna terminals (see Fig. 65). Unfortunately, low-pass filters must be operated into a load of close to their design impedance or their filtering properties will be impaired, and damage may occur to the filter if high power is used. For this reason, if the filter load impedance is not within limits, a device must be used to transform the load impedance of the antenna system (as seen at the transmitter end of the feed line) into the proper value. We will, hereafter, assume this will be the commonly used value of 50 ohms.

The impedance-matching device is variously referred to as a Transmatch, a matchbox or an *antenna coupler*. The

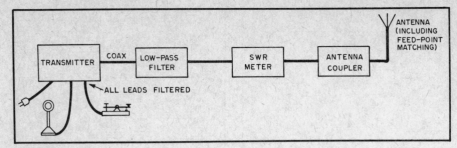

Fig. 65 — Proper connecting arrangement for a low-pass filter and antenna coupler. The SWR meter is included for use as a tuning indicator for the antenna coupler.

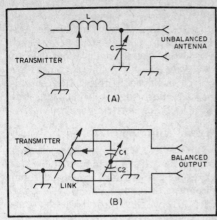

Fig. 66 — At A is an L-network antenna coupler, usable for unbalanced feed. The inductively coupled circuit at B is used with balanced feed line.

L network (Fig. 66A) will match any unbalanced load with a series resistance higher than 50 ohms. (This assumes unlimited choice of values for L and C.) Most unbalanced antennas will satisfy this condition. If, however, no combination of L and C will perform the proper impedance transformation, the network may be reversed input-to-output by moving the capacitor to the transmitter side of the coil. To adjust this tuner, the coil tap is moved one turn at a time, each time adjusting C for lowest SWR. Eventually a combination should be found that will give a low value of SWR.

You can convert an L network into a *pi network* by adding a variable capacitor to the transmitter side of the coil. Using this circuit, any value of load impedance can be matched using some values of coil and capacitors.

Balanced feed lines may be tuned by means of the circuit of Fig. 66B. A capacitor may be added in series with the input to tune out link inductance. As with the L network, the coil taps and tuning capacitor settings are adjusted for lowest SWR, with higher impedance loads being tapped further out from the center of the coil. For very low load impedances, it may

be necessary to put C1 and C2 in *series* with the antenna leads (with the coil taps at the extreme ends of the coil). A more complete discussion of antenna couplers appears in chapter 3 of *The ARRL Antenna Book*, and several practical examples are included in the *Handbook*.

Antenna Radiation Patterns and Directivity

A radiation pattern is a graph showing actual or relative signal intensity, at a fixed distance, as a function of the direction from the antenna system. At the outset it must be realized that such a pattern is a three-dimensional affair and therefore cannot be represented in a plane drawing. The "solid" radiation pattern of an antenna in free space would be found by measuring the field strength at every point on the surface of an imaginary sphere having the antenna at its center. The information so obtained is then used to construct a solid figure such that the distance from a fixed point (representing the antenna) to the surface, in any direction, is proportional to the field strength from the antenna in that direction.

The Isotropic Radiator

The radiation from a practical antenna never has the same intensity in all directions. The intensity may even be zero in some directions from the antenna; in others it may be greater than one would expect from an antenna that *did* radiate equally well in all directions. But even though no actual antenna radiates with equal intensity in all directions, it is nevertheless useful to assume that such an antenna exists. It can be used as a "measuring stick" for comparing the

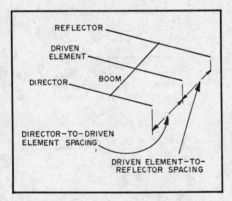

Fig. 67 — A three-element Yagi antenna. More directors may be added for additional gain.

properties of actual antenna systems. Such a hypothetical antenna is called an *isotropic radiator.*

The solid pattern of an isotropic radiator, therefore, would be a sphere, since the field strength is the same in all directions. In any plane containing the isotropic antenna (which may be considered as a point in space, or a "point source") the pattern is a circle with the antenna at its center. The isotropic antenna has the simplest possible directive pattern; that is, it has no directivity at all.

An infinite variety of pattern shapes,

some quite complicated, is possible with actual antenna systems.

Antennas

A *Yagi beam* antenna is made up of one half-wave dipole driven directly from the feed line plus one or more parallel *parasitic elements* (see Fig. 67). Parasitic elements perform their function by intercepting part of the transmitted energy from the driven element and reradiating the rf with a phase and amplitude that depend on the parasitic element length and distance to other nearby elements. Those placed on the maximum radiation side of the driven element are called *directors.* These usually contribute maximum gain if they are made about five percent shorter than a half-wave resonant dipole. The *reflector* is placed at the back of the beam and is usually about five percent longer than a resonant dipole. Invariably, no more than one reflector is used, the rest of the parasitic elements being directors.

Spacing between elements is less critical than the element lengths. Optimum reflector-driven element spacing is between about 0.15 and 0.23 wavelength at the frequency in use. Director spacing is generally greatest, the more elements there are between it and the driven element. For example, typical first director-to-driven element spacings range from about 0.13 to 0.19 wavelength while optimum spacings between adjacent directors beyond the sixth are about 0.35 to 0.42 wavelength. Yagi antennas are covered in chapter 20 of the ARRL *Handbook* and more extensively in chapter 4 of *The ARRL Antenna Book*.

Phased Vertical Antennas

Two or more vertical antennas spaced a half wavelength apart can be operated as a single antenna system to obtain additional gain and a directional pattern. There are practical ways that verticals can be combined, end-fire and broadside. In the broadside configuration, the two verticals are fed in phase, producing a figure-eight pattern that is broadside to the plane of the verticals. In an end-fire arrangement, the two verticals are fed 180° out of phase, and a figure-eight pattern that is in line with the two antennas is obtained. These arrangements are shown in Figs. 68 and 69.

If an end-fire pair of verticals is fed 90° out of phase and spaced a quarter wavelength apart, the resulting pattern will be unidirectional. The direction of maximum radiation is in line with the two verticals, and in the direction of the vertical receiving the lagging excitation. This is illustrated in Fig. 70. Other spacings and phasing line lengths will result in a wide variety of pattern shapes. The systems outlined here are some of the more popular types.

VHF and UHF Antennas

Vhf and uhf Yagis are built on the same basic design principles as those used at lower frequencies. However, when constructing vhf and uhf antennas with large-diameter tubing, element lengths must be shortened slightly. The smaller an element length/diameter ratio, the more the element must be shortened.

There is no upper limit to the gain of a Yagi array — the longer the boom length the greater the gain, assuming the antenna is properly designed and constructed. At hf, antennas of more than four or five elements are too big to use conveniently, but at vhf and above, *long Yagis* are of more manageable size. Large Yagi antennas must be constructed with care, however, since element lengths, diameters and spacings are more critical than with smaller antennas.

Even the *insulators* used in antennas above about 100 MHz must be selected with care. Common porcelain insulators can be lossy, especially when installed at high-voltage points. Insulators should have low loss and high dielectric strength. Two good materials for the purpose are quartz glass and Teflon. Polystyrene and polyethylene are also good if their loss of strength at high heat is acceptable.

The final difference between hf and vhf antennas is that vertical *polarization* is

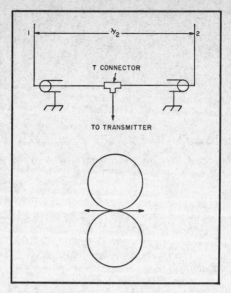

Fig. 68 — Pattern for two 1/4 λ verticals spaced one-half wavelength apart and fed in phase. The arrow represents the axis of the elements.

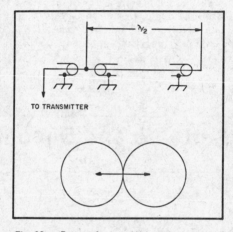

Fig. 69 — Pattern for two 1/4 λ verticals spaced one-half wavelength apart and fed out of phase. The arrow represents the axis of the elements.

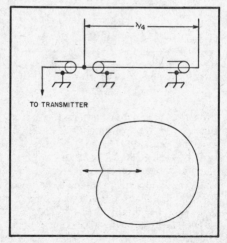

Fig. 70 — Pattern for two 1/4 λ verticals spaced one-quarter wavelength apart and fed 90° out of phase. The arrow represents the axis of the elements, with the element on the right being the one of lagging phase.

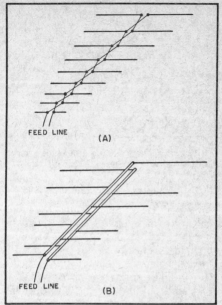

Fig. 71 — The log-periodic antenna. At A, each element must be fed 180° out of phase with those adjacent so that the feed line must be twisted a half turn between each pair of elements. Using this construction technique, each element must be insulated from the boom (not shown). At B, two booms are used, and the elements are attached in such a manner that adjacent elements are fed out of phase.

more often used at vhf. Man-made rf noise tends to have a predominantly vertical component, so that horizontal polarization may be advantageous in noisy areas, but otherwise the choice of polarization will depend on custom. Since simple whip antennas are common for mobile operation, most fm work is carried out using vertical polarization while most cw or ssb activity is on horizontal polarization.

Because of their large size compared to a Yagi of equivalent gain, *log-periodic antennas* are most often used at vhf and above. The basic principle of this antenna is that over a certain frequency range its dimensions are independent of frequency (see Fig. 71). At low frequencies, the largest two or three elements are nearly self-resonant and thus do most of the radiating. At progressively higher frequencies, shorter and shorter groups of elements are used. The point is that at any frequency, a group of elements is used that is nearly identical to every other group except that the element lengths and spacings are scaled to the frequency in use. Thus, the log-periodic antenna is usable over a wide band of frequencies.

One rather unusual antenna that is well suited for vhf work is the *discone* (Fig. 72), so-called because it is in the shape of a disc placed at the apex of a cone. This is vertically polarized, wide-band antenna which is capable of providing a nearly constant 50-ohm load and omnidirectional radiation over a very wide frequency range. Distance L should be at least a

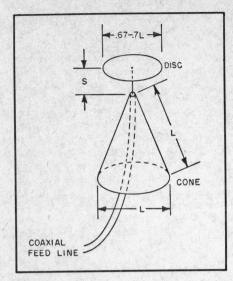

Fig. 72 — The discone antenna. The coax braid is attached to the top of the cone, and the center conductor connects to the center of the disc.

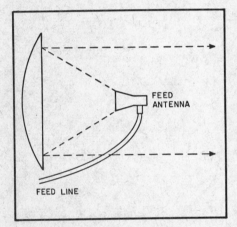

Fig. 73 — a parabolic dish reflector.

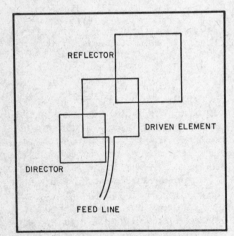

Fig. 74 — The cubical quad antenna. Sometimes the elements are mounted at a 45° angle and the antenna fed at one corner. In any case, if the antenna is fed at the bottom, the polarization will be horizontal; if fed at the side, the antenna will have vertical polarization. The elements are usually attached at the corners to X-shaped bamboo or fiberglass "spreaders" which are connected at the crossover point to a common metal boom.

quarter-wavelength at the lowest frequency in use. Distance S is not particularly critical, but often-used lengths range from about six inches at 14 MHz to about an inch at 144 MHz. Constructional details may be found in chapter 16 of *The ARRL Antenna Book.*

The *rhombic* is an often-overlooked antenna for vhf use. This diamond-shaped antenna is fed at one end with a balanced feed line (or coaxial cable and a balun). The antenna is basically bidirectional, but it may be made unidirectional by cutting the corner opposite the feedpoint and inserting a 600- to 800-ohm resistor (exact value determined experimentally). At hf, any rhombic with reasonable gain is monstrous, but on 2 meters, for example, a four-wavelength per leg rhombic would be about 50 feet long. Complete design information on rhombic antennas appears in chapter 5 of *The ARRL Antenna Book.*

Parabolic dish reflectors are rarely used in the amateur bands below 420 MHz. Above this frequency, reasonably small high-gain dishes may be constructed (Fig. 73). A 10-foot diameter dish, for example, will have a theoretical gain over a dipole of about 21 dB at 432 MHz and 30 dB at 1296 MHz. (Practical antennas will have about 3 dB less gain.) The same dish may be used on different bands merely by changing the feed antenna. The feed antenna must be unidirectional with a beamwidth narrow enough that most of the energy radiated falls within the perimeter of the dish. The dish itself need not be of solid metal — wind resistance and weight are greatly reduced if you substitute wire screen or an array of wires strung on a roughly parabolic framework of metal tubing. If the wires run in only one direction (that is, there are not two perpendicular sets of wire as with wire screening), then the wires must be run parallel with the antenna polarization. Wire separation must be less than about 0.1 wavelength or so at the highest frequency in use to ensure efficient reflection. Construction details of a practical dish appear in chapter 12 of *The ARRL Antenna Book.*

The *quad* beam antenna is most often used at hf. Like the Yagi, it consists of a driven element and one or more parasitic elements. Each element, however, instead of being basically a half-wave length dipole, is in the form of a full-wave loop (see Fig. 74). As with the Yagi, the director(s) and reflector should be slightly shorter and longer respectively (about three percent) than the driven element. For the same boom length and number of elements, the quad will have about 2-dB greater gain than the Yagi. In addition, the turning radius of a quad is less than that of a Yagi of equal boom length since quad elements are only one-quarter wavelength wide. These advantages, however, are often offset by greater mechanical

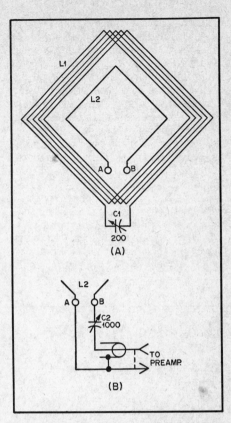

Fig. 75 — A multiturn frame antenna is shown at A. L2 is the coupling loop. The drawing at B shows how L2 is connected to a preamplifier.

complexity of the quad. Further information on quads is found in chapters 4 and 14 of *The ARRL Antenna Book.*

Radio Direction Finding Technique

The art of radio direction finding is as old as radio itself. Anyone who has seen antique broadcast receivers has likely noticed the large multiturn wire antennas mounted atop the receivers. These antennas were rotated in azimuth to optimize reception. Modern broadcast receivers make use of small ferrite-loaded rod antennas that are an integral part of the receiver.

Radio direction finding is just what the name implies — finding the direction or location of a transmitted signal. It is interesting to note that the old-fashioned wire-loop antennas are still used for direction finding, primarily on the lower hf bands (160, 80 and 40 meters) and to some extent on the higher hf bands (20, 15 and 10 meters). An example of a practical loop antenna is shown in Fig. 75. The main drawback of this antenna for radio direction finding applications is that the pattern is bidirectional, broadside to the loop. Since the antenna is bidirectional, some ambiguity will be noticed. An antenna that is directional (a cardioid pattern), and not prohibitively large at these frequencies is the Adcock array. This antenna is presented in the reference listed at the end of this section.

Radio direction finding on the higher hf

bands (20, 15 and 10 meters) has become somewhat easier with the proliferation of rotatable beam antennas at many stations. These antennas are characterized by good front-to-back and front-to-side pattern ratios which are precisely what is needed for direction finding. Although the main lobe off the front of the antenna may be fairly broad, worthwhile direction finding can be done especially when triangulation is used. More on this technique later.

At vhf and uhf, the job of direction finding is even easier. High-gain, small-beamwidth antennas are physically small at these frequencies and can be hand carried along with portable transceivers. Many clubs sponsor hidden transmitter hunts on these frequencies in order to enhance the skills of operators should

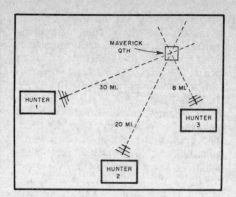

Fig. 76 — Method for triangulation when locating a signal source.

they be needed in emergency or malicious interference trackdown.

Although any one station equipped for direction finding can estimate the direction from which the signal is emanating, one station cannot estimate the distance between the transmitter and receiver. To obtain this information, a technique called triangulation must be used. This is illustrated in Fig. 76. Stations 1, 2 and 3 rotate their directional antennas to obtain maximum response from the transmitted signal. The beam headings are noted, compared and plotted on an area map. The point where the three headings converge is the approximate location of the transmitter. Additional information on radio direction finding can be found in an article entitled "Maverick Trackdown," which appeared in the July 1980 issue of *QST*.

Radio Communication Practices

Test Equipment, Measurements and Adjustments

The Wheatstone bridge shown in Fig. 77A is a device used for measuring an unknown resistance R_d. When R_b is adjusted such that $R_a/R_b = R_c/R_d$, then the voltmeter will indicate zero and the bridge is said to be *balanced*. Since we presumably know the values of R_a, R_b and R_c, we can compute R_d. If $R_a = R_c$ then the bridge will be balanced only when $R_b = R_d$.

If the battery is replaced by a source of radio-frequency voltage, the same circuit can be used to measure the rf resistance of an antenna. However, since radio antennas rarely exhibit a pure resistive impedance, the *rf impedance bridge* of Fig. 77A includes a coil and capacitor. When the total series reactance and resistance of R_b, L and C equals the antenna impedance, the bridge will balance. There are several other possible ways to arrange the components in the various arms of the bridge that allow measurement of an unknown impedance using the formula $Z_a/Z_b = Z_c/Z_d$ where Z_a, Z_b, Z_c and Z_d are the *complex* impedances (including both magnitude and phase angle) of the various arms of the bridge. One practical circuit is included in chapter 16 of the ARRL *Handbook*.

A *sweep generator* is simply an rf signal generator that can constantly sweep the signal back and forth across a specified range of frequencies, usually at about 60-Hz rate. The sweep signal voltage is also available to drive the horizontal input of an oscilloscope so that the frequency response of an intermediate frequency amplifier system, rf filter of any other circuit can be displayed graphically on the oscilloscope face (see Fig. 78). In this way, you can easily adjust the circuit to have any desired frequency-response charac-

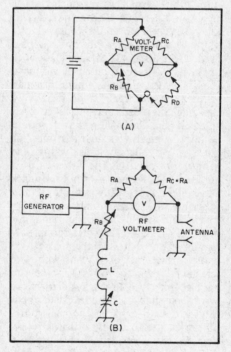

Fig. 77 — A Wheatstone bridge, shown at A, used for measuring unknown resistances. The rf impedance bridge at B will measure the equivalent series resistance *and* reactance of an antenna or other circuit. The variable resistor R_b may be provided with a tuning dial reading directly in ohms, and the capacitor dial may also be calibrated directly in ohms reactance for any particular frequency. Usually the coil is a plug-in type, a different coil used for each band, and a conversion factor is applied to the capacitor dial to compute ohms reactance for each frequency band in use.

teristics. If the device is an i-f amplifier, the vertical scope input may be connected to the a-m detector, if one is present, instead of the rf detector.

If the device in question is to be adjusted for maximum selectivity, (that is,

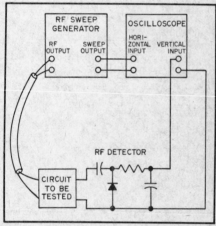

Fig. 78 — Proper setup of an rf sweep generator. The oscilloscope face will be a graph of amplitude response of the circuit being tested versus frequency. Frequently the sweep generator is equipped with crystal-controlled marker oscillators to provide reference calibration frequencies for precise alignment of i-f filters.

the sharpest peak in the frequency-response pattern), then a fixed-tuned rf generator may be used. All tuned circuits are adjusted for maximum output with the generator frequency set for the passband center frequency.

By coupling an a-m or ssb phone signal directly to the vertical deflection plates of an oscilloscope and adjusting the horizontal sweep for a slow audio rate, you can view the voice-*modulated* wave pattern on the scope face to check for "flat topping" or other indications of amplitude distortion. Methods for doing this are shown in the ARRL *Handbook*.

In an a-m transmitter, a small sample of the audio-frequency voltage from the plate-modulation transformer may be applied to the horizontal input of the oscilloscope with the internal sweep generator turned off. The modulated rf signal is again coupled to the vertical deflection plates. The resulting *trapezoidal*-shaped pattern provides an easily interpretable way of checking for modulation defects. Further information is in the ARRL *Handbook*.

An even easier method of checking amplifier linearity is to use a *linearity tracer*. This consists of two rf detectors, one connected to the input of the amplifier and one to the output. You connect the output of one detector to the horizontal input of an oscilloscope and the other to the vertical input. If the amplifier is truly linear, the scope pattern will be a tilted straight line. If the line bends or has a sharp break in it, then the amplifier has distortion. Best results are had if the rf coupling to each detector is adjusted so that approximately equal outputs are obtained from both.

Spectrum Analysis

Spectrum analysis is most often performed with the aid of a piece of sophisticated test equipment called a *spectrum analyzer*. The spectrum analyzer can be likened to an oscilloscope in that both characterize an electrical signal through graphical representation. The oscilloscope is used to observe electrical signals in the *time* domain (amplitude as a function of time). However, not all signals can be properly represented in just the time domain. Amplifiers, mixers, oscillators, detectors, modulators, filters and transmitters are best characterized in terms of their *frequency spectrum*. This information is obtained by viewing electrical signals in the frequency domain (amplitude as a function of frequency). An instrument that can display the frequency domain is the spectrum analyzer.

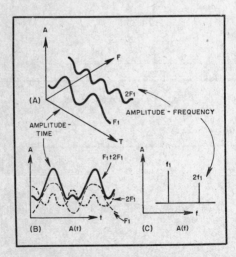

Fig. 79 — Here are several ways in which a complex signal may be characterized. At A is a three-dimensional display of amplitude, time and frequency. At B, this information is shown only in the time domain as would be seen on an oscilloscope. At C the same information is shown in the frequency domain as it would be viewed on a spectrum analyzer.

So that we can more easily understand the concepts of time and frequency domain, let's look at Fig. 79. The three-dimensional coordinates show time (as the line rising toward the top/right) and amplitude (as the vertical axis). The two discrete frequencies shown are harmonically related so we'll refer to them as f_1 and $2f_1$.

In the representation of time domain at Fig. 79B, all frequency components of the signal are summed together. In fact, if the two discrete frequencies shown were applied to the input of an oscilloscope we would see the solid line (which corresponds to $f_1 + 2f_1$) on the display.

In the frequency domain, complex signals (signals composed of more than one frequency) are separated into their individual frequency components. Additionally, a measurement is made as to the power level at each discrete frequency. The display depicted at Fig. 79C is typical of that obtained with a spectrum analyzer.

The frequency domain can contain information not found in the time domain and therefore the spectrum analyzer offers advantages over the oscilloscope for certain measurements. As might be expected, some measurements require data gathering to be done in the time domain, and in these cases the oscilloscope is an invaluable instrument.

Spectrum analyzers are calibrated in both frequency and amplitude for relative and absolute measurements. The frequency range displayed on the screen of the analyzer is controlled by the scan-width control, which is calibrated in hertz, kilohertz or megahertz per division (graticule marking). Each horizontal division on the screen, for example, might correspond to 10 MHz, 1 MHz or 10 kHz.

The vertical axis of the display is calibrated for amplitude. Common calibrations for the amplitude axis are 1 dB, 2 dB and 10 dB per division (graticule marking). For transmitter analysis, the 10-dB-per-division range is the most used, as it allows for large-range viewing of the fundamental signal, harmonics and spurious signals.

Displayed at Fig. 80A is the output from a transmitter operating "key down" in the 40 meter band. The horizontal scale has been set for 5 MHz per division and the vertical scale is 10 dB per division. The "pip" (white line) at the far left-hand edge of the display is generated within the spectrum analyzer. This signal corresponds to "zero" frequency and is used to mark this spot on the analyzer display. Moving to the right at 5 MHz per division, the next tall "pip" may be seen at roughly 7 MHz. This signal is the fundamental frequency. Since the vertical scale is adjusted for 10 dB per division, all other signals (spurious outputs from the transmitter) can be accurately referenced to the power of the fundamental. Moving farther to the right, the next signal can be seen at

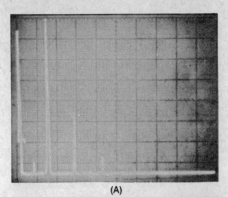

(A)

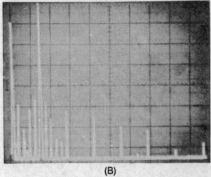

(B)

Fig. 80 — Spectrum-analyzer photographs of two different pieces of equipment operating on the 40-meter band. Each horizontal division represents 5 MHz and each vertical division is 10 dB. The photograph at A represents a "clean" transmitted signal and that at B is not. Both transmitters are legal, though, according to the FCC rules and regulations.

roughly 14 MHz — the second harmonic of the fundamental. The level of this signal is 46 dB below the fundamental. Moving even farther to the right, another signal is down 67 dB from the level of the fundamental. Backtracking to the left, another signal is visible at about 4 MHz. This is most likely a spurious mixing product or oscillator leakage to the final amplifier since it is not harmonically related to the fundamental. The level of this signal is quite low, some 70 dB below that of the fundamental. This photograph is typical of the output of a well-designed transmitter.

The photograph shown at Fig. 80B is that of a not-so-well-designed transmitter. The horizontal and vertical calibration for this photograph is identical to that shown at A. In addition to the higher-order harmonics, a number of mixing products are seen above and below the fundamental. Generally speaking, the chances of causing interference to other services is greater with the transmitter output shown at B than that depicted at A.

Another area of concern in the realm of transmitter spectral purity has to do with the intermodulation distortion (IMD) levels associated with ssb transmitters and amplifiers. IMD occurs within an amplifier stage when it is supplied with more than one input tone (frequency). These tones combine in such a manner as to produce additional amplifier output

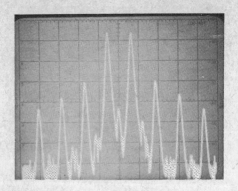

Fig. 81 — Here is a spectrum analyzer photograph showing the result of a two-tone test of an ssb transmitter. Each horizontal division is equal to 1 kHz and each vertical division is equal to 10 dB. The third-order products can be seen at 30 dB below the PEP (top line), the fifth-order products down 37 dB and seventh-order products down 44 dB. This represents acceptable, but not ideal, performance. See text for a detailed discussion of the tone levels involved.

signals that were not present at the input. Since human speech is made up of a con-glomeration of different frequencies, a high-level amplifier stage amplifying an ssb signal will produce a certain amount of IMD. A detailed discussion of IMD can be found in chapter 12 of *The Radio Amateur's Handbook*.

One convenient method for measuring IMD from a transmitter or amplifier is to inject two equal amplitude tones (at different frequencies) into the microphone jack of the test transmitter and view the output signal on a spectrum analyzer. This is called a *two-tone IMD test*. The photograph shown in Fig. 81 is typical of the two-tone test obtained from an ssb transmitter or amplifier. In this case, each horizontal division represents 1 kHz and each vertical division represents 10 dB. Responses other than the two individual tones near the center are distortion products; third-order products are down 30 dB, fifth-order products are down 37 dB and seventh-order products are down 44 dB from the PEP output. This represents an acceptable level of performance. A more detailed discussion of spectrum analyzer measurements can be found in an article entitled "Spectrum Analysis — One Picture's Worth a . . ." in the August 1979 issue of *QST*.

The Logic Probe

Most amateurs are familiar with the use of the standard multimeter for trouble shooting, but just how do you go about testing digital logic circuitry? There are only two states to worry about in digital circuits; these are the logical "one" and "zero" states. One could use a voltmeter or oscilloscope to monitor these logic states, but most of the time it is only necessary to know if you have either a one or zero at the input or output of a gate. The logic probe is just the answer. This small piece of test equipment will indicate at a glance whether there is a one or zero state, or high-impedance point (one that isn't directly connected with the actual logic circuit). This particular unit is for use with TTL circuitry and the circuit of the probe is shown in Fig. 82. Analysis of the circuit is left to the reader.

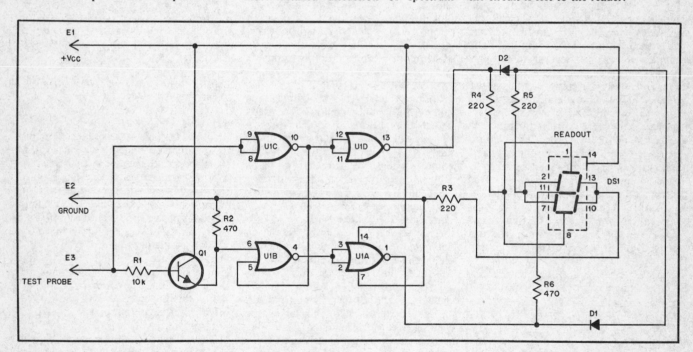

Fig. 82 — Schematic diagram of the TTL logic probe. The readout will indicate a zero for a zero state, a one for a one state and an "H" for a high-impedance state (one that isn't directly connected with the actual logic circuit).

Radio Phenomena

Tropospheric Bending

The troposphere consists of atmospheric layers close to the earth's surface. Although *tropospheric bending* is evident over a wide range of frequencies, it is most useful in the vhf/uhf region, especially at 144 MHz and above. The bending action is caused by a change in the refractive index of adjacent air masses having significantly different temperature, relative humidity or barometric pressure. The boundary layer between these different air masses is the point where the radio wave is bent, much as light is bent when it passes from air into water or from water into air. Normally, this boundary layer is formed within the first few thousand feet above the surface of the earth with a resulting propagation range of from 50 to 400 miles.

Even under normal conditions, *some* bending does take place. The *true* or *geometric horizon* is the most distant point one can see and is limited by the height of the observer above ground. Because of the slight bending of radio waves in the troposphere, however, signals return to earth somewhat beyond the geometric horizon. This *radio-path horizon* is generally about 33 percent farther away than the true horizon.

Under normal conditions, the

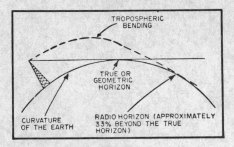

Fig. 83 — Under normal conditions, tropospheric bending causes radio waves to be returned to earth about 33 percent beyond the visual or geometric horizon.

temperature of the air gradually decreases with increasing height above ground. However, under certain conditions a mass of warm air may actually overrun cold air so that there is an area above the surface of the earth where cold air is covered by a blanket of warm air. This is called a *thermal inversion*. If the two air masses are more or less stationary, waves can become trapped between the air-mass boundary and the earth, and travel great distances with very little attenuation. Sometimes the wave can become trapped between two air-mass boundaries above the surface of the earth. The area between the two boundaries is known as a *duct*. Both the transmitting and receiving antennas must be within the duct if communication is to take place.

The manner in which the radio waves are guided along the inversion is very similar to the way microwaves travel through a waveguide. Because of this, radio wave propagation through a duct is called *guided propagation*. Usually ducts form over water, though they can form over land as well. The lowest usable frequency depends on the depth of the duct and the amount the reflective index changes at the boundaries.

Transequatorial Propagation

High-frequency radio wave propagation is limited by the degree to which the ionosphere is ionized. The upper frequency limit is called the *maximum usable frequency* (muf). Except during the peaks (maxima) of the 11-year sunspot cycle, the muf seldom reaches 50 MHz. However, stations located within a zone ranging from 1500 to 2500 miles from the geomagnetic equator can often communicate with stations located in a similar zone in the opposite hemisphere by *transequatorial* ionospheric propagation. Although this form of propagation is also affected by solar activity, frequencies up to 1.5 times the high-frequency muf can be used. Ionospheric scatter is also optimized over north-south equatorial paths. Such *transequatorial scatter* can be useful for contacts up to about 5000 miles at frequencies up to almost 80 MHz at times.

Stratospheric Reflection

The term *stratospheric reflection* applies to all forms of propagation in which radio waves bounce off stratospheric phenomena such as meteor trails and aurora borealis curtains. Meteor trails are ionized tracks formed by meteors passing through the atmosphere. Although they last only a few seconds at most, these ionized tracks will reflect vhf radio waves. During periods of intense meteor bombardment, called meteor showers, sustained radio propagation is possible.

Auroral propagation is characterized by

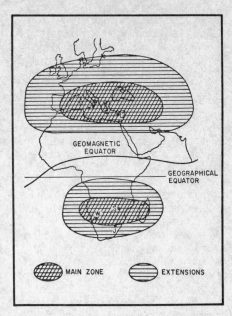

Fig. 84 — Frequent and occasional zones of transequatorial 50-MHz propagation, as described by ZE2JV, show Limassol, Cyprus, and Salisbury, Zimbabwe, to be almost ideally positioned with respect to the curbing geomagnetic equator. Windhoek, Namibia, is also in a favorable spot; Johannesburg, somewhat less so.

a rapid modulation or buzzing sound. During magnetic storms and visual displays of aurora borealis, vhf radio signals can be reflected over distances up to 700 miles. Because most stratospheric reflection is characterized by rapid signal fluctuations, cw is normally the only effective transmission mode.

Radio propagation is discussed further in chapter 18 of the ARRL *Handbook* and chapter 1 of the *Antenna Book*.

Operating Procedures

Amateur Fast-Scan Television

With the most resemblance to broadcast-quality television, because it uses the same technical standards, fast-scan television can be used by any amateur holding a Technician or higher-class license. Popularly known as ATV (amateur television), it is permitted in the 420- to 450-MHz band and above. Because the power density is comparatively low, typically 10 to 100 watts spread across 4 MHz, reliable amateur coverage is only on the order of 20 miles (about 32 km). Nevertheless, you might find yourself exchanging pictures with stations up to 200 miles (320 km) away when tropospheric conditions are good.

Most wide-band A5 activity occurs in the 420- to 450-MHz band. The exact frequency used depends on local custom, but a 439.25-MHz picture carrier is common in the East, while 427.0 MHz is popular in California. Some population centers have ATV repeaters, typically 439.25/427.25 MHz. ATVers try to avoid interfering with the weak-signal work (moonbounce, for example) being done around 43.2 MHz and repeater operation above 442 MHz.

There are at least three ways to transmit the voice information. The most popular is by talking on another band, often 2-meter fm. This has the advantage of letting other local hams listen in on what you are doing — a good way to pick up some ATV converts this way! Rather than tie up a busy repeater for this, it is best to use simplex. In southern California, for example, 146.43 MHz is commonly used.

Commercial TV has an fm voice subcarrier 4.5 MHz above the TV picture carrier. This can easily be received in the usual way on a regular TV set. Many of the surplus fm rigs that are available, however, do not have enough bandwidth to pass both the picture carrier and the voice subcarrier at the same time.

Another way to go is frequency modulation of the video subcarrier. Since the video is amplitude modulated, it should not interfere with the fm audio, or vice versa. The usual way to receive this is with the fm receiver section of the surplus uhf rig. It is also possible to use a low-band police/fire monitor coupled into the TV set 44-MHz i-f.

Signal reporting on ATV differs from the RST system used on cw and phone. For example, "closed circuit" is the ATVers term for "armchair copy"! The received signal strength is indicated by the amount of snow on the screen — the more snow, the weaker the signal. Some operators use a reporting system running from P0 to P5, roughly corresponding to readibility reports on voice or cw.

The resolution or sharpness is the number of distinguishable lines that can be displayed across the TV screen. Although commercial TV transmissions have 525 lines of resolution, acceptable pictures can be sent with systems capable of only 200 to 300 lines.

Signal reports are very useful for "talking the picture in" on the air while the sending station makes transmitter adjustments. In fact, this is the only reliable way to adjust the video modulator since receiver overloading will give misleading results when you monitor your own signal — a picture that looks fine on your own TV receiver will likely have low contrast on a distant station's set.

Camera procedures on ATV are similar to those presented in a previous section, "Setting Up Your Studio." The major difference is greater flexibility in lighting. Camera adjustments are best made with it connected directly to the monitor receiver video input. If you don't want to modify the TV set for this, most CCTV cameras have provisions for generating a vhf TV signal on one of the lower TV channels for monitoring purposes.

Using Amateur Radio Satellites

The first step in working the satellite is to find out where it is. As the spacecraft is constantly moving, some type of tracking calculator is needed. The simplest type of tracking device is an OSCARLOCATOR, available from ARRL. Briefly, you use one reference point each day, usually the first time in a given (UTC) day that the satellite crosses the equator in a northerly equation. The equator crossing (EQX) time and longitude, when and where the satellite passes over the equator, is available from numerous sources such as W1AW Bulletins and the various amateur publications. With this information, you can easily determine the satellite's approximate location and where to point your antenna at any given time from any point in the Northern Hemisphere.

More-sophisticated calculating techniques are also possible. Actual antenna bearings can be mathematically calculated and recorded for a large number of points during a satellite pass. Programmable calculators and even computers facilitate this approach.

As home computers become more popular, mechanized tracking systems will doubtless become standard, further simplifying the tracking routine. Several hams already use computerized systems, and the heavy involvement of computers in the Phase III project will bring more computers into use in the ham shack.

Regardless of the approach taken, it is a good idea to document your calculations well in advance of the pass. Jot down all the information in a logical fashion on a work sheet that is easy to read. You will have enough to do during a pass, with turning your receiver and transmitter, aiming

antennas, logging and actually making contacts, without adding the burden of calculating the orbital data at the same time!

Using your system, whatever it may be, figure out when AOS (acquisition of signal) is for your location and the azimuth (compass heading) to where the satellite will rise. Since the satellite will come into "view" on the horizon, you automatically know that the required antenna elevation at AOS is 0°; in other words the antenna points parallel to the ground. Record on the chart your calculated AOS time, and the associated antenna azimuth and elevation. Now, recalculate the antenna readings for the time one minute after AOS. Record these values on the chart. Continue for every one-minute interval until LOS (loss of signal). If you later find that your antennas are very sharp in beamwidth and require greater pointing accuracy, reduce the interval to 30 seconds.

Using all this information is much simpler than it sounds. At the times indicated on your chart, simply point your antennas in the azimuth and elevation shown. It's that simple. Stick with the chart. Often times satellite users won't have calculated too well, or they figure that they don't need advance planning. Signals start fading or are weak to begin with, so they wildly start rotating their antennas in an attempt to find the satellite. Quite obviously, this is not the most effective approach. Find a tracking system you are comfortable with and plan the pass in advance.

Now that the preliminaries are completed, the actual fun of working through the satellite can begin once it's in range. The best procedure is to have your antennas pointed toward the AOS point and begin listening at the transponder beacon frequency several minutes before you expect acquisition. You'll probably have to tune a little off the published frequency as Doppler shift makes the signal appear higher or lower than expected. If you don't hear the beacon within a minute or so of what your chart predicts, something is wrong. Likely possibilities are miscalculations on your part, inaccurate orbital data, listening to the wrong transponder for that day, equipment failure, or even a miss-set clock. The keynote of satellites is reliability; failure is rare compared with various equipment failures and mistakes encountered on the ground.

Once the satellite is accessed, you can set about the task of making a contact. The toughest part is setting your transmitter frequency so that it is retransmitted on the proper downlink frequency. Calculating the expected downlink frequency for a given uplink frequency will put you fairly close. An alternative is to use a reference chart, which plots output frequency versus input frequency. With either of these methods, Doppler shifts and equipment frequency inaccuracies will only place you close to the correct frequencies, but close enough so that sending

a few words of sideband or a few dits will enable you to pinpoint yourself. The key word is few. Unfortunately, you'll often hear a series of dits swishing up and down the passband. Not only is this inconsiderate, it also wastes time, which is in very short supply during a pass. Initially this may seem like an impossible task or one best suited to an octopus. With a little practice, however, the longing for an extra set of hands gradually subsides.

Since you're listening on an entirely different band from that on which you're transmitting, full duplex operation is possible; you hear what you're sending through the satellite as you send it! (Traffic handlers often go to great effort to achieve this.) The ability of the station you're working to interrupt you while you're transmitting greatly improves the natural flow of the contact. It is even common for a CQ to be answered while it's being sent. Once again, anything to save time is to your advantage.

Typical contacts through the satellite are short contest-type exchanges. Exchanging calls, signal reports, locations and names is the extent of most contacts. Time is of the essence: Long-windedness doesn't work. Like an fm repeater, the satellite eventually times out, in this case, by going out of range.

A typical contact might go like this:

```
CQ CQ CQ DE W1AW W1AW W1...
   W1AW DE K1XA 579 CONN BOB
K1XA DE W1AW 569 CONN CHUCK    73
W1AW DE K1JX...
```

There is one other very important aspect for the satellite user to consider. The transponder's internal automatic gain control system reduces the receiver's sensitivity as the signal input level increases. This is done for two reasons. The first is to prevent receiver overload which might produce spurious signals within the transmitter passband. Second and more important, is that theoretically a very loud signal would be retransmitted with as much power as the transponder's transmitter can muster. If this were to occur, serious damage could be sustained by the satellite. Even with the agc system, transmitter current drain rises with very strong input signals, placing unnecessary and undesirable burden on the spacecraft batteries. It is every satellite user's responsibility to ensure that he or she does not transmit too great a signal to the satellite.

The proper transmitter power level is easy to determine. Since the downlink signal you receive indicates the effectiveness of your uplink, adjustments of your uplink power are reflected in the strength of the downlink signal strength. Your downlink strength should be no louder than the transponder beacon. Following this simple rule prevents receiver desense and guarantees easy transponder access for others as well as preventing satellite damage.

Rules and Regulations

Frequency Bands Available to U.S. Radio Amateurs (§§97.61, 97.95)

U.S. radio amateurs are permitted operating privileges on many frequency bands. However, the radio frequency spectrum is a finite resource and some bands must be shared with other users. FCC has imposed some limitations and conditions on amateurs operating on these frequencies to protect sharing partners. For example, the dc plate input power to the final transmitter stage of an amateur station operating in the 420- to 450-MHz band may not exceed 50 watts in some portions of California, New Mexico and Texas, and in all of Arizona and Florida. Section 97.61 of the Amateur Rules lists these and other restrictions.

ITU Regions

The United States is located in ITU Region 2 as defined in the table of world frequency allocations. See the map in §97.95 of the Amateur Rules. Note that §97.95 has lists of frequencies on which amateurs located in Region 1 or Region 3 must operate.

Space Amateur Radio Stations (Subpart H)

Subpart H of the Amateur Rules applies to the Amateur Satellite Service. *Space operation* is space-to-earth and space-to-space Amateur Radio communication from a station that is beyond, is intended to go beyond, or has been beyond the major portion of the earth's atmosphere. *Earth operation* is earth-to-space-to-earth Amateur Radio communication by means of radio signals automatically retransmitted by stations in space operation. Only Amateur Extra Class stations are eligible for space operation; however, the station licensee may permit any Amateur Radio operator to be the control operator, subject to the privileges of the control operator's class of license. In other words, the control operator may not exceed his or her own frequency privileges to control a station in space operation. Any Amateur Radio station is eligible for *earth operation*, subject to the privileges of the control operator's class of license.

Purity of Emissions (§97.73)

All spurious emissions or radiation from an amateur transmitter, transceiver or external radio frequency power amplifier shall be reduced or eliminated in accordance with good engineering practice. See §97.73 for more information about minimum performance standards for amateur transmitters, transceivers and amplifiers.

Mobile Operation Aboard Ships or Aircraft (§97.101)

Even though your airplane or ship travels may take you into international waters or territory, as long as you operate from a U.S.-registered vessel or aircraft[1] or hold a U.S. Amateur license,[2] you must comply with all provisions of the FCC Rules. In addition, you may operate from within the territorial jurisdiction of another country only if you have the permission of that government in advance.[3]

An amateur station operated on board a ship or aircraft must comply with all of the following conditions:

1) The installation and operation of the amateur mobile station shall be approved by the master of the ship or captain of the aircraft;

2) The amateur mobile station shall be separate from and independent of all other radio equipment, if any, installed on board the same ship or aircraft;

3) The electrical installation of the amateur mobile station shall be in accord with the rules applicable to ships or aircraft as promulgated by the appropriate government agency;

4) The amateur mobile station and its associated equipment, either in itself or in its method of operation, shall not constitute a hazard to the safety of life or property.

RACES Operation (Subpart F)

The Radio Amateur Civil Emergency Service provides for amateur operation for civil defense communications purposes only, during periods of local, regional or national civil emergencies, including any emergency that may necessitate invoking of the President's War Emergency Powers under the provisions of Section 606 of the Communications Act. RACES stations are permitted one hour per week of air time for tests and drills.

Points of Communications (§97.89)

Amateur stations may communicate with:

1) Other amateur stations.

2) Stations in other services licensed by the Commission and with the U.S. Government stations for civil defense purposes in accordance with subpart F of Part 97 of the Commission's Rules, in emergencies and, on a temporary basis, for test purposes.

3) Any station that is authorized by the Commission to communicate with amateur stations.

In addition, amateur stations may be used for transmitting signals, communications or energy to receiving apparatus for the measurement of emissions, temporary observation of transmission phenomena, radio control of remote objects, and similar experimental purposes and for emergency communications, emergency drill practice transmissions, information bulletins (if related solely to Amateur Radio interests), code practice transmissions (see §97.91) and net-type and round-table operations and discussions.

---

[1]The United States Communications Act of 1934, as amended, Section 301, reads as follows:
". . . No person shall use or operate any apparatus for the transmission of energy or communications or signals by radio . . . (e) upon any vessel or aircraft of the United States; . . . except under and in accordance with this Act and with a license in that behalf granted under the provisions of this Act."
[2]See §97.95(b)(4) of the Amateur Rules.
[3]Canada and the United States permit each other's amateurs to operate within their boundaries without prior notification. See §97.41 of the Amateur Rules.

Sample Study Questions

While the following questions are written in a format similar to that found in the Extra Class examination, the questions will not be the same as those found on the FCC exam. You should review the FCC Study Outline at the beginning of this chapter before taking the test.

1) Which of the following is an Amateur Extra Class Exclusive subband?
A) 1800-1825 kHz
B) 14100-14125 kHz
C) 21250-21270 kHz
D) 28000-28025 kHz

2) On which of the following frequencies would fast-scan television be permitted?
A) 7.12 MHz
B) 14.275 MHz
C) 146.52 MHz
D) 1225.0 MHz

3) Which of the following is *not* an authorized emission in the amateur bands?
A) A5
B) A9
C) F4
D) P

4) From the top of your tower, you can see the horizon 10 miles away. Approximately how far away is the radio-path horizon? (Assume flat terrain.)
A) 3 miles
B) 7 miles
C) 10 miles
D) 13 miles

5) Ducts form in the
A) ionosphere
B) stratosphere
C) troposphere
D) ectosphere

6) Stations in the northern hemisphere can often work stations in a similar latitude in the southern hemisphere on frequencies up to 1-1/2 times the muf using
A) guided propagation
B) stratospheric reflection
C) transequatorial propagation
D) backscatter

7) Cw is usually preferred to voice modes when auroral propagation is taking place because
A) a higher information rate can be maintained
B) auroral effects are most profound in the Novice bands where cw is the most common mode
C) cw techniques are more common on the vhf bands
D) when the signal strength is fluttering rapidly, cw is easier to copy

8) Tropospheric propagation takes place as a result of
A) ionized layers of the atmosphere

B) irregularity of terrain over which signals pass
C) sharp or rapid changes in the density and humidity of air
D) ultraviolet radiation from the sun

9) Which of the following is a method of high-level modulation?
A) Grid modulation
B) Plate modulation
C) Screen modulation
D) Frequency modulation

10) On which of the following frequencies is pulse modulation permitted?
A) 14.225 MHz
B) 222.5 MHz
C) 1296.0 MHz
D) None of the above

11) A 1-volt, 1-kHz tone fed into the microphone jack of a phase-modulation transmitter produces 6-kHz deviation. A 0.5-volt, 3-kHz tone produces a deviation of
A) 1 kHz
B) 3 kHz
C) 6 kHz
D) 9 kHz

12) Which of the following is an advantage of speech compression over audio speech clipping?
A) Higher average modulation level
B) Doesn't require a dc power source
C) Higher peak-to-average power ratio
D) Less distortion

13) You are transmitting facsimile on a frequency of 146.52 MHz. Assuming the transmission is legal, what is the correct classification of the emission?
A) A2
B) A4
C) F2
D) F4

14) The transmission of a slow-scan television signal requires
A) a 20-kHz bandwidth for satisfactory operation
B) that such transmission be limited to A5 emissions
C) a 100-watt minimum transmitter power output
D) sync pulse duration of 5 milliseconds

15) What is the *smallest* value variable capacitor that will tune a 10-µH coil to 3.5 MHz?
A) 50 pF
B) 100 pF

C) 150 pF
D) 250 pF

16) A 0.01-µF capacitor has a 2-megohm resistor connected across it. If the capacitor is initially charged to 20 volts, how long will it take for the voltage to die down to 1 volt?
A) 0.06 second
B) 0.2 second
C) 2 seconds
D) 200 seconds

17) Which of the following is an *incorrect* statement?
A) Unshielded wire should be used to connect a transmitter to the low-pass filter
B) Random-length, end-fed wires may be coupled to a 50-ohm, unbalanced-transmitter output connection with an L network
C) Harmonic radiation from an antenna can be reduced with an antenna coupler
D) A broadband balun can match a 200-ohm load to a 50-ohm transmitter

18) Which of the waveforms shown represents the output of an integrator fed with a square-wave input?

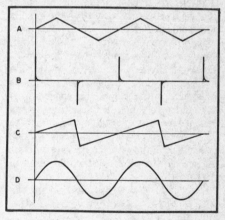

19) What is the impedance of the circuit below at a frequency of 10 Hz?

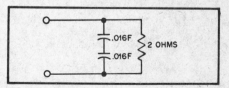

A) 0.7 ohm
B) 1 ohm
C) 1.4 ohms
D) 1.7 ohms

20) What is the phase angle of the current with respect to the voltage in the circuit on the previous page? Assume an input voltage of 120 volts, 10 Hz.
A) −90 degrees
B) −67 degrees
C) 30 degrees
D) 45 degrees

21) Your vertical antenna has a feed-point impedance of 30 ohms resistive. What is the standing-wave ratio if you feed the antenna with 50-ohm transmission line?
A) 0.6
B) 1.29
C) 1.67
D) 2.78

22) What is the Q of the circuit below if the series resistance of the inductor is 100 ohms?

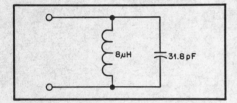

A) 1
B) 3
C) 5
D) 7

23) Which of the following statements is *incorrect?*
A) A capacitor represents a series-tuned circuit, resonant at the frequency where its capacitance and inductance have the same reactance
B) At frequencies well above their natural resonant frequencies, a capacitor acts like an inductor and an inductor acts like a capacitor
C) At a frequency near the natural resonant frequency, an inductor will have its highest impedance and a capacitor will have its lowest impedance
D) The amount of capacitance or inductance that may be used in a given circuit is independent of frequency

24) What would be the approximate output voltage (V_o) if R_L were changed to 500 ohms?

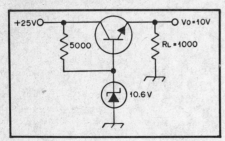

A) 2.5 volts
B) 5 volts

C) 10 volts
D) 20 volts

25) A Class C rf amplifier is to be operated under the following conditions: plate voltage, 600 volts; screen voltage, 200 volts; grid voltage, 50 volts; plate current, 150 mA; screen current, 10 mA and grid current, 1 mA. What should be the approximate load impedance?
A) 1000 ohms
B) 2000 ohms
C) 4000 ohms
D) 8000 ohms

26) Shown below is a diagram of a

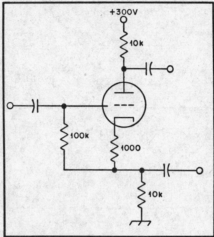

A) tetrode amplifier
B) phase inverter
C) Pierce oscillator
D) dc amplifier

27) You want to build a low-pass filter for you 20-meter transmitter that will attenuate the second harmonic without significantly attenuating the fundamental. Which of the following filters could be designed to give the best second-harmonic attenuation for a specified number of filter components?
A) Constant-k filter
B) Constant-m filter
C) K-derived filter
D) M-derived filter

28) Which of the following statements is correct?
A) A reflex klystron makes a good uhf linear amplifier
B) A parametric amplifier is easier to adjust than a transistor amplifier
C) A high pump frequency is used in a parametric amplifier to improve the noise figure
D) At frequencies above 100 MHz or so, electrons move so fast that we can assume that they travel from cathode to plate almost instantaneously

29) A 427-MHz transmitter uses a low-loss coaxial tank in the final amplifier plate circuit. Assuming the final amplifier is grid-modulated with a 5-MHz band-

width TV signal, what would be the optimum loaded Q of the tank circuit?
A) 85
B) 155
C) 170
D) 340

30) Which one of the following would not be utilized as part of a repeater control system?
A) Transmission limiter
B) Carrier-operated relay
C) Encoder
D) De-emphasis network

31) What should be the value of R if the transistor current gain is 50?

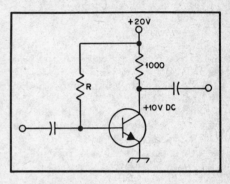

A) 50,000 ohms
B) 100,000 ohms
C) 200,000 ohms
D) 400,000 ohms

32) If the transistor in the figure below has a current gain of 50 and base and collector resistances of 2,000 and 50,000 ohms respectively, what is the voltage gain of the circuit?
A) 25
B) 50
C) 100
D) 200

33) Which of the following would most likely be used in a remotely tuned, solid-state vfo?
A) Hot-carrier diode
B) Vidicon
C) Silicon-controlled rectifier (thyristor)
D) Varactor

34) Point-contact diodes are often used as
A) Variable-capacitance diodes
B) High-voltage rectifiers
C) High-current rectifiers
D) Uhf mixers

35) A device that converts a light image into an electronic signal is a
A) Cathode-ray tube
B) Lighthouse tube
C) Vidicon
D) Light-emitting diode

36) In a transistor, the ratio of a change in dc collector current to a change in emitter current is known as
A) The alpha cutoff frequency

B) Beta
C) The maximum average forward current
D) The current amplification factor

37) Which of the following is an important consideration when choosing an insulator for use in a vhf antenna?
A) Dielectric strength
B) Dielectric loss
C) Resistance to high temperature
D) All of the above

38) Which of the following antennas commonly used at vhf/uhf is omnidirectional?
A) Discone
B) Parabolic reflector
C) Yagi
D) Log-periodic

39) Why is feed-line radiation generally to be avoided?
A) It can upset the antenna radiation pattern
B) It can reduce the gain of the antenna
C) It can cause increased interference to home-entertainment devices if they are located close to the feed line
D) All of the above

40) A given antenna is found to have a maximum field strength of 25.0 V per meter at a distance of 25 miles. What is the field intensity at the half-power points?
A) 15 V/meter
B) 1.0 V/meter
C) 17.6 V/meter
D) 47 V/meter

41) In fast-scan television transmission, the fm subcarrier
A) is normally sent at a frequency of about 455 kHz
B) carries the video information
C) carries the color (chrominance) information
D) appears on only one side of the picture carrier frequency because the TV transmission is sent as a vestigal sideband signal

42) A sweep generator can be used for
A) determining the frequency response of a filter
B) generating an ac power-supply voltage
C) generating a pulsating dc voltage
D) measuring the rf impedance of an antenna

43) Strip-line filters are usually used at uhf in preference to coil-capacitor tuned circuits because
A) the strip-line filters are usually smaller than the coil-capacitor equivalent
B) it is difficult to build uhf tuned circuits with high enough Q (low enough loss)

C) uhf coils are difficult to wind
D) uhf capacitors tend to be bulky

44) An auxiliary detector to be used with an oscilloscope for quick observation of amplifier adjustments and parametric variations is
A) wobbulator
B) transducer
C) linearity tracer
D) lissajous figure

45) What are the three logical operations in digital electronics?
A) On, off and don't care
B) And, or and not
C) Yes, no and maybe
D) Addition, multiplication and inversion

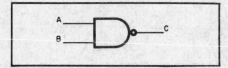

46) The above device is a(n):
A) NAND gate
B) inverter
C) storage register
D) OR gate

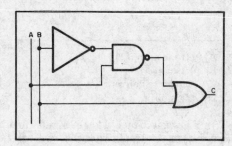

47) The Boolean equation for the above circuit is:
A) $C = AB$
B) $C = \overline{AB}$
C) $C = \overline{A} + \overline{B}$
D) $C = \overline{AB} + B$

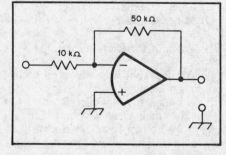

48) What voltage gain can be expected from the above op-amp circuit?
A) 1
B) 5
C) 10
D) 50

49) Which of the following is not a characteristic of op amps?

A) Low output impedance
B) High voltage gain
C) Low input impedance
D) Gain set by feedback element

50) Identify the circuit shown in Ques. 48.
A) Inverting amplifier
B) Noninverting amplifier
C) Difference amplifier
D) Active filter

51) Which of the following is not a possible use for a phase-locked-loop circuit?
A) Voltage regulator
B) A-m demodulator
C) Fm demodulator
D) Frequency synthesis

52) Identify the unlabeled box in this PLL block diagram.

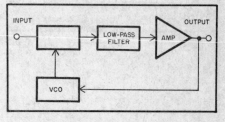

A) Phase inverter
B) Amplifier
C) Modulator
D) Phase detector

53) What is the basic structure of a solar cell?
A) Electrical interconnection of many transistors
B) Large area p-n junction
C) A mixture of phosphorous and boron
D) Photosynthesis

54) What can be said about the Q and $\overline{Q}$ outputs of a flip flop?
A) They are in phase
B) They are 90° out of phase
C) They are 180° out of phase
D) They are 270° out of phase

55) How many flip flops are required in order to divide a signal by 8?
A) 1
B) 2
C) 3
D) 4

56) The 4000 series of integrated circuits are
A) RTL
B) DTL
C) TTL
D) CMOS

57) What baud rate is permissible below 21.250 MHz?
A) 110
B) 600
C) 1200
D) 1800

58) Narrow-band voice modulation

makes use of which of the following techniques?
A) Frequency dithering
B) Amplitude synthesis
C) Frequency compandering
D) Distribution of harmonic energy

59) Noise figure is a measure of receiver
A) ability to function in the presence of strong signals.
B) i-f gain.
C) rf gain.
D) sensitivity.

60) What is the theoretical minimum noise floor of a receiver with a 400 Hz bandwidth?
A) − 148 dBm
B) − 104 dBm
C) − 174 dBm
D) − 290 dBm

61) If two tones are injected into a receiver at 14.020 and 14.040 MHz, where would you expect to find the third-order distortion products?
A) Outside the amateur band
B) At 14.020 and 14.040 MHz
C) At 14.000 and 14.060 MHz
D) At 14.060 and 14.080 MHz

62) The Smith Chart can be used to

A) determine power output from an amplifier.
B) determine impedances along a transmission line.
C) calculate ASCII signal bandwidths.
D) determine receiver distortion products.

63) A 1/4 λ of transmission line shorted at the far end
A) looks like a short at this end.
B) looks inductive at this end.
C) looks capacitive at this end.
D) looks like an open circuit at this end.

64) An isotropic radiator is used as which of the following?
A) An effective antenna for 80 meter operation
B) A measuring stick for comparing the performance of other antennas
C) A broadband vhf/uhf antenna
D) The driven element of a Yagi antenna

65) What pattern would result from two 1/4 λ verical antennas separated by one-half wavelength and fed 180° out of phase?
A) A figure-eight pattern broadside to the direction of the verticals
B) A figure-eight pattern in the direction of the verticals

C) A perfect circle
D) A heart-shaped pattern toward the vertical receiving lagging energy

66) The spectrum analyzer is used to view signals in the
A) Time domain
B) Amplitude domain
C) Vhf domain
D) Frequency domain

67) In the above photograph, how far below the fundamental signal is the third harmonic, assuming that the vertical axis is calibrated at 10 dB per division?
A) 6 dB
B) 12 dB
C) 64 dB
D) 68 dB

Chapter 8

International Regulations

Radio is not like a truck, a motor bike or an automobile. They all must stop at national boundaries. Radio, on the other hand, respects no boundary lines. So by its very nature, radio is international in nature. But it wasn't always this way. Prior to advanced technology and major developments made by the Amateur Radio operators of yesteryear, radio sometimes made it from one *county* to another — sometimes! But we sure outdid ourselves, and now when we put our signals on the air, there's a good chance they're being heard in another nation.

Thus, there must be international agreements on the assignment of frequencies, procedures used in the Maritime services and so on. Countries have to get together, and there must be an organization. The organization is the International Telecommunication Union, and as its name suggests, the countries of the world regularly hold worldwide and regional conferences. They discuss radio problems and come to conclusions and agreements.

The radio authority in each nation must set up radio services which fit the general pattern established by the worldwide and regional conferences. The very life of Amateur Radio, therefore, dangles on one string: Will Amateur Radio be included in the allocations tables? Especially on the lower-frequency amateur bands, providing for several services in addition to amateur in "our" bands. Under such joint allocations, each government may assign the band to a particular service, or hand it out to various services mentioned in the allocations.

In the case of the United States and Canada, almost without exception our governments have given to amateurs every frequency band possible under international regulations. In some cases, our governments have actually left out services which are eligible to use a band ac-

cording to international allocation. A good example of this is 3500-4000 kHz (see Table 1). It's easy to see that this band is available in this hemisphere (Region 2) for all the amateur, fixed or mobile services. The governments must decide who ends up with the band. Both Canada and the United States elected to give the whole 3.5-4.0 MHz band to amateurs exclusively.

In other areas of the world, particularly Europe, amateurs get to use only part of this 500-kHz band. In fact, they must *share* with other radio services what portion they do operate on.

Intruders

But the radio regulations have an "escape clause." And what an escape clause! Any national administration may assign any station, whatever type it is, to any frequency, provided that no interference is caused to any station of another country operating legitimately, according to the allocations table.

What this means is that if amateurs fail to object to the interference from non-amateur stations in the amateur bands, the administration responsible can go along thinking it's complying with the regulations. *Enter the ARRL Intruder Watch*! The Intruder Watch is hundreds of amateurs listening to their receivers for two or more hours a week. They're listening for intruders, stations which have no business operating in the amateur bands. These hard-working volunteers establish the fact that interference is indeed being caused by these stations, and all vital facts (emission, frequency, time and location) are sent to ARRL headquarters. There, the various intercept reports are matched up and the consolidated report sent through the appropriate government channels. The worst that can happen is that a record of disregard of agreements

can be built up, to be used as "ammunition" against the offending government at the next international conference. Most of the time, though, the reports by amateurs to the League result in removal of the station from the airwaves.

Other Provisions

The agreements among the various nations at international radio conferences are long and drawn-out, dealing with many different matters in addition to allocations. In the Geneva documents, there are two definitions of interest to us:

Amateur service: A service of self-training, intercommunication and technical investigations carried on by amateurs, that is, by duly authorized persons interested in radio technique solely with a personal aim and without pecuniary interest.

Amateur station: A station in the amateur service.

The documents further deal with the amateur service as follows:

Article 41 — Amateur Stations

Section 1
Radiocommunications between amateur stations of different countries shall be forbidden if the administration of one of the countries concerned has notified that it objects to such radiocommunications.

Section 2
1) When transmissions between amateur stations of different countries are permitted, they shall be made in plain language and shall be limited to messages of a technical nature relating to tests and to remarks of a personal character for which, by reason of their unimportance, recourse to the public telecommunications service is not justified. It is absolutely forbidden for amateur stations to be used for

transmitting international communications on behalf of third parties.

2) The preceding provisions may be modified by special arrangements between the administrations of the countries concerned.

Section 3

1) Any person operating the apparatus of an amateur station shall have proved that he is able to send correctly by hand and to receive correctly by ear, texts in Morse code signals. Administrations concerned may, however, waive this requirement in the case of stations making use exclusively of frequencies above 144 MHz.

2) Administrations shall take such measures as they judge necessary to verify the technical qualifications of any person operating the apparatus of an amateur station.

Section 4

The maximum power of amateur stations shall be fixed by the administrations concerned, having regard to the technical qualifications of the operators and to the conditions under which these stations are to work.

Section 5

1) All the general rules of the Convention and of these Regulations shall apply to amateur stations. In particular, the emitted frequency shall be as stable and as free from spurious emissions as the state of technical development for such stations permits.

2) During the course of their transmissions amateur stations shall transmit their call sign at short intervals.

Section 6

Space stations in the Amateur-Satellite Service operating in bands shared with other services shall be fitted with appropriate devices for controlling emissions in the event that harmful interference is reported in accordance with the procedure laid down in Article 15. Administrations authorizing such space stations shall inform the International Frequency Registration Board (IFRB) and shall insure that sufficient earth command stations are established before launch to guarantee that any harmful interference that might be reported can be terminated by the authorizing Administration.

International Message Traffic

The international regulation quoted above says that when amateur stations of different countries are in contact, the transmissions should be in plain language with remarks either of a technical or personal nature. The remarks must be so unimportant that the use of public telecommunications is not justified. Also, transmitting international communications on behalf of third parties is absolutely forbidden for amateur stations.

In most foreign countries, the communications system is a government monopoly. These countries obviously forbid their amateurs to handle any formal messages or any communications on behalf of third parties, even friendly greetings. But this restriction can be modified slightly by special arrangements between nations. For example, Australia permits third party traffic pertaining *strictly* to the Amateur Satellite Service.

Table 2 lists the countries which have entered into third-party agreements with the United States permitting amateurs to handle messages under the conditions shown in each case.

Conditions: (1) We may handle messages on behalf of third parties provided that they are of the character that would not normally be sent by any existing means of electrical communication or except for the availability of the amateur station. (2) We may handle messages

Table 1
Geneva Amateur Allocations Summary

Band	Worldwide	Region 1 (Europe-Africa)	Region 2 (N & S America)	Region 3 (Rest of World)
1800-2000 kHz		Fixed¹ Mobile	Amateur Fixed Mobile Radionavigation	Same as Region 2
3500-4000 kHz		3500-3800 Amateur Fixed Mobile	3500-4000 Amateur Fixed Mobile	3500-3900 Amateur Fixed Mobile
		3800-3900 Aero mobile Fixed Land mobile		
		3900-3950 Aero mobile		3900-3950 Aero mobile Broadcasting
		3950-4000 Broadcasting Fixed		3950-4000 Broadcasting Fixed
7000-7100 kHz	7000-7100 Amateur			
7100-7300 kHz		7100-7300 Broadcasting	7100-7300 Amateur	7100-7300 Broadcasting
14,000-14,350 kHz	Amateur			
21,000-21,450 kHz	Amateur			
26,960-27,230 kHz (In Region 2, Australia and New Zealand, the amateur service may operate between the frequencies 26,960-27,230 kHz.)				
28,000-29,700 kHz	Amateur			
50-54 MHz		Broadcasting	Amateur	Amateur
144-146 MHz	144-146 Amateur			
146-148 MHz		146-148 Fixed Mobile	146-148 Amateur	146-148 Amateur
220-225 MHz		Aero navigation	Amateur Radiolocation	Aero navigation Radiolocation
420-450 MHz		430-440 Amateur Radiolocation	420-450 Radiolocation Amateur	420-450 Radiolocation Amateur

¹Austria, Denmark, Finland, Ireland, Netherlands, Federal Republic of Germany, Zimbabwe, Republic of Malawi, United Kingdom, Switzerland, Czechoslovakia, and the Republic of South Africa and Namibia may allocate up to 200 kHz to their amateur service within the band 1715-2000 kHz, taking steps to protect the fixed and mobile services of other countries from harmful interference. The mean power of these amateur stations shall not exceed 10 watts.

Table 2
U.S. Third-Party Agreements

Country	Condition*
Argentina	1, 3b
Bolivia	1, 3b
Brazil	1, 3b
Canada	1, 2, 3a
Chile	1
Colombia	1, 3b
Costa Rica	1, 3b
Cuba	1, 3b
Dominican Republic	1, 3b
Ecuador	1, 3b
El Salvador	1, 3b
Ghana	1, 3b
Guatemala	1, 3b
Guyana	1, 3b
Haiti	1, 3b
Honduras	1, 3b
Israel	1, 3b
Jamaica	1, 2, 3b
Jordan	1, 3b
Liberia	1, 3b
Mexico	1, 3b
Nicaragua	1, 3b
Panama	1, 3b
Paraguay	1, 3b
Peru	1
Trinidad & Tobago	1, 3b
Uruguay	1, 3b
Venezuela	1, 3b

*See text.

WD5AJE/SU is authorized to conduct third-party communications between Egypt and the U.S.

---

from radio stations in isolated points not connected into the regular electrical communication network, such messages to be handed to the local office of the commercial telegraph company for transmission to final destination. (3a) In cases of emergency, where the regular communication system is interrupted, amateurs may handle messages of any importance, same to be handed to the nearest point of the commercial telegraph system remaining in operation, (3b) Amateurs may handle, in emergencies, traffic relating directly to the safety of life or property.

Canada: Canadian amateurs may handle traffic, under general conditions noted, with Bolivia, Chile, Colombia, Costa Rica, Dominican Republic, El Salvador, Guatemala, Guyana, Honduras, Israel, Jamaica, Mexico, Nicaragua, Paraguay, Peru, Trinidad & Tobago, U.S., Uruguay and Venezuela.

U.S. Possessions: Message traffic may be freely handled by American amateurs with U.S. possessions and territories where amateur stations are licensed by the FCC, as well as with stations in the Canal Zone. This message handling is under the same conditions as domestic traffic in the States. There must be no pecuniary interest, direct or indirect.

G.I. Stations: U.S. personnel stationed overseas who are amateurs are no longer licensed by the U.S. Instead, the national governments do the licensing. This means that third-party traffic is no longer per-

mitted, if there are no special third-party agreements between the two countries involved. Only amateur stations identified by authorized call signs having a one- or two-letter prefix beginning with A, K, W or N or licensed by the U.S. government. Third-party traffic may be handled freely with these stations, except for the KA prefix followed by a number other than 1 and two letters. Because a current U.S.-Japanese agreement provides that operation by U.S. personnel will be under regulations similar to those existing for Japanese nationals, third-party traffic privileges are denied KA stations in Japan as well as JAs. During holidays, special permission is often granted for third-party messages. Listen for bulletins over W1AW.

Australia: Although traffic is normally prohibited, certain stations of the Wireless Institute of Australia may handle messages concerning WIA internal administration, including the exchange of messages between WIA and ARRL headquarters concerning arrangements for contests and so on. Also, messages concerning the amateur satellite program may be handled until four months after OSCAR 7 ceases to transmit. Absolutely no third-party traffic is permitted, however.

Germany (Federal Republic): Traffic is normally prohibited, but communications concerning amateur satellites may be handled internationally.

Rest of the World: In general, traffic is prohibited with amateur stations in the rest of the world. This is not through reluctance on the part of the U.S. government but because of prohibitions by the other governments concerned. The amateur at the other end is commonly forbidden all traffic handling. Amateurs must abide by this restriction and have no participation in the handling of third-party traffic in such cases.

Amateur Radio Operation in a Foreign Country

One thing all of us must remember is that every country has the right to determine who may and who may not operate an Amateur Radio station within its jurisdiction. Holding a U.S. or Canadian Amateur Radio license does not automatically give *any* person the right to operate his station while a guest in a foreign country, except that now reciprocity is automatic between the U.S. and Canada *only*.

Some countries have allowed U.S. and/or Canadian amateurs to operate their stations while visiting; however, a visiting amateur must make proper application to the government for permission and abide by the rules of the host government. By the same token, a foreign amateur visiting the U.S. or Canada must apply for permission from the Federal Communications Commission or the De-

Table 3
Countries with which the United States shares reciprocal operating agreements:

Argentina	Ireland
Austria	Israel
Australia	Jamaica
Barbados	Jordan
Belgium	Kuwait
Bolivia	Liberia
Brazil	Luxembourg
Canada*	Monaco
Chile	Netherlands
Colombia	Netherlands
Costa Rica	Antilles
Denmark	New Zealand
Dominica	Nicaragua
Dominican Republic	Norway
Ecuador	Panama
El Salvador	Paraguay
Fiji	Peru
Finland	Philippines
France	Portugal
Germany (Federal Republic)	Sierra Leone
Greece	Spain
Guatemala	Surinam
Guyana	Sweden
Haiti	Switzerland
Honduras	Trinidad & Tobago
Iceland	United Kingdom
India	Uruguay
Indonesia	Venezuela
	Yugoslavia

*Automatic. Written permit not required.

Table 4
Countries with which Canada shares reciprocal operating agreements:

Austria	India
Barbados	Indonesia
Belgium	Israel
Bermuda	Luxembourg
Botswana	Netherlands
Brazil	New Zealand
Chile	Nicaragua
Columbia	Norway
Costa Rica	Panama
Denmark	Peru
Dominica	Philippines
Dominican Republic	Poland
Ecuador	Portugal
Finland	Senegal
France	Sweden
Germany (Federal Republic)	Switzerland
Greece	United Kingdom
Guatamala	United States
Haiti	of America*
Honduras	Uruguay
Iceland	Venezuela

*Automatic. Written permit not required.

---

partment of Communications, whichever the case may be, and abide by either FCC or DOC regulations.

Some countries have signed treaties with the governments of the U.S. and/or Canada to facilitate the application procedures. More information about operating in foreign countries can be found in chapter 1. However, for your convenience, Tables 3 and 4 list those countries with which the U.S. and Canada have concluded reciprocal operating agreements.

New Bands for the 1980s

A Summary of the Results of the World Administrative Radio Conference and How it Affects U.S. Amateurs

In 1979, the nations of the world met to consider comprehensive changes in the International Table of Frequency Allocations and other important parts of the Radio Regulations of the International Telecommunication Union (ITU). The last such meeting was held in 1959. WARC-79 was a major challenge for the Amateur Radio community because the Conference had the power to make sweeping changes in the privileges enjoyed by Radio Amateurs.

The world Amateur Radio community was represented at WARC-79 by the International Amateur Radio Union (IARU). The IARU is an organization of Amateur Radio societies from around the world, and its headquarters society is the American Radio Relay League. Over 16 years of preparation brought about a bright picture for Amateur Radio for the years ahead. A complete chronicle of these international efforts can be found in February 1980 QST, pages 52-73. A summary of how U.S. amateurs fared in the decisions made at WARC-79 appears below.

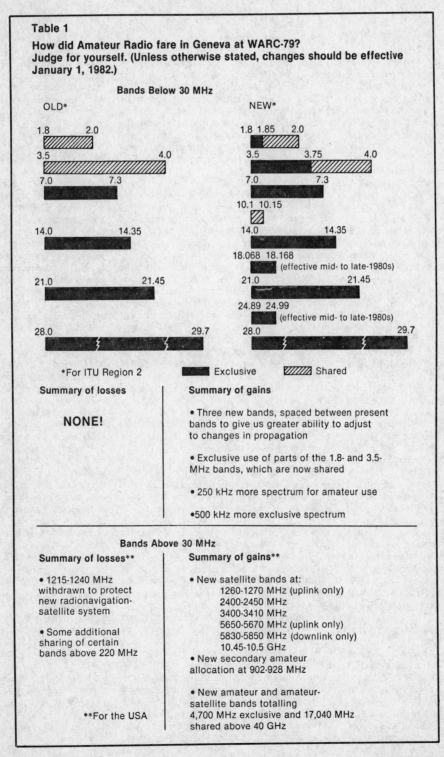

Table 1

How did Amateur Radio fare in Geneva at WARC-79?
Judge for yourself. (Unless otherwise stated, changes should be effective January 1, 1982.)

Bands Below 30 MHz

OLD* / NEW*

*For ITU Region 2 — Exclusive / Shared

Summary of losses

NONE!

Summary of gains

• Three new bands, spaced between present bands to give us greater ability to adjust to changes in propagation

• Exclusive use of parts of the 1.8- and 3.5-MHz bands, which are now shared

• 250 kHz more spectrum for amateur use

• 500 kHz more exclusive spectrum

Bands Above 30 MHz

Summary of losses**

• 1215-1240 MHz withdrawn to protect new radionavigation-satellite system

• Some additional sharing of certain bands above 220 MHz

Summary of gains**

• New satellite bands at:
    1260-1270 MHz (uplink only)
    2400-2450 MHz
    3400-3410 MHz
    5650-5670 MHz (uplink only)
    5830-5850 MHz (downlink only)
    10.45-10.5 GHz
• New secondary amateur allocation at 902-928 MHz

• New amateur and amateur-satellite bands totalling 4,700 MHz exclusive and 17,040 MHz shared above 40 GHz

**For the USA

Chapter 9

U.S. Amateur Regulations

The complete text of the Communications Act of 1934 would occupy many pages. The only parts given are those most applicable to Amateur Radio station licensing and regulations in this country (with which every amateur should be familiar). Note particularly Sections 324, 325 and 605 and the penalties outlined in Sections 501 and 502.

Be it enacted by the Senate and House of Representatives of the United States of America in Congress assembled,

Section 1. For the purpose of regulating interstate and foreign commerce in communication by wire and radio so as to make available, so far as possible, to all the people of the United States a rapid, efficient, nationwide and worldwide wire and radio communication service with adequate facilities at reasonable charges, for the purpose of the national defense, for the purpose of promoting safety of life and property through the use of wire and radio communication, and for the purpose of securing a more effective execution of this policy by centralizing authority heretofore granted by law to several agencies and by granting additional authority with respect to interstate and foreign commerce in wire and radio communication, there is hereby created a commission to be known as the "Federal Communications Commission," which shall be constituted as hereinafter provided, and which shall execute and enforce the provisions of this Act.

Section 2. (a) The provisions of the Act shall apply to all interstate and foreign communication by wire or radio and all interstate and foreign transmission of energy by radio, which orginates and/or is received within the United States, and to all the licensing and regulating of all radio stations as hereinafter provided; but it shall not apply to persons engaged in wire or radio communication or transmission in the Canal Zone, or to wire or radio communication or transmission wholly within the Canal Zone . . .

Section 4. (a) The Federal Communications Commission (in this Act referred to as the "Commission") shall be composed of seven commissioners appointed by the President, by and with the advice and consent of the Senate, one of whom the President shall designate as chairman.

Section 301. It is the purpose of this Act, among other things, to maintain the controls of the United States over all the channels of interstate and foreign radio transmission; and to provide for the use of such channels, but not the ownership thereof, by persons for limited periods of time, under licenses granted by Federal authority, and no such license shall be construed to create any right, beyond the terms, conditions and periods of the license. No person shall use or operate any apparatus for the transmission of energy or communications or signals by radio . . . except under and in accordance with this Act and with a license in that behalf granted under the provisions of this Act.

Section 302. (a) The Commission may . . . make reasonable regulations governing the interference potential of devices which in their operation are capable of emitting radio frequency energy . . . in sufficient degree to cause harmful interference to radio communications. Such regulations shall be applicable to the manufacture, import, sale, offer for sale, shipment or use of such devices. (b) No person shall manufacture, import, sell, offer for sale, ship or use devices which fail to comply with regulations promulgated pursuant to this section . . .

Section 303 Except as otherwise provided in this Act, the Commission from time to time, as public convenience, interest or necessity requires, shall —

a) Classify radio stations

b) Prescribe the nature of the service to be rendered

c) Assign bands of frequencies . . .

d) Determine the location of stations . . .

e) Regulate the kind of apparatus to be used with respect to its external effects and the purity and sharpness of the emissions from each station and from the apparatus therein

f) Make such regulations not inconsistent with law as it may deem necessary to prevent interference between stations and to carry out the provisions of this Act . . .

g) Study new uses for radio, provide for experimental uses of frequencies, and generally encourage the larger and more effective use of radio in the public interest . . .

j) Have authority to make general rules and regulations requiring stations to keep such records . . . as it may deem desirable . . .

l) 1) Have authority to prescribe the qualifications of station operators . . . and to issue licenses to such citizens or nationals of the United States or citizens of the Trust Territory of the Pacific Islands . . . as the Commission finds qualified . . . 2) Notwithstanding paragraph (1) of this subsection, an individual to whom a radio station is licensed under the provisions of this Act may be issued an operator's license to operate that station. 3) In addition to amateur operator licenses which the Commission may issue to aliens pursuant to paragraph (2) of this subsection, and notwithstanding section 301 of this Act and paragraph (1) of this subsection, the Commission may issue authorizations, under such conditions and terms as it may prescribe, to permit an alien licensed by his government as an Amateur Radio operator to operate his Amateur Radio station licensed by his government in the United States, its possessions, and the Commonwealth of Puerto Rico provided there is in effect a bilateral agreement between the United States and the alien's government for such operation on a reciprocal basis by United States Amateur Radio operators. Other provisions of this Act and of the Administrative Procedure Act shall not be applicable to any request or application for or modification, suspension or cancellation of any such authorization.

m) 1) Have authority to suspend the license of any operator upon proof sufficient to satisfy the Commission that the licensee — (A) has violated any provision of any Act, treaty or convention binding on the United States, which the Commission is authorized to administer, or any regulation made by the Commission under any such Act, treaty or convention; or (B) has failed to carry out a lawful order of the master or person lawfully in charge of the ship or aircraft on which he is employed; or (C) has willfully damaged or permitted radio apparatus or installations to be damaged; or (D) has transmitted superfluous radio communications or signals or communications containing profane or obscene words, language or meaning, or has knowingly transmitted — (1) false or deceptive signals or communications; or (2) a call signal or letter which has not been assigned by proper authority to the station he is operating; or (E) has willfully or maliciously interfered with any other radio communications or signals; or (F) has obtained or attempted to obtain, or has assisted another to obtain or attempt to obtain, an operator's license by fraudulent means.

2) No order of suspension of any operator's license shall take effect until fifteen days' notice in writing thereof, stating the cause for the proposed suspension has been given to the operator licensee who may make written application to the Commission at any time within said fifteen days for a hearing upon such order . . .

n) Have authority to inspect all radio installations . . .

o) Have authority to designate call letters of all stations.

p) Have authority to cause to be published such call letters.

q) Have authority to require the painting and/or illumination of radio towers if and when in its judgment such towers constitute, or there is a reasonable possiblity that they may constitute, a menace to air navigation.

r) Make rules and regulations . . . to carry out the provisions of this Act, or any international radio or wire communications treaty or convention . . .

Section 310. (a) The station license required under this Act shall not be granted to or held by any foreign government or the representative thereof. (b) No broadcast or common carrier or aeronautical . . . radio station license shall be granted to or held by (1) an alien . . . (c) In addition to amateur station licenses which the Commission may issue to aliens pursuant to this Act, the Commission may issue authorizations, under such conditions and terms as it may prescribe, to permit an alien licensed by his government as an Amateur Radio operator to operate his Amateur Radio station licensed by his government in the United States, its possessions, and the Commonwealth of Puerto Rico provided there is in effect a bilateral agreement between the United States and the alien's government for such operation on a reciprocal basis by United States Amateur Radio operators. Other provisions of this Act and of the Administrative Procedure Act shall not be applicable to any request or application for or modification, suspension or cancellation of any such authorization.

Section 318. The actual operation of all transmitting apparatus in any radio station for which a station license is required by this Act shall be carried on only by a person holding an operator's license issued hereunder. No person shall operate any such apparatus in such station except under and in accordance with an operator's license issued to him by the Commission . . .

Section 321 . . . (b) All radio stations, including Government stations and stations on board foreign vessels when within the territorial waters of the United States, shall give absolute priority to radio communications or signals relating to ships in distress.

Section 324. In all circumstances, except in case of radio communications or signals relating to vessels in distress, all radio stations, including those owned and operated by the United States, shall use the minimum amount of power necessary to carry out the communication desired.

Section 325. (a) No person within the jurisdiction of the United States shall knowingly utter or transmit, or cause to be uttered or transmitted, any false or fraudulent signal of distress, or communication relating thereto, nor shall any broadcasting station rebroadcast the program or any part thereof of another broadcasting station without the express authority of the originating station.

Section 501. Any person who willfully and knowingly does or causes or suffers to be done any act, matter or thing, in this Act prohibited or declared to be unlawful, or who willfully or knowingly omits or fails to do any act, matter or thing in this Act required to be done, or willfully or knowingly causes or suffers such omission or failure, shall, upon conviction thereof, be punished for such offense, for which no penalty (other than a forfeiture) is provided in this Act, by a fine of not more than $10,000 or by imprisonment for a term not exceeding one year, or both . . .

Section 502. Any person who willfully or knowingly violates any rule, regulation, restriction or condition made or imposed by the Commission under authority of this Act, or any rule, regulation, restriction or condition made or imposed by any international radio or wire communications treaty or convention, or regulations annexed thereto, to which the United States is or may hereafter become a party, shall, in addition to any other penalties provided by law, be punished, upon conviction thereof, by a fine of not more than $500 for each and every day during which such offense occurs . . .

Section 503 . . . (b) Any person who is determined by the Commission, in accordance with paragraph (3) or (4) of this subsection, to have — (A) willfully or repeatedly failed to comply substantially with the terms and conditions of any license, permit, certificate, or other instrument or authorization issued by the Commission; (B) willfully or repeatedly failed to comply with any of the provisions of this Act or of any rule, regulation, or order shall be liable to the United States for a forfeiture penalty . . . (2) The amount of any forfeiture penalty determined under this subsection shall not exceed $2000 for each violation. Each day of a continuing violation shall constitute a separate offense . . .

Section 605 . . . No person receiving or assisting in receiving, or transmitting or assisting in transmitting, any interstate or foreign communication by wire or radio shall divulge or publish the existence, contents, substance, purport, effect or meaning thereof, . . . to any person other than the addressee, his agent or attorney . . . or in response to a subpoena issued by a court of competent jurisdiction, or on demand or other lawful authority . . . and no person not being entitled thereto shall receive or assist in receiving any interstate or foreign communication by wire or radio and use the same or any information therein contained for his own benefit or for the benefit of another not entitled thereto . . . This section shall not apply to the receiving, divulging, publishing or utilizing the contents of any radio communication, which is broadcast or transmitted by amateurs or others for the use of the general public, or which relates to ships in distress.

Section 606 . . . (c) Upon proclamation by the President that there exists war or a threat of war or a state of public peril or disaster or other national emergency, or in order to preserve the neutrality of the United States, the President . . . may suspend or amend, for such time as he may see fit, the rules and regulations applicable to any or all stations . . . within the jurisdiction of the United States as prescribed by the Commission, and may cause the closing of any station for radio communication . . . and the removal therefrom of its apparatus and equipment, or he may authorize the use or control of any such station . . . and/or its apparatus and equipment by any department of the Government under such regulations as he may prescribe, upon just compensation to the owners . . .

Contents — Part 97

Authority: §§97.1 to 97.313 issued under 48 Stat. 1066, 1082, as amended; 47 U.S.C. 154, 303. Interpret or apply 48 Stat. 1064-1068, 1081-1105, as amended; 47 U.S.C. Sub-chap. I, III-VI.

Subpart A — General

§ 97.1 Basis and purpose.

The rules and regulations in this part are designed to provide an amateur radio service having a fundamental purpose as expressed in the following principles:

(a) Recognition and enhancement of the value of the amateur service to the public as a voluntary noncommercial communication service, particularly with respect to providing emergency communications.

(b) Continuation and extension of the amateur's proven ability to contribute to the advancement of the radio art.

(c) Encouragement and improvement of the amateur radio service through rules which provide for advancing skills in both the communication and technical phases of the art.

(d) Expansion of the existing reservoir within the amateur radio service of trained operators, technicians, and electronics experts.

(e) Continuation and extension of the amateur's unique ability to enhance international good will.

§ 97.3 Definitions.

(a) *Amateur radio service.* A radio communication service of self-training, intercommunication, and technical investigation carried on by amateur radio operators.

(b) *Amateur radio communication.* Noncommercial radio communication by or among amateur radio stations solely with a personal aim and without pecuniary or business interest.

(c) *Amateur radio operator* means a person holding a valid license to operate an amateur radio station issued by the Federal Communications Commission.

(d) *Amateur radio license.* The instrument of authorization issued by the Federal Communications Commission comprised of a station license, and in the case of the primary station, also incorporating an operator license.

Operator license. The instrument of authorization including the class of operator privileges.

Interim Amateur Permit. A temporary operator and station authorization issued to licensees successfully completing Commission supervised examinations for higher class operator licenses.

Station license. The instrument of authorization for a radio station in the Amateur Radio Service.

(e) *Amateur radio station.* A station licensed in the amateur radio service embracing necessary apparatus at a particular location used for amateur radio communication.

(f) *Primary station.* The principal amateur radio station at a specific land location shown on the station license.

(g) *Military recreation station.* An amateur radio station licensed to the person in charge of a station at a land location provided for the recreational use of amateur radio operators, under military auspices of the Armed Forces of the United States.

(h) *Club station* A separate Amateur radio station licensed to an Amateur radio operator acting as a station trustee for a *bona fide* amateur radio organization or society. A *bona fide* Amateur Radio organization or society shall be composed of at least two persons, one of whom must be a licensed Amateur operator, and shall have:

(1) A name,

(2) An instrument of organization (e.g., constitution),

(3) Management, and

(4) A primary purpose which is devoted to Amateur Radio activities consistent with §97.1 and constituting the major portion of the club's activities.

(i) (Reserved)

(j) *Terrestrial location.* Any point within the major portion of the earth's atmosphere, including aeronautical, land and maritime locations.

(k) (Reserved)

(l) *Amateur Radio operation.* Amateur Radio communication conducted by Amateur Radio operators from Amateur Radio station, including the following:

Fixed operation. Radio communication conducted from the specific geographical land location shown on the station license.

Portable operation. Radio communication conducted from a specific geographical location other than that shown on the station license.

Mobile operation. Radio communication conducted while in motion or during halts at unspecified locations.

Repeater operation. Radio communication, other than auxiliary operation, for retransmitting automatically the radio signals of other Amateur Radio stations.

Auxiliary operation. Radio communication for remotely controlling other Amateur Radio stations, for automatically relaying the radio signals of other Amateur Radio stations in a system of stations, or for intercommunicating with other Amateur Radio stations in a system of Amateur Radio stations.

(m) *Control* means techniques used for accomplishing the immediate operation of an Amateur Radio station. Control includes one or more of the following:

(1) *Local control.* Manual control, with the control operator monitoring the operation on duty at the control point located at a station transmitter with the associated operating adjustments directly accessible. (Direct mechanical control, or direct wire control of a transmitter from a control point located on board any aircraft, vessel, or on the same premises on which the transmitter is located, is also considered local control.)

(2) *Remote control.* Manual control, with the control operator monitoring the operation on duty at a control point located elsewhere than at the station transmitter, such that the associated operating adjustments are accessible through a control link.

(3) *Automatic control* means the use of devices and procedures for control so that a control operator does not have to be present at the control point at all times. (Only rules for automatic control of stations in repeater operation have been adopted.)

(n) *Control link.* Apparatus for effecting remote control between a control point and a remotely controlled station.

(o) *Control operator.* An amateur radio operator designated by the licensee of an amateur radio station to also be responsible for the emissions from that station.

(p) *Control point.* The operating position of an amateur radio station where the control operator function is performed.

(q) *Antenna structures.* Antenna structures include the radiating system, its supporting structures, and any appurtenances mounted thereon.

(r) *Antenna height above average terrain.* The height of the center of radiation of an antenna above an averaged value of the elevation above sea level for the surrounding terrain.

(s) *Transmitter.* Apparatus for converting electrical energy received from a source into radio-frequency electromagnetic energy capable of being radiated.

(t) *Effective radiated power.* The product of the radio frequency power, expressed in watts, delivered to an antenna, and the relative gain of the antenna over that of a halfwave dipole antenna.

(u) *System network diagram.* A diagram showing each station and its relationship to the other stations in a network of stations, and to the control point(s).

(v) *Third-party traffic.* Amateur radio communication by or under the supervision of the control operator at an amateur radio station to another amateur radio station on behalf of anyone other than the control operator.

(w) *Emergency communication.* Any amateur radio communication directly relating to the immediate safety of life of individuals or the immediate protection of property.

(x) *Automatic retransmission.* Retransmission of signals by an amateur radio station whereby the retransmitting station is actuated solely by the presence of a received signal through electrical or electro-mechanical means, i.e., without any direct, positive action by the control operator.

(y) *External radio frequency power amplifier.* Any device which, (1) when used in conjunction with a radio transmitter as a signal source, is capable of amplification of that signal, and (2) is not an integral part of the transmitter as manufactured.

(z) *External radio frequency power amplifier kit.* Any number of electronic parts, usually provided with a schematic diagram or printed circuit board, which, when assembled in accordance with instructions, results in an external radio frequency power amplifier, even if additional parts of any type are required to complete assembly.

Subpart B — Amateur Operator and Station Licenses

§ 97.5 Classes of operator licenses.

Amateur extra class.
Advanced class (previously class A).
General class (previously class B).
Conditional class (previously class C).
Technician class.
Novice class.

§ 97.7 Privileges of operator licenses.

(a) *Amateur Extra Class and Advanced Class.* All authorized amateur privileges including exclusive frequency operating authority in accordance with the following table:

Frequencies	Class of license authorized
3500-3525 kHz 3775-3800 kHz 7000-7025 kHz 14,000-14,025 kHz 21,000-21,025 kHz 21,250-21,270 kHz	Amateur Extra Only
3800-3890 kHz 7150-7225 kHz 14,200-14,275 kHz 21,270-21,350 kHz	Amateur Extra and Advanced.

(b) *General Class.* All authorized amateur privileges except those exclusive operating privileges which are reserved to the Advanced Class and/or Amateur Extra Class.

(c) *Conditional Class.* Same privileges as General Class. New Conditional Class licenses will not be issued. Present Conditional Class licensees will be issued General Class licenses at time of renewal or modification.

(d) *Technician Class.* All authorized amateur privileges on the frequencies 50.0 MHz and above. Technician Class licenses also convey the full privileges of Novice Class licenses.

(e) *Novice Class.* Radiotelegraphy in the frequency bands 3700-3750 kHz, 7100-7150 kHz (7050-7075 kHz when the terrestrial station location is not within Region 2), 21,100-21,200 kHz, and 28,100-28,200 kHz, using only Type A1 emission.

§ 97.9 Eligibility for new operator license.

Anyone except a representative of a foreign government is eligible for an amateur operator license.

§ 97.11 Application for operator license.

(a) An application (FCC Form 610) for a new operator license, including an application for change in operating privileges, which will require an examination supervised by Commission personnel at a regular Commission examining office shall be submitted to such office in advance of or at the time of examination, except that, whenever an examination is to be taken at a designated examination point away from a Commission office, the application, together with the necessary filing fee should be submitted in advance of the examination date to the office which has jurisdiction over the examination point involved.

(b) An application (FCC Form 610) for a new operator license, including an application for change in operating privileges, which requests an examination supervised by a volunteer examiner under the provisions of § 97.27, shall be submitted to the FCC field office nearest the applicant. Applications for the Novice license should be sent to the Commission's offices in Gettysburg, PA 17325. All applications should be accompanied by any necessary filing fee.

(c) An application (FCC Form 610) for renewal and/or modification of license when no change in operating privileges is involved shall be submitted, together with any necessary filing fee, to the Commission's office at Gettysburg, Pennsylvania 17325.

§ 97.13 Renewal or modification of operator license.

(a) An Amateur operator license may be renewed upon proper application.

(b) The applicant shall qualify for a new license by examination if the requirements of this section are not fulfilled.

(c) Application for renewal and/or modification of an amateur operator license shall be submitted on FCC Form 610 and shall be accompanied by the applicant's license. Application for renewal of unexpired licenses must be made during the license term and should be filed within 90 days but not later than 30 days prior to the end of the license term. In any case in which the licensee has, in accordance with the provisions of this chapter, made timely and sufficient application for renewal of an unexpired license, no license with reference to any activity of a continuing nature shall expire until such application shall have been finally determined.

(d) If a license is allowed to expire, application for renewal may be made during a period of grace of five years after the expiration date. During this five-year period of grace, an expired license is not valid. A license renewed during the grace period will be dated currently and will not be backdated to the date of its expiration. Application for renewal shall be submitted on FCC Form 610 and shall be accompanied by the applicant's expired license.

(e) When the name of a licensee is changed or when the mailing address is changed a formal application for modification of license is not required. However, the licensee shall notify the Commission promptly of these changes. The notice, which may be in letter form, shall contain the name and address of the licensee as they appear in the Commission's records, the new name and/or address, as the case may be, the radio station call sign and class of license. The notice shall be sent to Federal Communications Commission, Gettysburg, PA 17325 and a copy shall be kept by the licensee until a new license is issued.

OPERATOR LICENSE EXAMINATIONS

§ 97.19 When examination is required.

Examination is required for the issuance of a new amateur operator license, and for a change in class of operating privileges. Credit may be given, however, for certain elements of examination as provided in § 97.25.

§ 97.21 Examination elements.

Examinations for amateur operator privileges will comprise one or more of the following examination elements:

(a) Element 1(A): Beginner's code test at five (5) words per minute;

(b) Element 1(B): General code test at thirteen (13) words per minute;

(c) Element 1(C): Expert's code test at twenty (20) words per minute;

(d) Element 2: Basic law comprising rules and regulations essential to beginners' operation, including sufficient elementary radio theory for the understanding of those rules;

(e) Element 3: General amateur practice and regulations involving radio operation and apparatus and provisions of treaties, statutes, and rules affecting amateur stations and operators;

(f) Element 4(A): Intermediate amateur practice involving intermediate level radio theory and operation as applicable to modern amateur techniques, including, but not limited to, radiotelephony and radiotelegraphy;

(g) Element 4(B): Advanced amateur practice involving advanced radio theory and operation as applicable to modern amateur techniques, including, but not limited to, radiotelephony, radiotelegraphy, and transmissions of energy for measurements and observations applied to propagation, for the radio control of remote objects and for similar experimental purposes.

§ 97.23 Examination requirements.

Applicants for operator licenses will be required to pass the following examination elements:

(a) Amateur Extra Class: Elements 1(C), 2, 3, 4(A) and 4(B);

(b) Advanced Class: Elements 1(B), 2, 3, 4(A)

(c) General Class: Elements 1(B), 2 and 3;

(d) Technician Class: Elements 1(A), 2 and 3;

(e) Novice Class: Elements 1(A) and 2.

§ 97.25 Examination credit.

(a) An applicant for a higher class of amateur operator license who holds any valid amateur license will be required to pass only those elements of the higher class examination that are not included in the examination for the amateur license held.

(b) Amateur Code Credit Certificates (FCC Form 845) will be issued by the Engineers-In-Charge of FCC Offices to applicants for amateur operator licenses who successfully complete telegraphy examinations elements 1(a), 1(b) or 1(c) but who fail the associated written examination element(s). Upon presentation of a properly completed Amateur Code Credit Certificate, the FCC shall give the applicant for an amateur radio operator license examination credit for the code speed listed on the Amateur Code Credit Certificate. An Amateur Code Credit Certificate is valid for a period of one year from the date of its issuance.

(c) An applicant for an amateur operator license will be given credit for either telegraph code element 1(A) or 1(B) if within 5 years prior to the receipt of his application by the

Commission he held a commercial radiotelegraph operator license or permit issued by the Federal Communications Commission. An applicant for an amateur Extra Class license will be given credit for the telegraph code element 1(C) if he holds a valid first class commercial radiotelegraph operator license or permit issued by the Federal Communications Commission containing an aircraft radiotelegraph endorsement.

(d) No examination credit, except as herein provided, shall be allowed on the basis of holding or having held any amateur or commercial operator license.

§ 97.27 Mail examinations for applicants unable to travel.

The Commission may permit the examinations for an Amateur Extra, Advanced, General or Technician class license to be administered at a location other than a Commission examination point by an examiner chosen by the Commission when it is shown by physician's certification that the applicant is unable to appear at a regular Commission examination point because of a protracted disability preventing travel.

§ 97.28 Manner of conducting examinations.

(a) Except as provided in § 97.27, all examinations for Amateur Extra, Advanced, General, and Technician Class operator licenses will be conducted by authorized Commission personnel or representatives at locations and times specified by the Commission. Examination elements given under the provisions of § 97.27 should be filed on FCC Form 610, and should be sent to the FCC field office nearest the applicant. (A list of these offices appears in § 0.121 of the Commission's Rules and can be obtained from the Regional Services Division, Field Operations Bureau, FCC, Washington, D.C. 20554, or any field office.)

(b) The examination for a Novice Class operator license shall be conducted and supervised by a volunteer examiner selected by the applicant, unless otherwise prescribed by the Commission. The volunteer examiner shall be at least 18 years of age, shall be unrelated to the applicant, and shall be the holder of an Amateur Extra, Advanced, or General Class operator license. The written portion of the Novice Class operator examination shall be obtained, administered, and submitted in accordance with the following procedure:

(1) Within 10 days after successfully completing telegraphy examination element 1(A), an applicant shall submit an application (FCC Form 610) to the Commission's office in Gettysburg, Pennsylvania 17325. The application shall include a written request from the volunteer examiner for the examination papers for Element 2. The examiner's written request shall include (i) the names and permanent addresses of the examiner and the applicant, (ii) a description of the examiner's qualifications to administer the examination, (iii) the examiner's statement that the applicant has passed telegraphy element 1(A) under his supervision within the 10 days prior to submission of the request, and (iv) the examiner's written signature. Examination papers will be forwarded only to the volunteer examiner.

(2) The volunteer examiner shall be responsible for the proper conduct and necessary supervision of the examination. Administration of the examination shall be in accordance

with the instructions included with the examination papers.

(3) The examination papers, either completed or unopened in the event the examination is not taken, shall be returned by the volunteer examiner to the Commission's office in Gettysburg, PA., no later than 30 days after the date the papers are mailed by the Commission (the date of mailing is normally stamped by the Commission on the outside of the examination envelope).

(c) The code test required of an applicant for an amateur radio operator license, in accordance with the provisions of §§ 97.21 and 97.23 shall determine the applicant's ability to transmit by hand key (straight key or, if supplied by the applicant, any other type of hand operated key such as a semi-automatic or electronic key, but not a keyboard keyer) and to receive by ear, in plain language, messages in the international Morse code at not less than the prescribed speed during a five minute test period. Each five characters shall be counted as one word. Each punctuation mark and numeral shall be counted as two characters.

(d) All written portions of the examinations for amateur operator privileges shall be completed by the applicant in legible handwriting or hand printing. Whenever the applicant's signature is required, his normal signature shall be used. Applicants unable to comply with these requirements, because of physical disability, may dictate their answers to the examination questions and the receiving code test. If the examination or any part thereof is dictated, the examiner shall certify the nature of the applicant's disability and the name and address of the person(s) taking and transcribing the applicant's dictation.

§ 97.31 Grading of examinations.

(a) Code tests for sending and receiving are graded separately.

(b) Seventy-four percent (74%) is the passing grade for written examinations. For the purpose of grading, each element required in qualifying for a particular license will be considered as a separate examination. All written examinations will be graded only by Commission personnel.

§ 97.32 Interim Amateur Permits.

(a) Upon successful completion of a Commission supervised Amateur Radio Service operator examination, an applicant already licensed in the Amateur Radio Service may operate his amateur radio station pending issuance of his permanent amateur operator and station licenses under the terms and conditions of an Interim Amateur Permit, evidenced by a properly executed FCC Form 660-B.

(b) An Interim Amateur Permit conveys all operating privileges of the applicant's new operator license classification.

(c) The transmissions of amateur radio stations operated under the authority of Interim Amateur Permits shall be identified in the manner specified in § 97.84.

(d) The original Interim Amateur Permit of an amateur radio operator shall be kept in the personal possession of or posted in a conspicuous place in the room occupied by such operator when operating an amateur radio station under the authority of an Interim Amateur Permit.

(e) Interim Amateur Permits are valid for a period of 90 days from the date of issuance or until issuance of the permanent station and

operator licenses, whichever comes first, but may be set aside by the Commission within the 90 day term if it appears that the permanent operator and station licenses cannot be granted routinely.

(f) Interim Amateur Permits shall not be renewed.

§ Eligibility for re-examination.

An applicant who fails an examination element required for an amateur radio operator license shall not apply to be examined for the same or higher examination element within thirty days of the date the examination element was failed.

STATION LICENSES

§ 97.37 General eligibility for station license.

(a) An Amateur Radio station license will be issued only to a licensed Amateur Radio operator, except that a military recreation station license may also be issued to an individual not licensed as an Amateur Radio operator (other than a representative of a foreign government), who is in charge of a proposed military recreation station not operated by the U.S. Government but which is to be located in approved public quarters.

(b) Only modification and/or renewal station licenses will be issued for club and military recreation stations. No new licenses will be issued for these types of stations.

§ 97.39 Eligibility of corporations or organizations to hold station license.

An amateur station license will not be issued to a school, company, corporation, association, or other organization, except that in the case of a *bona fide* Amateur Radio organization or society meeting the criteria set forth in Section 97.3, a station license may be issued to a licensed amateur operator, other than the holder of a Novice class license, as trustee for such society.

§ 97.40 Station license required.

(a) No transmitting station shall be operated in the Amateur Radio Service without being licensed by the Federal Communications Commission, except that an Amateur Radio station licensed by the Government of Canada may, in accordance with Section 97.41, be operated in the United States without the prior approval of the Commission.

(b) Every Amateur Radio operator shall have one, but only one, primary Amateur Radio station license.

§ 97.41 Operation of Canadian amateur stations in the United States.

(a) An Amateur Radio station licensed by the Government of Canada may be operated in the United States without the prior approval of the Federal Communications Commission.

(b) Operation of a Canadian amateur station in the United States must comply with all of the following:

(1) The terms of the Convention between the United States and Canada (TIAS No. 2508) relating to the operation by citizens of either country of certain radio equipment or stations in the other country. (See Appendix 4 to Part 97.)

(2) The operating terms and conditions of the amateur station license issued by the Government of Canada.

(3) The provisions of subparts A through E of Part 97.

(4) Any further conditions the Commission may impose upon the privilege of operating in the United States.

(c) At any time the Commission may, in its discretion, modify, suspend, or cancel the privilege of any Canadian licensee operating an Amateur Radio station in the United States.

§ 97.42 Application for station license.

(a) Each application for a club or military recreation station license in the Amateur Radio Service shall be made on the FCC Form 610-B. Each application for any other Amateur Radio license shall be made on the FCC Form 610.

(b) One application and all papers incorporated therein and made a part thereof shall be submitted for each amateur station license. If the application is only for a station license, it shall be filed directly with the Commission's Gettysburg, Pennsylvania office. If the application also contains an application for any class of amateur operator license, it shall be filed in accordance with the provisions of § 97.11.

(c) Each applicant in the Safety and Special Radio Services (1) for modification of a station license involving a site change or a substantial increase in tower height or (2) for a license for a new station must, before commencing construction, supply the environmental information, where required, and must follow the procedure prescribed by Subpart 1 of Part 1 of this chapter (§§ 1.1301 through 1.1319) unless Commission action authorizing such construction would be a minor action with the meaning of Subpart 1 of Part 1.

(d) Protection for Federal Communications Commission Monitoring Stations:

(1) Applicants for an Amateur Radio station license to operate in the vicinity of an FCC monitoring station are advised to give consideration, prior to filing applications, to the possible need to protect the FCC stations from harmful interference. Geographical coordinates of the facilities which require protection are listed in Section 0.121(c) of the Commission's Rules. Applications for stations (except mobile stations) in the vicinity of monitoring stations may be reviewed by Commission staff on a case-by-case basis to determine the potential for harmful interference to the monitoring station. Depending on the theoretical field strength value and existing root-sum-square or other ambient radio field signal levels at the indicated coordinates, a clause protecting the monitoring station may be added to the station license.

(2) Advance consultation with the Commission is suggested prior to filing an initial application for station license if the proposed station will be located within one mile of any of the above-referenced monitoring station coordinates and is to be operated on frequencies below 1000 MHz. Such consultations are also suggested for proposed stations operating above 1000 MHz if they are to be located within one mile of any monitoring station designated in Section 0.121(c) as a satellite monitoring facility.

(3) Regardless of any coordination prior to filing initial applications, it is suggested that licensees within one mile of a monitoring station consult the Commission before initiating any changes in the station which would increase the field strength produced over the monitoring station.

(4) Applicants and licensees desiring such consultations should communicate with: Chief, Field Operations Bureau, Federal Communications Commission, Washington, DC 20054, Telephone 202-632-6980.

(5) The Commission will not screen applications to determine whether advance consultation has taken place. However, applicants are advised that such consultation can avoid objections from the Federal Communications Commission or modification of any authorization which will cause harmful interference.

§ 97.43 Mailing address furnished by licensee.

Each application shall set forth and each licensee shall furnish the Commission with an address in the United States to be used by the Commission in serving documents or directing correspondence to that licensee. Unless any licensee advises the Commission to the contrary, the address contained in the licensee's most recent application will be used by the Commission for this purpose.

§ 97.44 Location of station.

Every Amateur Radio station shall have one land location, the address of which appears on the station license, and at least one control point.

§ 97.45 Limitations on antenna structures.

(a) Except as provided in paragraph (b) of this section, an antenna for a station in the Amateur Radio Service which exceeds the following height limitations may not be erected or used unless notice has been filed with both the FAA on FAA Form 7460-1 and with the Commission on Form 714 or on the license application form, and prior approval by the Commission has been obtained for:

(1) Any construction or alteration of more than 200 feet in height above ground level at its site (§ 17.7[a] of this chapter).

(2) Any construction or alteration of greater height than an imaginary surface extending outward and upward at one of the following slopes (§17.7[b] of this chapter):

(i) 100 to 1 for a horizontal distance of 20,000 feet from the nearest point of the nearest runway of each airport with at least one runway more than 3,200 feet in length, excluding heliports and seaplane bases without specified boundaries, if that airport is either listed in the Airport Directory of the current Airman's Information Manual or is operated by a Federal military agency.

(ii) 50 to 1 for a horizontal distance of 10,000 feet from the nearest point of the nearest runway of each airport with its longest runway no more than 3,200 feet in length, excluding heliports and seaplane bases without specified boundaries, if that airport is either listed in the Airport Directory or is operated by a Federal military agency.

(iii) 25 to 1 for a horizontal distance of 5,000 feet from the nearest point of the nearest landing and takeoff area of each heliport listed in the Airport Directory or operated by a Federal military agency.

(3) Any construction or alteration on an airport listed in the Airport Directory of the Airman's Information Manual (§17.7[c] of this chapter).

(b) A notification to the Federal Aviation Administration is not required for any of the following construction or alteration:

(1) Any object that would be shielded by existing structures of a permanent and substantial character or by natural terrain or topographic features of equal or greater height, and would be located in the congested area of a city, town, or settlement where it is evident beyond all reasonable doubt that the structure so shielded will not adversely affect safety in air navigation. Applicants claiming such exemption shall submit a statement with their application to the Commission explaining the basis in detail for their finding (§ 17.14(a) of this chapter).

(2) Any antenna structure of 20 feet or less in height except one that would increase the height of another antenna structure (§ 17.14[b] of this chapter).

(c) Further details as to whether an aeronautical study and/or obstruction marking and lighting may be required, and specifications for obstruction marking and lighting when required, may be obtained from Part 17 of this chapter, "Construction, Marking, and Lighting of Antenna Structures." Information regarding the inspection and maintenance of antenna structures requiring obstruction marking and lighting is also contained in Part 17 of this chapter.

§ 97.47 Renewal and/or modification of amateur station license.

(a) Application for renewal and/or modification of an individual station license shall be submitted on FCC Form 610, and application for renewal and/or modification of an amateur club or military recreation station shall be submitted on FCC Form 610-B. In every case the application shall be accompanied by the applicant's license or photocopy thereof. Applications for renewal of unexpired licenses must be made during the license term and should be filed not later than 60 days prior to the end of the license term. In any case in which the licensee has in accordance with the provisions of this chapter, made timely and sufficient application for renewal of an unexpired license, no license with reference to any activity of a continuing nature shall expire until such application shall have been finally determined.

(b) If a license is allowed to expire, application for renewal may be made during a period of grace of 1 year after the expiration date. During this 1-year period of grace, an expired license is not valid. A license renewed during the grace period will be dated currently and will not be backdated to the date of expiration. An application for an individual station license shall be submitted on FCC Form 610. An application for an amateur club or military recreation station license shall be submitted on FCC Form 610-B. In every case the application shall be accompanied by the applicant's expired license or a photocopy thereof.

§ 97.49 Commission modification of station license.

(a) Whenever the Commission shall determine that public interest, convenience, and necessity would be served, or any treaty ratified by the United States will be more fully complied with, by the modification of any radio station license either for a limited time, or for the duration of the term thereof, it shall issue an order for such licensee to show cause why such license should not be modified.

(b) Such order to show cause shall contain a statement of the grounds and reasons for such proposed modification, and shall specify wherein the said license is required to be modified. It shall require the licensee against whom it is directed to appear at a place and time therein named, in no event to be less than 30 days from the date of receipt of the order, to show cause why the proposed modification should not be made and the order of modification issued.

(c) If the licensee against whom the order to show cause is directed does not appear at the time and place provided in said order, a final order of modification shall issue forthwith.

CALL SIGNS

§ 97.51 Assignment of call signs.

(a) The Commission shall assign the call sign of an amateur radio station on a systematic basis.

(b) The Commission shall not grant any request for a specific call sign.

(c) From time to time the Commission will issue public announcements detailing the policies and procedures governing the systematic assignment of call signs and any changes in those policies and procedures.

DUPLICATE LICENSES AND LICENSE TERM

§ 97.57 Duplicate license.

Any licensee requesting a duplicate license to replace an original which has been lost, mutilated, or destroyed, shall submit a statement setting forth the facts regarding the manner in which original license was lost, mutilated, or destroyed. If, subsequent to receipt by the licensee of the duplicate license, the original license is found, either the duplicate or the original license shall be returned immediately to the Commission.

§ 97.59 License Term

(a) Amateur operator licenses are normally valid for a period of five years from the date of issuance of a new, modified or renewed license.

(b) Amateur station licenses are normally valid for a period of five years from the date of issuance of a new, modified or renewed license. All amateur station licenses, regardless of when issued, will expire on the same date as the licensee's amateur operator license.

(c) A duplicate license shall bear the same expiration date as the license for which it is a duplicate.

Subpart C — Technical Standards

§ 97.61 Authorized frequencies and emissions.

(a) The following frequency bands and associated emissions are available to amateur radio stations for amateur radio operation, other than repeater operation and auxiliary operation, subject to the limitations of § 97.65 and paragraph (b) of this section:

Frequency band	Emissions	Limitations (See paragraph (b))	Frequency band	Emissions	Limitations (See paragraph (b))
kHz					
1800-2000	A1, A3	1, 2	220-225	AØ, A1, A2, A3, A4, A5, FØ, F1, F2, F3, F4, F5	5
3500-4000	A1		420-450	AØ, A1, A2, A3, A4, A5 FØ, F1, F2, F3, F4, F5	5, 7
3500-3775	F1				
3775-3890	A5, F5		1215-1300	AØ, A1, A2, A3, A4, A5, FØ, F1, F2, F3, F4, F5	5
3775-4000	A3, F3	4			
4383.8	A3J/A3A	13	2300-2450	AØ, A1, A2, A3, A4, A5, FØ, F1, F2, F3, F4, F5 P	5, 8
7000-7300	A1	3, 4			
7000-7150	F1	3, 4	3300-3500	AØ, A1, A2, A3, A4, A5, FØ, F1, F2, F3, F4, F5, P	5, 12
7075-7100	A3, F3	11			
7150-7225	A5, F5	3, 4	5650-5925	AØ, A1, A2, A3, A4, A5, FØ, F1, F2, F3, F4, F5, P	5, 9
7150-7300	A3, F3	3, 4			
14000-14350	A1				
14000-14200	F1		*GHz*		
14200-14275	A5, F5		10.000-10.500	AØ, A1, A2, A3, A4, A5 FØ, F1, F2, F3, F4, F5	5
14200-14350	A3, F3				
			24.000-24.250	AØ, A1, A2, A3, A4, A5, FØ, F1, F2, F3, F4, F5, P	5, 10
MHz					
21.000-21.450	A1		48.000-50.000	AØ, A1, A2, A3, A4, A5, FØ, F1, F2, F3, F4, F5, P	
21.000-21.250	F1				
21.250-21.350	A5, F5		71.000-76.000	AØ, A1, A2, A3, A4, A5, FØ, F1, F2, F3, F4, F5, P	
21.250-21.450	A3, F3				
28.000-29.700	A1		165.000-170.000	AØ, A1, A2, A3, A4, A5, FØ, F1, F2, F3, F4, F5, P	
28.000-28.500	F1				
28.500-29.700	A3, F3, A5, F5		240.000-250.000	AØ, A1, A2, A3, A4, A5, FØ, F1, F2, F3, F4, F5, P	
50.0-54.0	A1				
50.1-54.0	A2, A3, A4, A5, F1, F2, F3, F5		Above 300.000	AØ, A1, A2, A3, A4, A5, FØ, F1, F2, F3, F4, F5, P	
51.0-54.0	AØ				
144-148	A1				
144.1-148.0	AØ, A2, A3, A4, A5, FØ, F1, F2, F3, F5				

(b) Limitations:

(1) The use of frequencies in this band is on a shared basis with the LORAN-A radionavigation system and is subject to cancellation or revision, in whole or in part, by order of the Commission, without hearing, whenever the Commission shall determine such action is necessary in view of the priority of the LORAN-A radionavigation system. The use of these frequencies by amateur stations shall not cause harmful interference to the LORAN-A system. If an amateur station causes such interference, operation on the frequencies involved must cease if so directed by the Commission.

(2) Operation shall be limited to:

	Maximum DC plate input power in watts							
Area	1800-1825 kHz	1825-1850 kHz	1850-1875 kHz	1875-1900 kHz	1900-1925 kHz	1925-1950 kHz	1950-1975 kHz	1975-2000 kHz
	Day/Night	Day/Night	Day/Night	Day/Night	Day/Night	Day/Night	Day/Night	Day/Night
Alabama	500/100	100/25	0	0	0	0	100/25	500/100
Alaska	1000/200	500/100	500/100	100/25	0	0	0	0
Arizona	1000/200	500/100	500/100	0	0	0	0	0
Arkansas	1000/200	500/100	100/25	0	0	100/25	100/25	500/100
California	1000/200	500/100	500/100	100/25	0	0	0	0
Colorado	1000/200	500/100	200/50	0	0	0	0	200/50
Connecticut	500/100	100/25	0	0	0	0	0	0
Delaware	500/100	100/25	0	0	0	0	0	100/25
District of Columbia	500/100	100/25	0	0	0	0	0	100/25
Florida	500/100	100/25	0	0	0	0	100/25	500/100
Georgia	500/100	100/25	0	0	0	0	0	200/50
Hawaii	0	0	0	0	200/50	100/25	100/25	500/100
Idaho	1000/200	500/100	500/100	100/25	100/25	100/25	100/25	500/100
Illinois	1000/200	500/100	100/25	0	0	0	0	200/50
Indiana	1000/200	500/100	100/25	0	0	0	0	200/50
Iowa	1000/200	500/100	200/50	0	0	100/25	100/25	500/100
Kansas	1000/200	500/100	100/25	0	0	100/25	100/25	500/100

Maximum DC plate input power in watts

Area	1800-1825 kHz Day/Night	1825-1850 kHz Day/Night	1850-1875 kHz Day/Night	1875-1900 kHz Day/Night	1900-1925 kHz Day/Night	1925-1950 kHz Day/Night	1950-1975 kHz Day/Night	1975-2000 kHz Day/Night
Kentucky	1000/200	500/100	100/25	0	0	0	0	200/50
Louisiana	500/100	100/25	0	0	0	0	100/25	500/100
Maine	500/100	100/25	0	0	0	0	0	0
Maryland	500/100	100/25	0	0	0	0	0	100/25
Massachusetts	500/100	100/25	0	0	0	0	0	0
Michigan	1000/200	500/100	100/25	0	0	0	0	100/25
Minnesota	1000/200	500/100	500/100	100/25	100/25	100/25	100/25	500/100
Mississippi	500/100	100/25	0	0	0	0	100/25	500/100
Missouri	1000/200	500/100	100/25	0	0	100/25	100/25	500/100
Montana	1000/200	500/100	500/100	100/25	100/25	100/25	100/25	500/100
Nebraska	1000/200	500/100	200/50	0	0	0	100/25	500/100
Nevada	1000/200	500/100	500/100	100/25	0	0	0	0
New Hampshire	500/100	100/25	0	0	0	0	0	0
New Jersey	500/100	100/25	0	0	0	0	0	0
New Mexico	1000/200	500/100	100/25	0	0	100/25	500/100	1000/200
New York	500/100	100/25	0	0	0	0	0	0
North Carolina	500/100	100/25	0	0	0	0	0	100/25
North Dakota	1000/200	500/100	500/100	100/25	100/25	100/25	100/25	500/100
Ohio	1000/200	500/100	100/25	0	0	0	0	100/25
Oklahoma	1000/200	500/100	100/25	0	0	100/25	100/25	500/100
Oregon	1000/200	500/100	500/100	0	0	0	0	0
Pennsylvania	500/100	100/25	0	0	0	0	0	0
Rhode Island	500/100	100/25	0	0	0	0	0	0
South Carolina	500/100	100/25	0	0	0	0	0	200/50
South Dakota	1000/200	500/100	500/100	100/25	100/25	100/25	100/25	500/100
Tennessee	1000/200	500/100	100/25	0	0	0	0	200/50
Texas	500/100	100/25	0	0	0	0	0	200/50
Utah	1000/200	500/100	500/100	100/25	100/25	0	0	100/25
Vermont	500/100	100/25	0	0	0	0	0	0
Virginia	500/100	100/25	0	0	0	0	0	100/25
Washington	1000/200	500/100	500/100	100/25	0	0	0	0
West Virginia	1000/200	500/100	100/25	0	0	0	0	100/25
Wisconsin	1000/200	500/100	200/50	0	0	0	0	200/50
Wyoming	1000/200	500/100	500/100	100/25	100/25	0	0	200/50
Puerto Rico	500/100	100/25	0	0	0	0	0	200/50
Virgin Islands	500/100	100/25	0	0	0	0	0	200/50
Swan Island	500/100	100/25	0	0	0	0	100/25	500/100
Serrana Bank	500/100	100/25	0	0	0	0	100/25	500/100
Roncador Key	500/100	100/25	0	0	0	0	100/25	500/100
Navassa Island	500/100	100/25	0	0	0	0	0	200/50
Baker, Canton, Enderbury Howland	100/25	0	0	100/25	100/25	0	0	100/25
Guam, Johnston, Midway, Northern Mariana	0	0	0	0	100/25	0	0	100/25
American Samoa	200/50	0	0	200/50	200/50	0	0	200/50
Wake	100/25	0	0	100/25	0	0	0	0
Palmyra, Jarvis	0	0	0	0	200/50	0	0	200/50

(3) Where, in adjacent regions or subregions, a band of frequencies is allocated to different services of the same category, the basic principle is the equality of right to operate. Accordingly, the stations of each service in one region or subregion must operate so as not to cause harmful interference to services in the other regions or subregions (No. 117, the Radio Regulations, Geneva, 1959).

(4) 3900-4000 kHz and 7100-7300 kHz are not available in the following U.S. possessions: Baker, Canton, Enderbury, Guam, Howland, Jarvis, the Northern Mariana Islands, Palmyra, American Samoa, and Wake Islands.

(5) Amateur stations shall not cause interference to the Government radiolocation service.

(6) (Reserved)

(7) In the following areas the d.c. plate input power to the final transmitter stage shall not exceed 50 watts, except when authorized by the appropriate Commission Engineer in Charge and the appropriate Military Area Frequency Coordinator.

(i) Those portions of Texas and New Mexico bounded by latitude 33°24' N., 31°53'., and longitude 105°40' W. and 106°40' W.

(ii) The State of Florida, including the Key West area and the areas enclosed within circles of 200-mile radius centered at 28°21' N., 80°43' W. and 30°30' N., 86°30'W.

(iii) The State of Arizona.

(iv) Those portions of California and Nevada south of latitude 37°10' N., and the area within a 200-mile radius of 34°09' N., 119°11' W.

(8) No protection in the band 2400-2500 MHz is afforded from interference due to the operation of industrial, scientific, and medical devices on 2450 MHz.

(9) No protection in the band 5725-5875 MHz is afforded from interference due to the operation of industrial, scientific and medical devices on 5800 MHz.

(10) No protection in the band 24.00-24.25 GHz is afforded from interference due to the operation of industrial, scientific and medical devices on 24.125 GHz.

(11) The use of A3 and F3 in this band is limited to amateur radio stations located outside Region 2.

(12) Amateur stations shall not cause interference to the Fixed-Satellite Service operating in the band 3400-3500 MHz.

(13) The frequency 4383.8 kHz, maximum power 150 watts, may be used by any station authorized under this part to communicate with any other station authorized in the State of Alaska for emergency communications. No airborne operations will be permitted on this frequency. Additionally, all stations operating on this frequency must be located in or within 50 nautical miles of the State of Alaska.

(c) All amateur frequency bands above 29.5 MHz are available for repeater operation, except 50.0-52.0 MHz, 144.0-144.5 MHz, 145.5-146.0 MHz, 220.0-220.5 MHz, 431.0-433.0 MHz, and 435.0-438.0 MHz. Both the input (receiving) and output (transmitting) frequencies of a station in repeater operation shall be frequencies available for repeater operation.

(d) All amateur frequency bands above 220.5 MHz, except 431-433 MHz, and 435-438 MHz, are available for auxiliary operation.

§ 97.63 Selection and use of frequencies.

(a) An amateur station may transmit on any frequency within any authorized amateur frequency band.

(b) Sideband frequencies resulting from keying or modulating a carrier wave shall be confined within the authorized amateur band.

(c) The frequencies available for use by a control operator of an amateur station are dependent on the operator license classification of the control operator and are listed in §97.7

Authorized Effective Radiated Power for Repeater Stations

Antena height above average terrain	Maximum effective radiated power for frequency bands above:			
	52 MHz	144.5 MHz	420 MHz	1215 MHz
Below 50 feet	100 watts	800 watts	Paragraphs (a) and (b)	Paragraphs (a) and (b)
50-99 feet	100 watts	400 watts	..do..	..do..
100-499 feet	50 watts	400 watts	800 watts	..do..
500-999 feet	25 watts	200 watts	800 watts	..do..
Above 1000 feet	25 watts	100 watts	400 watts	..do..

§ 97.65 Emission limitations.

(a) Type AØ emission, where not specifically designated in the bands listed in §97.61, may be used for short periods of time when required for authorized remote control purposes or for experimental purposes. However, these limitations do not apply where type AØ emission is specifically designated.

(b) Whenever code practice, in accordance with §97.91(d), is conducted in bands authorized for A3 emission, tone modulation of the radiotelephone transmitter may be utilized when interspersed with appropriate voice instructions.

(c) On frequencies below 29.0 MHz, the bandwidth of an F3 emission (frequency or phase modulation) shall not exceed that of an A3 emission having the same audio characteristics.

(d) On frequencies below 50 MHz, the bandwidth of A5 and F5 emissions shall not exceed that of an A3 single sideband emission.

(e) On frequencies between 50 MHz and 225 MHz, single sideband or double sideband, A5 emissions may be used and the bandwidth shall not exceed that of an A3 single sideband or double sideband signal respectively. The bandwidth of F5 emission shall not exceed that of an A3 single sideband emission.

(f) Below 225 MHz, A3 and A5 emissions may be used simultaneously on the same carrier frequency provided the total bandwidth does not exceed that of an A3 double sideband emission.

§ 97.67 Maximum authorized power.

(a) Except for power restrictions as set forth in §97.61 and paragraph (d) below each amateur transmitter may be operated with a power input not exceeding one kilowatt to the plate circuit of the final amplifier stage of an amplifier oscillator transmitter or to the plate circuit of an oscillator transmitter. An amateur transmitter operating with a power input exceeding 900 watts to the plate circuit shall provide means for accurately measuring the plate power input to the vacuum tube or tubes supplying power to the antenna.

(b) Notwithstanding the provisions of paragraph (a) of this section, amateur stations shall use the minimum amount of transmitter power necessary to carry out the desired communications.

(c) Within the limitations of paragraphs (a) and (b) of this section, the effective radiated power of an amateur radio station in repeater operation shall not exceed the power specified for the antenna height above average terrain [in the table above.]

(d) In the frequency bands 3700-3750 kHz, 7100-7150 kHz (7050-7075 kHz when the terrestrial location of the station is not within

Region 2), 21,100-21,200 kHz and 28,100-28,200 kHz, the power input to the transmitter final amplifying stage supplying radio frequency energy to the antenna shall not exceed 250 watts, exclusive of power for heating the cathode of a vacuum tube(s).

§ 97.69 Digital transmission.

Subject to the special conditions contained in paragraphs (a) and (b) below, the use of the International Telegraphic Alphabet No. 2 (also known as the Baudot Code) and the American Standard Code for Information Interchange (ASCII) may be used for such purposes as (but not restricted to) radio teleprinter communications, control of amateur radio stations, models and other objects, transfer of computer programs or direct computer-to-computer communications, and communications in various types of data networks (including so-called "packet switching" systems); provided that such operations are carried out in accordance with the other regulations set forth in this Part.

(a) Use of the International Telegraphic Alphabet No. 2 (Baudot Code) and subject to the following requirements:

(1) The transmitting speed shall consist of a single channel five unit (start-stop) teleprinter code conforming to International Telegraphic Alphabet No. 2 with respect to all letters and numerals (including the slant sign or fraction bar); however, in "figures" for positions not utilized for numerals, special signals may be employed for the remote control of receiving printers, or for other purposes indicated in this section.

(2) The transmitting speed shall be maintained within 5 words per minute of one of the following standard speeds: 60 (45 bauds), 67 (50 bauds), 75 (56.25 bauds) or 100 (75 bauds) words per minute.

(3) When frequency shift keying (type F1 emission) is utilized, the deviation in frequency from the mark signal to the space signal, or from the space signal to the mark signal, shall be less than 900 Hertz.

(4) When audio frequency shift keying (type A2 or F2 emission) is utilized, the highest fundamental modulating frequency shall not exceed 3000 Hertz, and the difference between the modulating audio frequency for the mark signal and that for the space signal shall be less than 900 Hertz.

(b) Use of the American Standard Code for Information Interchange (ASCII) is subject to the following requirements:

(1) The code shall conform to the American Standard Code for Information Interchange (ASCII) as defined in American National Standards Institute (ANSI) standard X3.4-1968.

(2) F1 emission shall be utilized on those fre-

quencies between 3.5 and 21.25 MHz where its use is permissible; and the sending speed shall not exceed 300 bauds.

(3) F1, F2 and A2 emissions may be utilized on those frequencies between 28 and 225 MHz where their use is permissible; and the sending speed shall not exceed 1200 bauds.

(4) F1, F2 and A2 emissions may be utilized on those frequencies above 420 MHz where their use is permissible; and the sending speed shall not exceed 19.6 kilobauds.

§ 97.71 Transmitter power supply

The licensee of an amateur station using frequencies below 144 megahertz shall use adequately filtered direct-current plate power supply for the transmitting equipment to minimize modulation from this source.

§ 97.73 Purity of emissions.

(a) Except for a transmitter or transceiver built before April 15, 1977 or first marketed before January 1, 1978, the mean power of any spurious emission or radiation from an amateur transmitter, transceiver, or external radio frequency power amplifier being operated with a carrier frequency below 30 MHz shall be at least 40 decibels below the mean power of the fundamental without exceeding the power of 50 milliwatts. For equipment of mean power less than five watts, the attenuation shall be at least 30 decibels.

(b) Except for a transmitter or transceiver built before April 15, 1977 or first marketed before January 1, 1978, the mean power of any spurious emission or radiation from an amateur transmitter, transceiver, or external radio frequency power amplifier being operated with a carrier frequency above 30 MHz but below 235 MHz shall be at least 60 decibels below the mean power of the fundamental. For a transmitter having a mean power of 25 watts or less, the mean power of any spurious radiation supplied to the antenna transmission line shall be at least 40 decibels below the mean power of the fundamental without exceeding the power of 25 microwatts, but need not be reduced below the power of 10 microwatts.

(c) Paragraphs (a) and (b) of this section notwithstanding, all spurious emissions or radiation from an amateur transmitter, transceiver, or external radio frequency power amplifier shall be reduced or eliminated in accordance with good engineering practice.

(d) If any spurious radiation, including chassis or power line radiation, causes harmful interference to the reception of another radio station, the licensee may be required to take steps to eliminate the interference in accordance with good engineering practice.

NOTE: For the purposes of this section, a spurious emission or radiation means any emission or radiation from a transmitter, transceiver, or external radio frequency power amplifier which is outside of the authorized Amateur Radio Service frequency band being used.

§ 97.74 Frequency measurement and regular check.

The licensee of an amateur station shall provide for measurement of the emitted carrier frequency or frequencies and shall establish procedures for making such measurement regularly. The measurement of the emitted carrier frequency or frequencies shall be made by means independent of the means used to control the radio frequency or frequencies generated by the transmitting apparatus and shall be of sufficient accuracy to assure operation within the amateur frequency band used.

§ 97.75 Use of external radio frequency (RF) power amplifiers.

(a) Until April 28, 1981, any external radio frequency (RF) power amplifier used or attached at any amateur radio station shall be type accepted in accordance with Subpart J of Part 2 of the FCC's Rules for operation in the Amateur Radio Service, unless one or more of the following conditions are met:

(1) The amplifier is not capable of operation on any frequency or frequencies below 144 MHz (the amplifier shall be considered incapable of operation below 144 MHz if the mean output power decreases, as frequency decreases from 144 MHz, to a point where 0 decibels or less gain is exhibited at 120 MHz and below and the amplifier is not capable of being easily modified to provide amplification below 120 MHz);

(2) The amplifier was originally purchased before April 28, 1978;

(3) The amplifier was —

(i) Constructed by the licensee, not from an external RF power amplifier kit, for use at his amateur radio station;

(ii) Purchased by the licensee as an external RF power amplifier kit before April 28, 1978 for use at his amateur radio station; or

(iii) Modified by the licensee for use at his amateur radio station in accordance with §2.1001 of the FCC's Rules;

(4) The amplifier was purchased by the licensee from another amateur radio operator who —

(i) Constructed the amplifier, but not from an external RF power amplifier kit;

(ii) Purchased the amplifier as an external RF power amplifier kit before April 28, 1978 for use at his amateur radio station; or

(iii) Modified the amplifier for use at his amateur radio station in accordance with §2.1001 of the FCC's Rules;

(5) The external RF power amplifier was purchased from a dealer who obtained it from an amateur radio operator who —

(i) Constructed the amplifier, but not from an external RF power amplifier kit;

(ii) Purchased the amplifier as an external RF power amplifier kit before April 28, 1978, for use at his amateur radio station; or

(iii) Modified the amplifier for use at his amateur radio station in accordance with §2.1001 of the FCC's Rules; or

(6) The amplifier was originally purchased after April 28, 1978 and has been issued a marketing waiver by the FCC.

(b) A list of type accepted equipment may be inspected at FCC headquarters in Washington, D.C. or at any FCC field office. Any external RF power amplifier appearing on this list as type accepted for use in the Amateur Radio Service may be used in the Amateur Radio Service.

NOTE: No more than one unit of one model of an external RF power amplifier shall be constructed or modified during any calendar year by an amateur radio operator for use in the Amateur Radio Service without a grant of type acceptance.

§ 97.76 Requirements for type acceptance of external radio frequency (RF) power amplifiers and external radio frequency power amplifier kits.

(a) Until April 28, 1981, any external radio frequency (RF) power amplifier or external RF power amplifier kit marketed (as defined in §2.815), manufactured, imported or modified for use in the Amateur Radio Service shall be type accepted for use in the Amateur Radio Service in accordance with Subpart J or Part 2 of the FCC's Rules. This requirement does not apply if one or more of the following conditions are met:

(1) The amplifier is not capable of operation on any frequency or frequencies below 144 MHz (the amplifier shall be considered incapable of operation below 144 MHz if the mean output power decreases, as frequency decreases from 144 MHz, to a point where 0 decibels or less gain is exhibited at 120 MHz and below and the amplifier is not capable of being easily modified to provide amplification below 120 MHz).

(2) The amplifier was originally purchased before April 28, 1978 by an amateur radio operator for use at his amateur radio station;

(3) The amplifier was constructed or modified by an amateur radio operator for use at his amateur radio station in accordance with §2.1001 of the FCC's Rules;

(4) The amplifier was constructed or modified by an amateur radio operator in accordance with §2.1001 of the FCC's Rules and sold to another amateur radio operator or to a dealer;

(5) The amplifier was constructed or modified by an amateur radio operator in accordance with §2.1001 of the FCC's Rules and sold by a dealer to an amateur radio operator for use at his amateur radio station; or

(6) The amplifier was manufactured before April 28, 1978 and has been issued a marketing waiver by the FCC.

(b) No more than one unit of one model of an external RF power amplifier shall be constructed or modified during any calendar year by an amateur radio operator for use in the amateur Radio Service without a grant of type acceptance.

(c) A list of type accepted equipment may be inspected at FCC headquarters in Washington, D.C. or at any FCC field office. Any external RF power amplifier appearing on this list as type accepted for use in the Amateur Radio Service may be marketed for use in the Amateur Radio Service.

§ 97.77 Standards for type acceptance of external radio frequency (RF) power amplifiers and external radio frequency power amplifier kits.

(a) An external radio frequency (RF) power amplifier or external RF power amplifier kit will receive a grant of type acceptance under this Part only if a grant of type acceptance would serve the public interest, convenience or necessity.

(b) To receive a grant of type acceptance under this Part, an external RF power amplifier shall meet the emission limitations of §97.73 when the amplifier is —

(1) Operated at its full output power;

(2) Placed in the "standby" or "off" positions, but still connected to the transmitter; and

(3) Driven with at least 50 watts mean radio frequency input power (unless a higher drive level is specified).

(c) To receive a grant of type acceptance under this part, an external RF power amplifier shall not be capable of operation on any frequency or frequencies between 24.00 MHz and 35.00 MHz. The amplifier will be deemed incapable of operation between 24.00 MHz and 35.00 MHz if —

(1) The amplifier has no more than 6 decibels of gain between 24.00 MHz and 26.00 MHz and between 28.00 MHz and 35.00 MHz. (This gain is determined by the ratio of the input RF driving signal (mean power measurement) to the mean RF output power of the amplifier.); and

(2) The amplifier exhibits no amplification (0 decibels of gain) between 26.00 MHz and 28.00 MHz.

(d) Type acceptance of external radio frequency power amplifiers or amplifier kits may be denied when denial serves the public interest, convenience or necessity by preventing the use of these amplifiers in services other than the Amateur Radio Service. Other uses of these amplifiers, such as in the Citizens Band Radio Service, are prohibited (Section 95.509). Examples of features which may result in dismissal or denial of an application for type acceptance of an external RF power amplifier include, but are not limited to, the following:

(1) Any accessible wiring which, when altered, would permit operation of the amplifier in a manner contrary to the FCC's Rules·

(2) Circuit boards or similar circuitry to facilitate the addition of components to change the amplifier's operating characteristics in a manner contrary to the FCC's Rules;

(3) Instructions for operation or modification of the amplifier in a manner contrary to the FCC's Rules;

(4) Any internal or external controls or adjustments to facilitate operation of the amplifier in a manner contrary to the FCC's Rules;

(5) Any internal radio frequency sensing circuitry or any external switch, the purpose of which is to place the amplifier in the transmit mode;

(6) The incorporation of more gain in the amplifier than is necessary to operate in the Amateur Radio Service. For purposes of this paragraph, an amplifier must meet the following requirements:

(i) No amplifier shall be capable of achieving designed output (or designed d.c. input) power when driven with less than 50 watts mean radio frequency input power;

(ii) No amplifier shall be capable of amplifying the input RF driving signal by more than 13 decibels. (This gain limitation is determined by the ratio of the input RF driving signal (mean power) to the mean RF output power of the amplifier. If the amplifier has a designed d.c. input power of less than 1000 watts, the gain allowance is reduced accordingly. (For example, an amplifier with a designed d.c. input power of 500 watts shall not be capable of amplifying the input RF driving signal (mean power measurement) by more than 10 decibels, compared to the mean RF output power of the amplifier.);

(iii) The amplifier shall not exhibit more gain than permitted by paragraph (d)(6)(ii) of this section when driven by a radio frequency input signal of less than 50 watts mean power; and

(iv) The amplifier shall be capable of sustained operation at its designed power level.

(7) Any attenuation in the input of the amplifier which, when removed or modified, would permit the amplifier to function at its designed output power when driven by a radio frequency input signal of less than 50 watts mean power.

Subpart D — Operating Requirements and Procedures

§ 97.78 Practice to be observed by all licensees.

In all respects not specifically covered by these regulations each amateur station shall be operated in accordance with good engineering and good amateur practice.

§ 97.79 Control operator requirements.

(a) The licensee of an amateur station shall be responsible for its proper operation.

(b) Every amateur radio station, when in operation, shall have a control operator at an authorized control point. The control operator shall be on duty, except where the station is operated under automatic control. The control operator may be the station licensee, if a licensed amateur radio operator, or may be another amateur radio operator with the required class of license and designated by the station licensee. The control operator shall also be responsible, together with the station licensee, for the proper operation of the station.

(c) An amateur station may only be operated in the manner and to the extent permitted by the operator privileges authorized for the class of license held by the control operator, but may exceed those of the station licensee provided proper station identification procedures are performed.

(d) The licensee of an amateur radio station may permit any third party to participate in amateur radio communication from his station, provided that a control operator is present and continuously monitors and supervises the radio communication to insure compliance with the rules.

§ 97.81 Authorized apparatus.

An amateur station license authorizes the use under control of the licensee of all transmitting apparatus at the fixed location specified in the station license which is operated on any frequency, or frequencies allocated to the amateur service, and in addition authorizes the use, under control of the licensee of portable and mobile transmitting apparatus operated at other locations.

§ 97.82 Availability of operator license.

Each amateur radio operator must have the original or photocopy of his or her operator license in his or her personal possession when serving as the control operator of an amateur radio station. The original license shall be available for inspection by any authorized government official upon request made by an authorized representative of the Commission, except when such license has been filed with application for modification or renewal thereof, or has been mutilated, lost or destroyed, and request has been made for a duplicate license in accordance with Section 97.57.

§ 97.83 Availability of station license.

The original license of each amateur station or a photocopy thereof shall be posted in a conspicuous place in the room occupied by the licensed operator while the station is being operated at a fixed location or shall be kept in his personal possession. When the station is operated at other than a fixed location, the original station license or a photocopy thereof shall be kept in the personal possession of the station licensee (or a licensed representative) who shall be present at the station while it is being operated as a portable or mobile station. The original station license shall be available for inspection by any authorized Government official at all times while the station is being operated and at other times upon request made by an authorized representative of the Commission, except when such license has been filed with application for modification or renewal thereof, or has been mutilated, lost, or destroyed, and request has been made for a duplicate license in accordance with §97.57

§ 97.84 Station identification.

(a) An amateur station shall be identified by the transmission of its call sign at the beginning and end of each single transmission or exchange of transmissions and at intervals not to exceed 10 minutes during any single transmission or exchange of transmissions of more than 10 minutes duration. Additionally, at the end of an exchange of telegraphy (other than teleprinter) or telephone transmissions between amateurs stations, the call sign (or the generally accepted network identifier) shall be given for the station, or for at least one of the group of stations, with which communication was established.

(b) Under conditions when the control operator is other than the station licensee, the station identification shall be the assigned call sign for that station. However, when a station is operated within the privileges of the operator's class of license but which exceeds those of the station licensee, station identification shall be made by following the station call sign with operator's primary station call sign (i.e., WN4XYZ/W4XX).

(c) An amateur radio station in repeater operation or a station in auxiliary operation used to relay automatically the signals of other stations in a system of stations shall be identified by radiotelephony or radiotelegraphy at a level of modulation sufficient to be intelligible through the repeated transmission at intervals not to exceed ten minutes.

(d) When an Amateur Radio station is in repeater or auxiliary operation, the following additional identifying information shall be transmitted:

(1) When identifying by radiotelephony, a station in repeater operation shall transmit the word "repeater" at the end of the station call sign. When identifying by radiotelegraphy, a station in repeater operation shall transmit the fraction bar DN followed by the letters "RPT" or "R" at the end of the station call sign. (The requirements of this subparagraph do not apply to stations having call signs prefixed by the letters "WR".)

(2) When identifying by radiotelephony, a station in auxiliary operation shall transmit the word "auxiliary" at the end of the station call sign. When identifying by radiotelegraphy, a station in auxiliary operation shall transmit the fraction bar DN followed by the letters "AUX" or "A" at the end of the station call sign.

(e) A station in auxiliary operation may be identified by the call sign of its associated station.

(f) When operating under the authority of an Interim Amateur Permit with privileges authorized by the Permit, but which exceed the privileges of the licensee's permanent operator license, the station must be identified in the following manner:

(1) On radiotelephony, by the transmission of the station call sign, followed by the word "interim", followed by the special identifier shown on the Interim Permit;

(2) On radiotelegraphy, by the transmission of the station call sign, followed by the fraction bar DN, followed by the special identifier shown on the interim permit.

(g) The identification required by this section shall be given on each frequency being utilized for transmission and shall be transmitted either by telegraphy, using the inernational Morse code, or by telephony, using the English language. If the identification required by this section is made by an automatic device used only for identification by telegraphy, the code speed shall not exceed 20 words per minute. The Commission encourages the use of a nationally or internationally recognized standard phonetic alphabet as an aid for correct telephone identification.

§ 97.85 Repeater operation.

(a) Emissions from a station in repeater operation shall be discontinued within five seconds after cessation of radiocommunications by the user station. Provisions to limit automatically the access to a station in repeater operation may be incorporated but are not mandatory.

(b) Except for operation under automatic control, as provided in paragraph (e) of this section, the transmitting and receiving frequencies used by a station in repeater operation shall be continuously monitored by a control operator immediately before and during periods of operation.

(c) A station in repeater operation shall not concurrently retransmit amateur radio signals on more than one frequency in the same amateur frequency band, from the same location.

(d) A station in repeater operation shall be operated in a manner ensuring that it is not used for one-way communications, except as provided in §97.91.

(e) A station in repeater operation, either locally controlled or remotely controlled, may also be operated by automatic control when devices have been installed and procedures have been implemented to ensure compliance with the rules when a duty control operator is not present at a control point of the station. Upon notification by the Commission of improper operation of a station under automatic control, operation under automatic control shall be immediately discontinued until all deficiencies have been corrected.

§ 97.86 Auxiliary operation.

(a) A station in auxiliary operation, either locally controlled or remotely controlled, may also be operated by automatic control when it is operated as part of a system of stations in

CHART OF REGIONS AS DEFINED IN TABLE OF FREQUENCY ALLOCATIONS

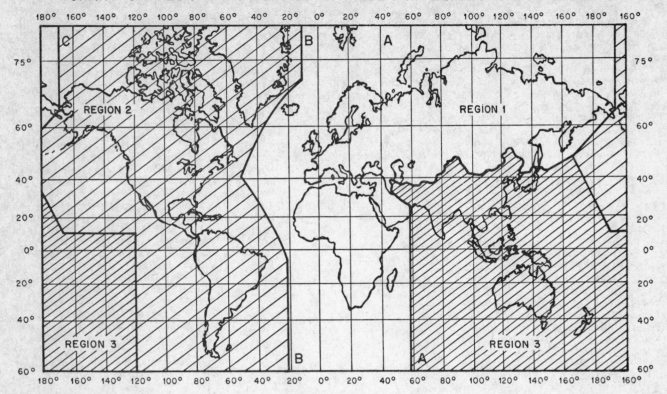

repeater operation operated under automatic control.

(b) If a station in auxiliary operation is relaying signals of another amateur radio station(s) to a station in repeater operation, the station in auxiliary operation may use an input (receiving) frequency in frequency bands reserved for auxiliary operation, repeater operation, or both.

(c) A station in auxiliary operation shall be used only to communicate with stations shown in the system network diagram.

§ 97.88 Operation of a station by remote control.

An amateur radio station may be operated by remote control only if there is compliance with the following:

(a) A photocopy of the remotely controlled station license shall be —

(1) posted in a conspicuous place at the remotely controlled transmitter location, and

(2) placed in the log of each authorized control operator.

(b) The name, address, and telephone number of the remotely controlled station licensee and at least one control operator shall be posted in a conspicuous place at the remotely controlled transmitter location.

(c) Except for operation under automatic control, a control operator shall be on duty when the station is being remotely controlled. Immediately before and during the periods the remotely controlled station is in operation, the frequencies used for emission by the remotely controlled station shall be monitored by the control operator. The control operator shall terminate all transmissions upon any deviation from the rules.

(d) Provisions must be incorporated to limit transmission to a period of no more than 3 minutes in the event of malfunction in the control link.

(e) A station in repeater operation shall be operated by radio remote control only when the control link uses frequencies other than the input (receiving) frequencies of the station in repeater operation.

§ 97.89 Points of Communications.

(a) Amateur stations may communicate with:

(1) Other amateur stations, excepting those prohibited by Appendix 2.

(2) Stations in other services licensed by the Commission and with the U.S. Government stations for civil defense purposes in accordance with Subpart F of this part, in emergencies and, on a temporary basis, for test purposes.

(3) Any station which is authorized by the Commission to communicate with amateur stations.

(b) Amateur stations may be used for transmitting signals, or communications, or energy, to receiving apparatus for the measurement of emissions, temporary observation of transmission phenomena, radio control of remote objects, and similar experimental purposes and for the purposes set forth in §97.91.

§ 97.91 One-way communications.

In addition to the experimental one-way transmission permitted by §97.89, the following kinds of one-way communications, addressed to amateur stations, are authorized and will not be construed as broadcasting: (a) Emergency communications, including bona fide emergency drill practice transmissions; (b) Information bulletins consisting solely of subject matter having direct interest to the amateur radio service as such; (c) Round-table discussions or net-type operations where more than two amateur stations are in communication, each station taking a turn at transmitting to other station(s) of the group; and (d) Code

practice transmissions intended for persons learning or improving proficiency in the international Morse code.

§ 97.93 Modulation of carrier.

Except for brief tests or adjustments, an amateur radiotelephone station shall not emit a carrier wave on frequencies below 51 megahertz unless modulated for the purpose of communication. Single audiofrequency tones may be transmitted for test purposes of short duration for the development and perfection of amateur radio telephone equipment.

STATION OPERATION AWAY FROM AUTHORIZED LOCATION

§ 97.95 Operation away from the authorized fixed station location.

(a) Operation within the United States, its territories or possessions is permitted as follows:

(1) When there is no change in the authorized fixed operation station location, an amateur radio station, other than a military recreation station, may be operated portable or mobile under its station license anywhere in the United States, its territories or possessions, subject to §97.61

(2) When the authorized fixed station location is changed, the licensee shall submit an application for modification of the station license in accordance with §97.47.

(b) When outside the continental limits of the United States, its territories, or possessions, an amateur radio station may be operated as portable or mobile only under the following conditions:

(1) Operation may not be conducted within the jurisdiction of a foreign government except pursuant to, and in accordance with express authority granted to the licensee by such foreign government. When a foreign govern-

ment permits Commission licensees to operate within its territory, the amateur frequency bands which may be used shall be as prescribed or limited by that government. (See Appendix 4 of this Part for the text of treaties or agreements between the United States and foreign governments relative to reciprocal amateur radio operation.)

(2) When outside the jurisdiction of a foreign government, amateur operation may be conducted within ITU Region 2 subject to the limitations of, and on those frequency bands listed in §97.61.

(3) When outside the jurisdiction of a foreign government, amateur operation may be conducted within ITU Regions 1 and 3 on the following frequencies, subject to the limitations and provisions of Section IV of Article 5 of the Radio Regulations of the ITU:

(i)

REGION 1	REGION 3
3.5-3.8 MHz	1.8-2.0 MHz
7.0-7.1 MHz	3.5-3.9 MHz
14.0-14.35 MHz	7.0-7.1 MHz
21.0-21.45 MHz	14.0-14.35 MHz
28.0-29.7 MHz	21.0-21.45 MHz
144-146 MHz	28.0-29.7 MHz
430-440 MHz	50.0-54.0 MHz
1215-1300 MHz	144-148 MHz
2300-2450 MHz	420-450 MHz
	1215-1300 MHz
	2300-2450 MHz

(ii) Operation on amateur frequency bands above 2450 MHz may be conducted subject to the limitations and provisions of Section IV of Article 5 of the Radio Regulations of the ITU.

(4) Except as otherwise provided, amateur operation conducted outside the jurisdiction of a foreign government shall comply with all requirements of Part 97 of this chapter.

SPECIAL PROVISIONS

§ 97.99 Stations used only for radio control of remote model crafts and vehicles.

An amateur transmitter when used for the purpose of transmitting radio signals intended only for the control of a remote model craft or vehicle and having mean output power not exceeding one watt may be operated under the special provisions of this section provided an executed Transmitter Identification Card (FCC Form 452-C) or a plate made of a durable substance indicating the station call sign and licensee's name and address is affixed to the transmitter.

(a) Station identification is not required for transmissions directed only to a remote model craft or vehicle.

(b) Transmissions containing only control signals directed only to a remote model craft or vehicle are not considered to be codes or ciphers in the context of the meaning of §97.117.

(c) Station logs need not indicate the times of commencing and terminating each transmission or series of transmissions.

§ 97.101 Mobile stations aboard ships or aircraft.

In addition to complying with all other applicable rules, an amateur mobile station operated on board a ship or aircraft must comply with all of the following special conditions: (a) The installation and operation of the amateur mobile station shall be approved by

the master of the ship or captain of the aircraft; (b) The amateur mobile station shall be separate from and independent of all other radio eqiupment, if any, installed on board the same ship or aircraft; (c) The electrical installation of the amateur mobile station shall be in accord with the rules applicable to ships or aircraft as promulgated by the appropriate government agency; (d) The operation of the amateur mobile station shall not interfere with the efficient operation of any other radio equipment installed on board the same ship or aircraft; and (e) The amateur mobile station and its associated equipment, either in itself or in its method of operation, shall not constitute a hazard to the safety of life or property.

LOGS

§ 97.103 Station log requirements.

An accurate legible account of station operation shall be entered into a log for each amateur radio station. The following items shall be entered as a minimum:

(a) The call sign of the station, the signature of the station licensee, or a photocopy of the station license.

(b) The locations and dates upon which fixed operation of the station was initiated and terminated. If applicable, the location and dates upon which portable operation was initiated and terminated at each location.

(1) The date and time periods the duty control operator for the station was other than the station licensee, and the signature and primary station call sign of that duty control operator.

(2) A notation of third party traffic sent or received, including names of all third parties, and a brief description of the traffic content. This entry may be in a form other than written, but one which can be readily transcribed by the licensee into written form.

(3) Upon direction of the Commission, additional information as directed shall be recorded in the station log.

(c) In addition to the other information required by this section, the log of a remotely controlled station shall have entered the names, addresses, and call signs of all authorized control operators and a functional block diagram of, and a technical explanation sufficient to describe the operation of the control link. Additionally, the following information shall be entered:

(1) A description of the measures taken for protection against access to the remotely controlled station by unauthorized persons;

(2) A description of the measures taken for protection against unauthorized station operation, either through activation of the control link, or otherwise;

(3) A description of the provisions for shutting down the station in the case of control link malfunction; and

(4) A description of the means used for monitoring the transmitting frequencies.

(d) When a station has one or more associated stations, that is, stations in repeater or auxiliary operation, a system network diagram shall be entered in the station log.

(e) In addition to the other information required by this section, the log of a station in repeater operation transmitting with an effective radiated power greater than the minimum effective radiated power listed in §97.67(c) for the frequency band in use shall contain the following:

(1) The location of the station transmitting

antenna, marked upon a topographic map having a scale of 1:250,000 and contour intervals;[1]

(2) The antenna transmitting height above average terrain;[2]

(3) The effective radiated power in the horizontal plane for the main lobe of the antenna pattern, calculated for maximum transmitter output power;

(4) The transmitter output power;

(5) The loss in the transmission line between the transmitter and the antenna, expressed in decibels;

(6) The relative gain in the horizontal plane of the transmitting antenna; and

(7) The horizontal and vertical radiation patterns of the transmitting antenna, with reference to true north (for horizontal pattern only), upon polar coordinate graph paper, and the method used in determining these patterns.

(f) In addition to the other information required by this section, the log of a station in auxiliary operation shall have the following information entered:

(1) A system network diagram for each system with which the station is associated;

(2) The station transmitting band(s);

(3) The transmitter input power; and

(4) If operated by remote control, the information required by paragraph (c) of this section.

(g) Notwithstanding the provisions of §97.105, the log entries required by paragraphs (c), (d), (e), and (f) of this section shall be retained in the station log as long as the information contained in those entries is accurate.

§ 97.105 Retention of logs.

The station log shall be preserved for a period of at least 1 year following the last date of entry and retained in the possession of the licensee. Copies of the log, including the sections required to be transcribed by §97.103, shall be available to the Commission for inspection.

EMERGENCY OPERATIONS

§ 97.107 Operation in emergencies.

In the event of an emergency disrupting normally available communication facilities in any widespread area or areas, the Commission, in its discretion, may declare that a general state of communications emergency exists, designate the area or areas concerned, and specify the amateur frequency bands, or segments of such bands, for use only by amateurs participating in emergency communication within or with such affected area or areas. Amateurs desiring to request the declaration of such a state of emergency should communicate with the Commission's Engineer in Charge of the area concerned. Whenever such declaration has been made, operation of and with amateur stations in the area concerned shall be only in accordance with the requirements set forth in this section, but such requirements shall in nowise affect other normal amateur communication in the affected areas when conducted on frequencies not designated for emergency operation.

(a) All transmissions within all designated

---

[1] Indexes and ordering information for suitable maps are available from the U.S. Geological Survey, Washington, D.C. 20242 or from the Federal Center, Denver, Colorado 80255.
[2] See Appendix 5.

amateur communications bands' other than communications relating directly to relief work, emergency service, or the establishment and maintenance of efficient Amateur Radio networks for the handling of such communications shall be suspended. Incidental calling, answering, testing or working (including casual conversations, remarks or messages) not pertinent to constructive handling of the emergency situation shall be prohibited within these bands.

(b) The Commission may designate certain amateur stations to assist in the promulgation of information relating to the declaration of a general state of communications emergency, to monitor the designated amateur emergency communications bands, and to warn non-complying stations observed to be operating in those bands. Such station, when so designated, may transmit for that purpose on any frequency or frequencies authorized to be used by that station, provided such transmissions do not interfere with essential emergency communica-

tions in progress; however, such transmissions shall preferably be made on authorized frequencies immediately adjacent to those segments of the amateur bands being cleared for the emergency. Individual transmissions for the purpose of advising other stations of the existence of the communications emergency shall refer to this section by number (§97.107) and shall specify, briefly and concisely, the date of the Commission's declaration, the area and nature of the emergency, and the amateur frequency bands or segments of such bands which constitute the amateur emergency communications bands at the time. The designated stations shall not enter into discussions with other stations beyond furnishing essential facts relative to the emergency, or acting as advisors to stations desiring to assist in the emergency, and the operators of such designated stations shall report fully to the Commission the identity of any stations failing to comply, after notice, with any of the pertinent provisions of this section.

(c) The special conditions imposed under the provisions of this section shall cease to apply only after the Commission or its authorized representative, shall have declared such general state of communications emergency to be terminated; however, nothing in this paragraph shall be deemed to prevent the Commission from modifying the terms of its declaration from time to time as may be necessary during the period of a communications emergency, or from removing those conditions with respect to any amateur frequency band or segment of such band which no longer appears essential to the conduct of the emergency communications.

---

[3]The frequency 4383.8 kHz may be used by any station authorized under this part to communicate with any other station in the State of Alaska for emergency communications. No airborne operations will be permitted on this frequency. Additionally, all stations operating on this frequency must be located in or within 50 nautical miles of the State of Alaska.

Subpart E — Prohibited Practices and Administrative Sanctions

PROHIBITED TRANSMISSIONS AND PRACTICES

§ 97.112 No remuneration for use of station.

(a) An amateur station shall not be used to transmit or receive messages for hire, nor for communication for material compensation, direct or indirect, paid or promised.

(b) Control operators of a club station may be compensated when the club station is operated primarily for the purpose of conducting amateur radiocommunication to provide telegraphy practice transmissions intended for persons learning or improving proficiency in the international Morse code, or to disseminate information bulletins consisting solely of subject matter having direct interest to the Amateur Radio Service provided:

(1) The station conducts telegraphy practice and bulletin transmission for at least 40 hours per week.

(2) The station schedules operations on all allocated medium and high frequency amateur bands using reasonable measures to maximize coverage.

(3) The schedule of normal operating times and frequencies is published at least 30 days in advance of the actual transmissions.

Control operators may accept compensation only for such periods of time during which the station is transmitting telegraphy practice or bulletins. A control operator shall not accept any direct or indirect compensation for periods during which the station is transmitting material other than telegraphy practice or bulletins.

§ 97.113 Broadcasting prohibited.

Subject to the provisions of §97.91, an amateur station shall not be used to engage in any form of broadcasting, that is, the dissemination of radio communications intended to be received by the public directly or by the intermediary of relay stations, nor for the retransmission by automatic means of programs or signals emanating from any class of station other than amateur. The foregoing provisions shall not be construed to prohibit amateur operators from giving their consent to the rebroadcast by broadcast stations of the transmissions of their amateur stations, provided, that the transmissions of the amateur station shall not contain any direct or indirect reference to the rebroadcast.

§ 97.114 Third party traffic.

The transmission or delivery of the following amateur radiocommunications is prohibited:

(a) International third party traffic except with countries which have assented thereto.

(b) Third party traffic involving material compensation, either tangible or intangible, direct or indirect, to a third party, a station licensee, a control operator, or any other person.

(c) Except for an emergency communication as defined in this part, third party traffic consisting of business communications on behalf of any party. For the purpose of this section business communication shall mean any transmission or communication the purpose of which is to facilitate the regular business or commercial affairs of any party.

§ 97.115 Music prohibited.

The transmission of music by an amateur station is forbidden.

§ 97.116 Amateur radiocommunication for unlawful purposes prohibited.

The transmission of radiocommunication or messages by an amateur radio station for any purpose, or in connection with any activity, which is contrary to Federal, State or local law is prohibited.

§ 97.117 Codes and ciphers prohibited.

The transmission by radio of messages in codes or ciphers in domestic and international communications to or between amateur stations is prohibited. All communications regardless of type of emission employed shall be in plain language except that generally recognized abbreviations established by regulation or custom and usage are permissible as are any other abbreviations or signals where the intent is not to obscure the meaning but only to facilitate communications.

§ 97.119 Obscenity, indecency, profanity.

No licensed radio operator or other person shall transmit communications containing obscene, indecent, or profane words, language, or meaning.

§ 97.121 False signals.

No licensed radio operator shall transmit false or deceptive signals or communications by radio, or any call letter or signal which has not been assigned by proper authority to the radio station he is operating.

§ 97.123 Unidentified communications.

No licensed radio operator shall transmit unidentified radio communciations or signals.

§ 97.125 Interference.

No licensed radio operator shall willfully or maliciously interfere with or cause interference to any radio communication or signal.

§ 97.126 Retransmitting radio signals.

(a) An amateur radio station, except a station in repeater operation or auxiliary operation, shall not automatically retransmit the radio signals of other amateur radio stations.

(b) A remotely controlled station, other than a remotely controlled station in repeater operation or auxiliary operation, shall automatically retransmit only the radio signals of stations in auxiliary operation shown on the remotely controlled station's system network diagram.

§ 97.127 Damage to apparatus.

No licensed radio operator shall willfully damage, or cause or permit to be damaged, any radio apparatus or installation in any licensed radio station.

§ 97.129 Fraudulent licenses.

No licensed radio operator or other person shall obtain or attempt to obtain, or assist another to obtain or attempt to obtain, an operator license by fraudulent means.

ADMINISTRATIVE SANCTIONS

§ 97.131 Restricted operation.

(a) If the operation of an amateur station causes general interference to the reception of transmissions from stations operating in the domestic broadcast service when receivers of good engineering design including adequate selectivity characteristics are used to receive such transmission and this fact is made known to the amateur station licensee, the amateur station shall not be operated during the hours from 8 p.m. to 10:30 p.m., local time, and on Sunday for the additional period from 10:30 a.m. until 1 p.m., local time, upon the frequency or frequencies used when the interference is created.

(b) In general, such steps as may be necessary to minimize interference to stations operating in other services may be required after investigation by the Commission.

§ 97.133 Second notice of same violation.

In every case where an amateur station licensee is cited within a period of 12 consecutive months for the second violation of the provisions of §§97.61, 97.63, 97.65, 97.71, or 97.73, the station licensee, if directed to do so by the Commission, shall not operate the station and shall not permit it to be operated from 6 p.m. to 10:30 p.m., local time, until written notice has been received authorizing the resumption of full-time operation. This notice will not be issued until the licensee has reported on the results of tests which he has conducted with at least two other amateur stations at hours other than 6 p.m. to 10:30 p.m., local time. Such tests are to be made for the specific purpose of aiding the licensee in determining whether the emissions of the station are in accordance with the Commission's rules. The licensee shall report to the Commission the observations made by the cooperating amateur licensee in relation to reported violations. This report shall include a statement as to the corrective measures taken to insure compliance with the rules.

§ 97.135 Third notice of same violation.

In every case where an amateur station licensee is cited within a period of 12 consecutive months for the third violation of §97.61, 97.63, 97.65, 97.71, or 97.73, the station licensee, if directed by the Commission, shall not operate the station and shall not permit it to be operated from 8 a.m. to 12 midnight, local time, except for the purpose of transmitting a prearranged test to be observed by a monitoring station of the Commission to be designated in each particular case. The station shall not be permitted to resume operation during these hours until the licensee is authorized by the Commission following the test, to resume full-time operation. The results of the test and the licensee's record shall be considered in determining the advisability of suspending the operator license or revoking the station license, or both.

§ 97.137 Answers to notices of violation.

Any licensee receiving official notice of a violation of the terms of the Communications Act of 1934, as amended, any legislative act, Executive order, treaty to which the United States is a party, or the rules and regulations of the Federal Communications Commission, shall, within 10 days from such receipt, send a written answer direct to the office of the Commission originating the official notice: *Provided, however,* That if an answer cannot be sent or an acknowledgement made within such 10-day period by reason of illness or other unavoidable circumstances, acknowledgement and answer shall be made at the earliest practicable date with a satisfactory explanation of the delay. The answer to each notice shall be complete in itself and shall not be abbreviated by reference to other communications or answers to other notices. If the notice relates to some violation that may be due to the physical or electrical characteristics of transmitting apparatus, the answer shall state fully what steps, if any are taken to prevent future violations, and if any new apparatus is to be installed, the date such apparatus was ordered, the name of the manufacturer, and promised date of delivery. If the notice of violation relates to some lack of attention to or improper operation of the transmitter, the name of the operator in charge shall be given.

Subpart F — Radio Amateur Civil Emergency Services (RACES)

GENERAL

§ 97.161 Basis and purpose.

The Radio Amateur Civil Emergency Service provides for amateur radio operation for civil defense communciations purposes only, during periods of local, regional or national civil emergencies, including any emergency which may necessitate invoking of the President's War Emergency Powers under the provisions of section 606 of the Communications Act of 1934, as amended.

§ 97.163 Definitions.

For the purposes of this Subpart, the following definitions are applicable:

(a) *Radio Amateur Civil Emergency Service.* A radiocommunication service conducted by volunteer licensed amateur radio operators, for providing emergency radiocommunications to local, regional, or state civil defense organizations.

(b) *RACES station.* An amateur radio station licensed to a civil defense organization, at a specific land location, for the purpose of providing the facilities for amateur radio operators to conduct amateur radiocommunications in the Radio Amateur Civil Emergency Service.

§ 97.165 Applicability of rules.

In all cases not specifically covered by the provisions contained in this Subpart, amateur radio stations and RACES stations shall be governed by the provisions of the rules governing amateur radio stations and operators (Subpart A through E of this part).

STATION AUTHORIZATIONS

§ 97.169 Station license required.

No transmitting station shall be operated in the Radio Amateur Civil Emergency Service unless:

(a) The station is licensed as a RACES station by the Federal Communications Commission, or

(b) The station is an amateur station licensed by the Federal Communications Commission, and is certified by the responsible civil defense organization as registered with that organization.

§ 97.171 Eligibility for RACES station license.

(a) A RACES station will only be licensed to a local, regional, or state civil defense organization.

(b) Only modification and/or renewal station licenses will be issued for RACES stations. No new licenses will be issued for RACES stations.

§ 97.173 Application for RACES station license.

(a) Each application for a RACES station license shall be made on the FCC Form 610-B.

(b) The application shall be signed by the civil defense official responsible for the coordination of all civil defense activities in the area concerned.

(c) The application shall be countersigned by the responsible official for the governmental entity served by the civil defense organization.

(d) If the application is for a RACES station to be in any special manner covered by §97.41, those showings specified for non-RACES stations shall also be submitted.

§ 97.175 Amateur radio station registration in civil defense organization.

No amateur radio station shall be operated in the Radio Amateur Civil Emergency Service unless it is certified as registered in a civil defense organization by that organization.

OPERATING REQUIREMENTS

§ 97.177 Operator requirements.

No person shall be the control operator of a RACES station, or shall be the control operator of an amateur radio station conducting communications in the Radio Amateur Civil Emergency Service unless that person holds a valid amateur radio operator license and is certified as enrolled in a civil defense organization by that organization.

§ 97.179 Operator privileges.

Operator privileges in the Radio Amateur Civil Emergency Service are dependent upon, and identical to, those for the class of operator license held in the Amateur Radio Service.

§ 97.181 Availability of RACES station license and operator licenses.

(a) The original license of each RACES station, or a photocopy thereof, shall be attached to each transmitter of such station, and at each control point of such station. Whenever a photocopy of the RACES station license is utilized in compliance with this requirement, the original station license shall be available for inspection by any authorized Government official at all times while the station is being operated and at other times upon request made by an authorized representative of the Commission, except when such license has been filed with application for modification or renewal thereof, or has been mutilated, lost, or destroyed, and request has been made for a duplicate license in accordance with §97.57.

(b) In addition to the operator license availability requirements of §97.82, a photocopy of the control operator's amateur radio operator license shall be posted at a conspicuous place at the control point for the RACES station.

TECHNICAL REQUIREMENTS

§ 97.185 Frequencies available.

(a) All of the authorized frequencies and emissions allocated to the Amateur Radio Service are also available to the Radio Amateur Civil Emergency Service on a shared basis.

(b) In the event of an emergency which necessitates the invoking of the President's War Emergency Powers under the provisions of §606 of the Communications Act of 1934 as amended, unless otherwise modified or directed, RACES stations and amateur radio stations participating in RACES will be limited in operation to the following:

Frequency or Frequency Bands

kHz	Limitations
1800-1825	1
1975-2000	1
3500-3510	
3510-3516	4
3516-3550	2, 4
3984-4000	
3997	3
7097-7103	4
7103-7125	2, 4
7245-7255	2, 4
14047-14053	4
14220-14230	2, 4
21047-21053	4

MHz	
28.55-28.75	
29.45-29.65	
50.35-50.75	
53.30	3
53.35-53.75	
145.17-145.71	
146.79-147.33	
220-225	5

(c) Limitations: (1) Use of frequencies in the band 1800-2000 kHz is subject to the priority of the LORAN system of radionavigation in this band and to the geographical, frequency, emission, and power limitations contained in §97.61 governing amateur radio stations and operators (Subparts A through E of this part).

(2) The availability of the frequency bands 3515-3550 kHz, 7103-7125 kHz, 7245-7247 kHz, 7253-7255 kHz, 14220-14222 kHz, and 14228-14230 kHz for use during periods of actual civil defense emergency is limited to the initial 30 days of such emergency, unless otherwise ordered by the Commission.

(3) For use in emergency areas when required to make initial contact with a military unit; also, for communications with military stations on matters requiring coordinations.

(4) For use by all authorized stations only in the continental United States, except that the bands 7245-7255 kHz and 14220-14230 kHz are also available in Alaska, Hawaii, Puerto Rico, and the Virgin Islands.

(5) Those stations operating in the band 220-225 MHz shall not cause harmful interference to the government radiolocation service.

§ 97.189 Point of communications.

(a) RACES stations may only be used to communicate with:

(1) Other RACES stations;

(2) Amateur radio stations certified as being registered with a civil defense organization, by that organization;

(3) Stations in the Disaster Communications Service;

(4) Stations of the United States Government authorized by the responsible agency to exchange communications with RACES stations;

(5) Any other station in any other service

regulated by the Federal Communications Commission, whenever such station is authorized by the Commission, to exchange communications with stations in the Radio Amateur Civil Emergency Service.

(b) Amateur radio stations registered with a civil defense organization may only be used to communicate with:

(1) RACES stations licensed to the civil defense organization with which the amateur radio station is registered:

(2) Any of the following stations upon authorization of the responsible civil defense official for the organization in which the amateur radio station is registered:

(i) Any RACES station licensed to other civil defense organizations;

(ii) Amateur radio stations registered with the same or another civil defense organization;

(iii) Stations in the Disaster Communications Service;

(iv) Stations of the United States Government authorized by the responsible agency to exchange communications with RACES stations;

(v) Any other station in any other service

regulated by the Federal Communications Commission, whenever such station is authorized by the Commission to exchange communications with stations in the Radio Amateur Civil Emergency Service.

§ 97.191 Permissible communications.

All communications in the Radio Amateur Civil Emergency Service must be specifically authorized by the civil defense organization for the area served. Stations in this service may transmit only civil defense communications of the following types:

(a) Communications concerning impending or actual conditions jeopardizing the public safety, or affecting the national defense or security during periods of local, regional, or national civil emergencies:

(1) Communications directly concerning the immediate safety of life or individuals, the immediate protection of property, maintenance of law and order, alleviation of human suffering and need, and the combating of armed attack or sabotage;

(2) Communications directly concerning the accumulation and dissemination of public in-

formation or instructions to the civilian population essential to the activities of the civil defense organization or other authorized governmental or relief agencies.

(b) Communications for training drills and tests necessary to ensure the establishment and maintenance of orderly and efficient operation of the Radio Amateur Civil Emergency Service as ordered by the responsible civil defense organization served. Such tests and drills may not exceed a total time of one hour per week.

(c) Brief one way transmissions for the testing and adjustment of equipment.

§ 97.193 Limitations on the use of RACES stations

(a) No station in the Radio Amateur Civil Emergency Service shall be used to transmit or to receive messages for hire, nor for communications for material compensation, direct or indirect, paid or promised.

(b) All messages which are transmitted in connection with drills or tests shall be clearly identified as such by use of the words "drill" or "test", as appropriate, in the body of the messages.

Subpart G — Operation of Amateur Radio Stations in the United States by Aliens Pursuant to Reciprocal Agreements

§ 97.301 Basis, purpose, and scope.

(a) The rules in this subpart are based on, and are applicable solely to, alien amateur operations pursuant to section 303(1)(3) and 310(a) of the Communications Act of 1934, as amended. (See Pub. L 93-505, 88 Stat. 1576.)

(b) The purpose of this subpart is to implement Public Law 88-383 by prescribing the rules under which an alien, who holds an amateur operator and station license issued by his government (hereafter referred to as an alien amateur), may operate an amateur radio station in the United States, in its possessions, and in the Commonwealth of Puerto Rico (hereafter referred to only as the United States).

§ 97.303 Permit required.

(a) Before he may operate an amateur radio station in the United States, under the provisions of sections 303(1)(2) and 310(a) of the Communications Act of 1934, as amended, an alien amateur licensee must obtain a permit for such operation from the Federal Communications Commission. A permit for such operation shall be issued only to an alien holding a valid amateur operator and station authorization from his government, and only when there is in effect a bilateral agreement between the United States and that government for such operation on a reciprocal basis by United States amateur radio operators.

§ 97.305 Application for permit.

(a) Application for a permit shall be made on FCC Form 610-A. Form 610-A may be obtained from the Commission's Washington, D.C., office, from any of the Commission's field offices and, in some instances, from United States missions abroad.

(b) The application form shall be completed in full in English and signed by the applicant. A photocopy of the applicant's amateur operator and station license issued by his government shall be filed with the application. The Commission may require the applicant to furnish additional information. The application must be filed by mail or in person with the Federal Communications Commission, Gettysburg, Pennsylvania 17325, U.S.A. To allow sufficient time for processing, the application should be filed at least 60 days before the date on which the applicant desires to commence operation.

§ 97.307 Issuance of permit.

(a) The Commission may issue a permit to an alien amateur under such terms and conditions as it deems appropriate. If a change in the terms of a permit is desired, an application for modification of the permit is required. If operation beyond the expiration date of a permit is desired, an application for renewal of the permit is required. In any case in which the permittee has, in accordance with the provisions of this subpart, made a timely and sufficient application for renewal of an unexpired permit, such permit shall not expire until the application has been finally determined. Applications for modification or for renewal of a permit shall be filed on FCC Form 610-A.

(b) The Commission, in its discretion may deny any application for a permit under this subpart. If an application is denied, the applicant will be notified by letter. The applicant may, within 90 days of the mailing of such letter, request the Commission to reconsider its action.

(c) Normally, a permit will be issued to expire 1 year after issuance but in no event after the expiration of the license issued to the alien amateur by his government.

§ 97.309 Modification, suspension, or cancellation of permit.

At any time the Commission may, in its discretion, modify, suspend, or cancel any permit issued under this subpart. In this event, the permittee will be notified of the Commission's action by letter mailed to his mailing address in the United States and the permittee shall comply immediately. A permittee may, within 90 days of the mailing of such letter, request the Commission to reconsider its action. The filing of a request for reconsideration shall not stay the effectiveness of that action, but the Commission may stay its action on its own motion.

§ 97.311 Operating conditions.

(a) The alien amateur may not under any circumstances begin operation until he has received a permit issued by the Commission.

(b) Operation of an amateur station by an alien amateur under a permit issued by the Commission must comply with all of the following:

(1) The terms of the bilateral agreement between the alien amateur's government and the government of the United States;

(2) The provisions of this subpart and of Subparts A through E of this part;

(3) The operating terms and conditions of the license issued to the alien amateur by his government; and

(4) Any further conditions specified on the permit issued by the Commission.

§ 97.313 Station identification.

(a) The alien amateur shall identify his station as follows:

(1) Radio telegraph operation: The amateur shall transmit the call sign issued to him by the licensing country followed by a slant (/) sign and the United States amateur call sign prefix letter(s) and number appropriate to the location of his station.

(2) Radiotelephone operation: The amateur shall transmit the call sign issued to him by the licensing country followed by the words "fixed", "portable" or "mobile", as appropriate, and the United States amateur call sign prefix letter(s) and number appropriate to the location of his station. The identification shall be made in the English language.

(b) At least once during each contact with another amateur station, the alien amateur shall indicate, in English, the geographical location of his station as nearly as possible by city and state, commonwealth, or possession.

Subpart H — Amateur-Satellite Service

General

§ 97.401 Purposes.

The Amateur-Satellite Service is a radiocommunication service using stations on earth satellites for the same purpose as those of the Amateur Radio Service.

§ 97.403 Definitions.

(a) *Space operation.* Space-to-earth, and space-to-space, Amateur Radio communication from a station which is beyond, is intended to go beyond, or has been beyond the major portion of the earth's atmosphere.

(b) *Earth operation.* Earth-to-space-to-earth amateur radiocommunication by means of radio signals automatically retransmitted by stations in space operation.

(c) *Telecommand operation.* Earth-to-space Amateur Radio communication to initiate, modify, or terminate functions of a station in space operation.

(d) *Telemetry.* Space-to-earth transmissions, by a station in space operation, of results of measurements made in the station, including those relating to the function of the station.

§ 97.405 Applicability of rules.

The rules contained in this Subpart apply to radio stations in the Amateur-Satellite Service. All cases not specifically covered by the provisions of this Subpart shall be governed by the provisions of the rules governing Amateur Radio stations and operators (Subpart A through E of this Part).

§ 97.407 Eligibility for space operation.

Amateur Radio stations licensed to Amateur Extra Class operators are eligible for space operation (see §97.403(a)). The station licensee may permit any Amateur Radio operator to be the control operator, subject to the privileges of the control operator's class of license (see §97.7).

§ 97.409 Eligibility for earth operation.

Any Amateur Radio station is eligible for earth operation (see §97.403(b)), subject to the privileges of the control operator's class of license (see §97.7).

§ 97.411 Eligibility for telecommand operation.

Any Amateur Radio station designated by the licensee of a station in space operation is eligible to conduct telecommand operation with the station in space operation, subject to the privileges of the control operator's class of license (see §97.7).

§ 97.413 Space operations requirements.

An Amateur Radio station may be in space operation where:

(a) The station has not been ordered by the Commission to cease radio transmissions.

(b) The station is capable of effecting a cessation of radio transmissions by commands transmitted by station(s) in telecommand operation whenever such cessation is ordered by the Commission.

(c) There are, in place, sufficient Amateur Radio stations licensed by the Commission capable of telecommand operation to effect cessation of space operation, whenever such is ordered by the Commission.

(d) The notifications required by §97.423 are on file with the Commission.

Technical Requirements

§ 97.415 Frequencies available.

The following frequency bands are available for space operation, earth operation, and telecommand operation:

Frequency bands

kHz	MHz	GHz
7000-7100	21.00-21.45	24-24.05
14,000-14,250	28.00-29.70	
	144-146	
	435-438[1]	

[1]Stations operating in the Amateur-Satellite Service shall not cause harmful interference to other stations between 435 and 438 MHz. (See International Radio Regulations, RR MOD 3644/320A.)

Special Provisions

§ 97.417 Space operation.

(a) Stations in space operation are exempt from the station identification requirements of §97.87 on each frequency band when in use.

(b) Stations in space operation may automatically retransmit the radio signals of other stations in earth operation, and space operation.

(c) Stations in space operation are exempt from the control operator requirements of §97.79 and from the provisions of §97.88 pertaining to the operation of a station by remote control.

(d) Stations in space operation are exempt from the station log requirements of §97.103.

§ 97.419 Telemetry.

(a) Telemetry transmission by stations in space operation may consist of specially coded messages intended to facilitate communications.

(b) Telemetry transmissions by stations in space operation are permissible one-way communications.

§ 97.421 Telecommand operation.

(a) Stations in telecommand operation may transmit special codes intended to obscure the meaning of command messages to the station in space operation.

(b) Stations in telecommand operation are exempt from the station identification requirements of §97.87.

§ 97.423 Notification required.

(a) The licensee of every station in space operation shall give written notifications to the Private Radio Bureau, Federal Communications Commission, Washington, DC 20554.

(b) *Pre-space operation notification.*

(1) Three notifications are required prior to initiating space operation. They are:

First notification. Required no less than twenty-seven months prior to initiating space operation.

Second notification. Required no less than fifteen months prior to initiating space operation.

Third notification. Required no less than three months prior to initiating space operation.

(2) The pre-space operation notification shall consist of:

Space operation date. A statement of the expected date space operations will be initiated, and a prediction of the duration of the operation.

Identity of satellite. The name by which the satellite will be known.

Service area. A description of the geographic area on the Earth's surface which is capable of being served by the station in space operation. Specify for both the transmitting and receiving antennas of this station.

Orbital parameters. A description of the anticipated orbital parameters as follows:

Non-geostationary satellite
1) Angle of inclination
2) Period
3) Apogee (kilometers)
4) Perigee (kilometers)
5) Number of satellites having the same orbital characteristics

Geostationary satellite
1) Nominal geographical longitude.
2) Longitudinal tolerance
3) Inclination tolerance
4) Geographical longitudes marking the extremities of the orbital arc over which the satellite is visible at a minimum angle of elevation of 10° at points within the associated service area.
5) Geographical longitudes marking the extremities of the orbital arc within which the satellite must be located to provide communications to the specified service area.
6) Reason when the orbital arc of (5) is less than that of (4).

Technical Parameters. A description of the proposed technical parameters for:

(1) the station in space operation; and

(2) a station in earth operation suitable for use with the station in space operation; and

(3) a station in telecommand operation suitable for use with the station in space operation.

The description shall include:

(1) Carrier frequencies if known; otherwise give frequency range where carrier frequencies will be located.

(2) Necessary bandwidth.

(3) Class of emission.

(4) Total Peak Power.

(5) Maximum power density (watts/Hz)

(6) Antenna radiation pattern[1]

(7) Antenna gain (main beam)[1]

(8) Antenna pointing accuracy (geostationary satellites only)[1]

(9) Receiving system noise temperature[2]

(10) Lowest equivalent satellite link noise temperature[3]

c. *In-space operation notification.* Notification is required after space operation has been initiated. The notification shall update the information contained in the pre-space operation notification. In-space operation notification is required no later than seven days following initiation of space operation.

d. *Post-space operation notification.* Notification of termination of space operation is required no later than three months after termination is complete. If the termination is ordered by the Commission, notification is required no later than twenty-four hours after termination is complete.

APPENDICES

APPENDIX 1

Examination Points

Examinations for Amateur Radio operator licenses are conducted at the Commission's office in Washington, D.C., and at each field office of the Commission on the days designated by the Engineer in Charge of each office. Specific dates should be obtained from the Engineer in Charge of the nearest field office of the Commission.

Examinations are also given at prescribed intervals in the cities listed in the Commission's current Examination Schedule, copies of which are available from the Federal Communications Commission Regional Services Division, Washington, D.C. 20554, or from any one of the Commission's field offices listed in §0.121.

APPENDIX 2

Extracts from Radio Regulations Annexed to the International Telecommunications Convention (Geneva 1959), as revised by the World Administrative Radio Conference for Space Telecommunications, Geneva, 1971.

---

[1] These antenna characteristics shall be provided for both transmitting and receiving antennas.

[2] For a station in space operation.

[3] The total noise temperature at the input of a typical amateur radio station receiver shall include the antenna noise (generated by external sources (ground, sky, etc.) peripheral to the receiving antenna and noise re-radiated by the satellite), plus noise generated internally to the receiver. The additional receiver noise is above thermal noise, kT_oB.

Referred to the antenna input terminals, the total system noise temperature is given by

$$T_s = T_a + (L - 1) T_o + L T_r$$

where:

T_a: antenna noise temperature

L: line losses between antenna output terminals and receiver input terminals

T_o: ambient temperature, usually given as 290°K

T_r: receiver noise temperature, this is also given as $(NF-1)T_o$, where NF is receiver noise figure.

Article 41 — Amateur Stations

SECTION 1. Radiocommunications between amateur stations of different countries[1] shall be forbidden if the administration of one of the countries concerned has notified that it objects to such radiocommunications.

SEC. 2.(1) When transmissions between amateur stations of different countries are permitted, they shall be made in plain language and shall be limited to messages of a technical nature relating to tests and to remarks of a personal character for which, by reason of their unimportance, recourse to the public telecommunications service is not justified. It is absolutely forbidden for amateur stations to be used for transmitting international communications on behalf of third parties.

(2) The preceding provisions may be modified by special arrangements between the administration of the countries concerned.

SEC. 3. (1) Any person operating the apparatus of an amateur station shall have proved that he is able to send correctly by hand and to receive correctly by ear, texts in Morse code signals. Administrations concerned may, however, waive this requirement in the case of stations making use exclusively of frequencies above 144 MHz.

(2) Administrations shall take such measures as they judge necessary to verify the technical qualifications of any person operating the apparatus of an amateur station.

SEC. 4. The maximum power of amateur stations shall be fixed by the administrations concerned, having regard to the technical qualifications of the operators and to the conditions under which these stations are to work.

SEC. 5. (1) All the general rules of the Convention and of these Regulations shall apply to amateur stations. In particular, the emitted frequency shall be as stable and as free from spurious emissions as the state of technical development for such stations permits.

(2) During the course of their transmissions, amateur stations shall transmit their call sign at short intervals.

Section 6. Space stations in the Amateur-Satellite Service operating in bands shared with other services shall be fitted with appropriate devices for controlling emissions in the event that harmful interference is reported in accordance with the procedure laid down in Article 15. Administrations authorizing such space stations shall inform the International Frequency Registration Board (IFRB) and shall insure that sufficient earth command stations are established before launch to guarantee that any harmful interference that might be reported can be terminated by the authorizing Administration.

Resolution No. 10

Relating to the use of the bands 7000 to 7100 kHz and 7100 to 7300 kHz by the Amateur Service and the Broadcasting Service.

The Administrative Radio Conference Geneva, 1959,

Considering

(a) That the sharing of frequency bands by amateur, fixed, and broadcasting services is undesirable and should be avoided;

(b) That it is desirable to have worldwide exclusive allocations for these services in Band 7;

---

[1] As may appear in public notices issued by the Commission.

(c) That the band 7000 to 7100 kHz is allocated on a worldwide basis exclusively to the amateur service;

(d) That the band 7100 to 7300 kHz is allocated in Regions 1 and 3 to the broadcasting service and in Region 2 to the amateur service;

resolves,

that the broadcasting service should be prohibited from the band 7000 to 7100 kHz and that broadcasting stations operating on frequencies in this band should cease such operation;

and noting,

the provisions of No. 117 of the Radio Regulations;

further resolves,

that interregional amateur contacts should be only in the band 7000 to 7100 kHz and that the administrations should make every effort to ensure that the broadcasting service in the band 7100 to 7300 kHz, in Regions 1 and 3, does not cause interference to the amateur service in Region 2; such being consistent with the provisions of No. 117 of the Radio Regulations.

APPENDIX 3

Classification of Emissions

For convenient reference the tabulation below is extracted from the classification of typical emissions in Part 2 of the Commission's Rules and Regulations and in the Radio Regulations, Geneva, 1959, and it includes only those general classifications which appear most applicable to the Amateur Radio Service.

Type of modulation	Type of transmission	Symbol
Amplitude	With no modulation	A0
	Telegraph without the use of modulating audio frequency (by on-off keying)	A1
	Telegraphy by the on-off keying of an amplitude modulating audio frequency or audio frequencies or by the on-off keying of the modulated emission (special case; an unkeyed emission amplitude modulated).	A2
	Telephony	A3[1]
	Facsimile	A4
	Television	A5
Frequency (or phase)	Telegraphy by frequency shift keying without the use of a modulating audio frequency	F1
	Telegraphy by the on-off keying of a frequency	F2

---

[1] (In Part 97) Unless specified otherwise, A3 includes single and double sideband with full, reduced or suppressed carrier.

modulating audio frequency or by the on-off keying of frequency modulated emission (special case; an unkeyed emission frequency modulated).

Telephone	F3
Facsimile	F4
Television	F5
Pulse	P

APPENDIX 4

Convention Between the United States of America and Canada, Relating to the operation by Citizens of Either Country of Certain Radio Equipment or Stations in the Other Country (Effective May 15, 1952)

Article III

It is agreed that persons holding appropriate amateur licenses issued by either country may operate their amateur stations in the territory of the other country under the following conditions:

(a) Each visiting amateur may be required to register and receive a permit before operating any amateur station licensed by his government.

(b) The visiting amateur will identify his station by;

(1) *Radiotelegraphy operation.* The amateur call sign issued to him by the licensing country followed by a slant (/) sign and the amateur call sign prefix and call area number of the country he is visiting.

(2) *Radiotelephone operation.* The amateur call sign in English issued to him by the licensing country followed by the words, "fixed" "portable" or "mobile," as appropriate, and the amateur call sign prefix and call area number of the country he is visiting.

(c) Each amateur station shall indicate at least once during each contact with another station its geographical location as nearly as possible by city and state or city and province.

(d) In other respects the amateur station shall be operated in accordance with the laws and regulations of the country in which the station is temporarily located.

APPENDIX 5

Determination of Antenna Height Above Average Terrain

The effective height of the transmitting antenna shall be the height of the antenna's center of radiation above "average terrain." For this purpose "effective height" shall be established as follows:

(a) On a U. S. Geological Survey Map having a scale of 1:250,000, lay out eight evenly spaced radials, extending from the transmitter site to a distance of 10 miles and beginning at (0°, 45°, 90°, 135°, 180°, 225°, 270°, 315°T.) If preferred, maps of greater scale may be used.

(b) By reference to the map contour lines, establish the ground elevation above mean sea level (AMSL) at 2, 4, 6, 8, and 10 miles from the antenna structure along each radial. If no elevation figure or contour line exists for any particular point, the nearest contour line elevation shall be employed.

(c) Calculate the arithmetic of these 40 points of elevation (5 points of each of 8 radials).

(d) The height above average terrain of the antenna is thus the height AMSL of the Antenna's center of radiation, minus the height of average terrain as calculated above.

NOTE 1: Where the transmitter is located near a large body of water, certain points of established elevation may fall over water. Where it is expected that service would be provided to land areas beyond the body of water, the points at water level in that direction should be included in the calculation of average elevation. Where it is expected that service would not be provided to land areas beyond the body of water, the points at water level should not be included in the average.

NOTE 2: In instances in which this procedure might provide unreasonable figures due to the unusual nature of the local terrain, applicant may provide additional data at his own discretion, and such data may be considered if deemed significant.

Word Index to Part 97

Answers — Chapter 5 — Technician/General Classes

1) A 100 ohms
2) B 10 to 1
3) D $P = \dfrac{R^2}{E}$
4) C 360 degrees
5) C 12 henrys
6) C 13 ohms
7) C Apparent power is measured in watts.
8) B 70.7 volts
9) D Add turns to the coil.
10) D It increases
11) A 10 ohms
12) A 4 μF
13) B 650 watts
14) B 5 volts
15) D Electrolytic
16) B 12.5 watts
17) C An acceptor
18) B Diode
19) A Ability to stand overvoltage
20) A 70 volts
21) D 140 volts
22) C Removing the carrier from an a-m signal
23) C A facsimile transmitter
24) A a-m
25) A Constant selectivity
26) D fm receiver
27) A mixer
28) C 375 W
29) C 215 kHz
30) A Prevent oscillation
31) C Isolate the two stages
32) B The diameter of the conductors and the spacing between them
33) C The transmission line and antenna impedances are identical.
34) A The radiation resistance
35) D It is the most common and practical antenna for use on the 80- and 40-meter bands.
36) B 33 feet
37) A Hf
38) C Good worldwide communication during most of the 24 hours
39) A A high solar-flux index
40) D 10-meter band
41) C 500 ohms
42) D A General class amateur licensee may not operate in the Advanced class phone bands.
43) C Israel
44) B 10 minutes
45) A (See the diagram in the question)
46) C 50 ohms
47) D Between the transmitter and antenna
48) C Code practice transmissions
49) A 3880 kHz
50) C Is a control operator
51) C On any amateur frequency (Technicians have all amateur frequencies above 50 MHz.)
52) D Always required
53) A Not exceeding 800 watts
54) C 144.5 to 145.5 MHz
55) B Azimuthal map
56) A Send the other station's call three times and your own call three times using A1 emission.
57) C A field strength meter
58) A No. 10 wire or copper ribbon
59) A Always tuned to resonance
60) B Repeater stations

Answers — Chapter 6 — Advanced Class

1) C Sporadic E-layer refraction
2) C Enhanced long-distance reception of television signals in the 420- to 450-MHz band
3) B F-layer refraction in the 10.0- to 10.5-GHz band
4) A 114 km
5) D 7.000121 MHz
6) D All of the above
7) B Dip oscillator
8) D A and C
9) B 144.022, 144.098, 144.174 and 144.250 MHz
10) D B and C
11) D All of the above
12) A Causes a well-designed fm receiver to respond only to the stronger of two signals having the same frequency
13) B Is the ratio of the power radiated to the power delivered by the feed line
14) D All of the above
15) A Is the ratio of voltage to current at the feedpoint if the system is resonant and lossless
16) B A half-wavelength dipole driven element, a reflector and four directors
17) A To establish resonance in each of the desired bands
18) B For a constant efficiency, gain increases with decreased bandwidth
19) D A and B
20) B An 8-foot whip with center or base loading
21) D B or C
22) A Variation of the load impedance
23) C A and/or B
24) D All of the above
25) A A linear amplifier
26) B An fm transmitter
27) A The balanced modulator
28) C A product detector
29) D A mixer
30) B The i-f amplifier
31) D F5
32) B PIN diode
33) A They can be used in relaxation oscillator circuits.
34) B Germanium
35) A Latching relays
36) B Uses crystal pairs having an approximately 2-kHz frequency difference
37) D None of the above
38) A f_o = 16.24 MHz, BW = 2.98 MHz, Q = 5.4
39) A The type of semiconductor material used
40) B C = 585 pF, BW = 186 kHz
41) D Replace the filter with one having 7 elements and the same ripple value.
42) B A notch filter
43) A The impedance transformation ratio
44) D 1000, 3000, 5000, 7000 and 9000 Hz
45) A Peak = rms $\times \sqrt{2}$
46) D PEP = 800 watts, average = 400 watts
47) C Vertical
48) D 108 ohms
49) A S/N increases with modulation index.
50) B 1.67
51) C The modulation index does not vary with the modulating frequency.
52) A A small loop in a plane perpendicular to the dipole
53) C 13.8 volts
54) C 1831 ohms
55) B 2.5 V
56) D skin effect
57) A indefinitely
58) A 18.7°, 0.947, 439.5 VA, 416.2 W
59) D 720 W
60) A 5-volt battery in series with a 43.4-ohm resistor

Answers — Chapter 7 — Amateur Extra Class License

1) C 21,250-21,270 kHz. (See paragraph 97.7 (a) of the FCC regulations)
2) D 1225.0 MHz (97.61 (a), 97.65 (d, e))
3) B A9 (97.61)
4) D 13 miles
5) C Troposphere
6) C Transequatorial propagation
7) D When the signal strength is fluttering rapidly, cw is easier to copy
8) C Sharp or rapid changes in the density and humidity of air
9) B Plate modulation
10) D None of the above (97.6(a))
11) D 9 kHz. Deviation of a pm signal is proportional to both amplitude and frequency of the modulating signal
12) D Less distortion
13) B A4. F4 is illegal on the 2-meter band. (97.61(a))
14) D A sync pulse duration of 5 milliseconds. Present SSTV standards call for 5-millisecond sync pulses. This is not actually required by FCC regulations, but since the other choices are incorrect, D is the best answer
15) D 250 pF. Use the formula $f = 1/2\pi\sqrt{LC}$. For $L = 10 \ \mu H$ (10×10^{-6} Hy) and $C = 150$ pF (150×10^{-12} farads) the frequency works out to be 4.11 MHz too high. For $C = 250$ pF the frequency works out to 3.18 MHz so that a 250-pF variable capacitor will tune a 10-μH coil through the 80-meter band
16) A .06 second. The time constant is $.01 \times 10^{-6}$ times 2×10^6 or .02 seconds. After three time constants, the voltage is $.368^3$ or .05 times the initial voltage, 20 volts. $.05 \times 20 = 1$ volt. So the answer is three time constants or 3×0.2 or .06 seconds.
17) A Unshielded wire should be used to connect a transmitter to the low-pass filter.
18) A Since the output signal is the integral of the input, think of the input as being velocity and the output as being distance. When the square-wave voltage (speed) is positive, the output voltage (distance) is increasing at a constant rate. When the square-wave voltage is negative, the output voltage is decreasing at a constant rate. Thus the output signal is a voltage that alternately increases at a constant rate and then decreases at a constant rate on successive half cycles of the square-wave input as in the figure
19) C 1.4 ohms. From $X_C = 1/(2\pi f C)$ each capacitor has a reactance of 1 ohm. The two in series thus have a reactance of 2 ohms. Thus the pair of capacitors in series and the resistor each had an admittance of .5 ohms. From the admittance formula $Y = \sqrt{B^2 + G^2} = .707$ so that $Z = 1/y$ or 1.414
20) D 45 degrees. Computed from $\theta = \arctan B/G$ or you can draw an admittance diagram. When $B = G$, the angle between Y and G is 45 degrees
21) C 1.67
22) C 5. Determine the tuned-circuit resonant frequency from $f = 1/(2\pi\sqrt{LC})$. Then $Q = X_L R_S$ where $X_L = 2\pi f L$.
23) D The amount of capacitance or inductance that may be used in a given circuit is independent of frequency. All the other statements are correct.
24) C 10 volts
25) B 2000 ohms
26) B Phase inverter
27) D M-derived filter. If the trap frequency $(f \pm)$ is set for the second harmonic, that frequency will be greatly attenuated.
28) C A high pump frequency is used in a parametric amplifier to improve the noise figure. A is incorrect because a *reflex* klystron can be used only as an oscillator
29) A 85. The band width of a resonant circuit is approximately $BW = f_c/Q_L$ where f_c is the center frequency and Q_L is the loaded Q. Since a bandwidth of at least 5 MHz is needed, maximum loaded Q is $Q_L = f_c/BW = 85.4$
30) D De-emphasis network
31) B 100,000 ohms
32) A 25
33) D Varactor. Variable-capacitor diodes are sometimes used in place of tuning capacitors in VFO circuits so that the frequency may be remotely controlled with a potentiometer
34) D Uhf mixers
35) C Vidicon
36) D The current amplification factor. The ratio of change in collector current to change in emitter current is the alpha current gain. Since this is not one of the choices, choose the only correct answer, D
37) D All of the above
38) A Discone
39) D All of the above
40) C 17.6 μV/meter. Since voltage is proportional to the square root of the power ($P = E^2/R$), at the half power point the field strength is $1/\sqrt{2} = .707$ times the maximum field strength
41) D Appears on only one side of the picture carrier frequency because the TV transmission is sent as a vestigial sideband signal
42) A Determining the frequency response of a filter
43) B It is difficult to build uhf tuned circuits with high enough Q (low enough loss).
44) C A linearity tracer
45) B AND, OR AND NOT
46) A NAND gate
47) D $C = \overline{AB} + B$
48) B
49) C
50) A
51) A
52) D A phase detector is required to compare the phase, and thus the frequency difference of the VCO and the incoming frequency
53) B
54) C
55) C $8 = 2^n$, $n = 3$
56) D
57) A Baud rates of 300 and below are usable from 3.500 to 21.250 MHz
58) C
59) D
60) A -174 dBm + 26 dBm = 148 dBm. The 26 dB figure represents the 400 Hz bandwidth factor
61) C These frequencies are determined according to the formulas $2f_1 - f_2$ and $2f_2 - f_1$.
62) B
63) D
64) B
65) B
66) D
67) C The fundamental is visible at 2.8 divisions from the left hand edge zero frequency marker. The next pip to the right of the fundamental is the second harmonic, which is down 64 dB from the fundamental. The next pip to the right of the second harmonic is the third harmonic, which is down 68 dB from the fundamental.

INDEX